HIGH SCHOOL
SUBJECTS
SELF TAUGHT

HIGH SCHOOL SUBJECTS SELF TAUGHT

Edited by
LEWIS COPELAND
and a Staff of Teachers and Editors

Introduction and Suggestions for Studying
By WILLIAM L. SCHAAF, Ph.D.
Professor of Education, Brooklyn College

FOURTH REVISED
AND ENLARGED EDITION

VOLUME IV

PHYSICS
CHEMISTRY
BIOLOGY
PHYSIOLOGY
PSYCHOLOGY
SOCIOLOGY

Published by
J. G. FERGUSON PUBLISHING COMPANY • Chicago

O-12

XXIV

Physics Self Taught

WHAT IS PHYSICS?

PHYSICS IS the science which deals with energy and matter and with physical changes in matter. It is customary to group Physics and Chemistry together as the physical sciences; and the two subjects supplement one another. Together they are playing a leading role in shaping the character of our present-day civilization.

Physics is usually divided into seven parts: mechanics, heat, sound, light, magnetism, electricity, and nuclear physics.

The subject of mechanics is very broad. It is subdivided into three parts: *mechanics of solids, mechanics of liquids,* and *mechanics of gases.* The mechanics of solids involves mostly the study of force and motion, and from this study have developed the sciences of civil and mechanical engineering. All machinery is based on an applied knowledge of force and motion.

The mechanics of liquids is the study of the behavior of liquids and the behavior of solids in liquids. The principle of flotation which governs the construction of all ships, as well as the very important science of hydraulics (including sanitary engineering), is included in this branch of mechanics. Without a knowledge of hydraulics and sanitary engineering, we could have developed no adequate means of disposing of sewage, and there would be no proper water supply.

The mechanics of gases deals with properties of different gases under pressure. The principle of the gasoline engine (the automobile) comes under this heading.

Under the subject of heat we study, among other aspects of heat, the behavior of metals when heated. The entire science of thermodynamics, which gives us the steam engine and the automobile, is based on a knowledge of heat.

From our knowledge of sound we are able to construct musical instruments as well as such important inventions as the phonograph, the radio, television, and the talking motion pictures.

Under the subject of light comes the vitally important subject of optics, including research and development in the field of lenses. As you know, the lens is very useful—without it we would have no telescopes, no cameras, no eyeglasses, no movies.

Magnetism and electricity are closely related. The tremendous advantages to civilization of these two branches of physics are obvious. The coincidence of electricity and magnetism gives us the electromagnet—one of the most important scientific discoveries ever made. The electromagnet is a part of such instruments as the telephone, the telegraph, the wireless telegraph, and such important machines as the dynamo and the motor. Nearly all electrical appliances are run by electric motors, and electrified railroads are run by the combination of the dynamo and the motor. The subject of electricity also includes the study of electromagnetic waves, such as the X-ray and radio waves.

Under the subject of nuclear physics comes the study of the atom and how we release energy from it. Other topics in nuclear physics are radioactivity, nuclear fission and fusion, and the applications of radioactive isotopes.

Until recently little was known about the nucleus or innermost portion of the atom. The rapid developments of the last decades, reaching a climax in the discovery of how to release nuclear energy on a large scale, have given rise to this new area of physics called nuclear physics. We have at our command today more energy than all of mankind has used up to this time. Modern atomic-power reactors can provide energy to drive ships, irrigate deserts, and perhaps even extend the average life span. Atomic energy has also put in our hands the most destructive force the world has ever known.

MEASUREMENT

The internationally used scientific system of measurement is called the *metric system*. It has decided advantages over the familiar so-called English system, for its divisions are decimal: that is, they are based on the multiple of 10. Whereas in the English system 12 inches equal one foot, in the metric system 10 millimeters equal one centimeter, and 100 (10×10) centimeters equal one meter. Every equivalent in the metric system is a multiple of 10, which makes computation very easy.

The common metric units for measuring length, with their English equivalents, are given in Table I. Notice that the meter is a little longer than the English yard—about 3⅓ inches longer.

Metric units of weight are also based on the multiple 10. The unit is the gram, which is the weight of one cubic centimeter of pure water at a temperature of 4° Centigrade. The common metric units for measuring weight, with their English equivalents, are given in Table II.

The measurement of area in the metric system involves square meters, square centimeters, and so on, just as in the English system it involves square yards and square inches. These units are given in Table III.

The measurement of volume is made clear in Table IV. The unit of liquid measure, a part of the measurement of volume, is the liter, which is almost exactly equal to the English quart, as you will observe.

TABLE I

UNITS OF LENGTH

ENGLISH.

$$1 \text{ foot (ft.)} = 12 \text{ inches (in.)}$$
$$1 \text{ yard (yd.)} = 3 \text{ feet}$$
$$1 \text{ mile (mi.)} = 5280 \text{ feet}$$

METRIC.

$$1 \text{ meter (m.)} = 1000 \text{ millimeters (mm.)}$$
$$1 \text{ meter} = 100 \text{ centimeters (cm.)}$$
$$1 \text{ kilometer (km.)} = 1000 \text{ meters}$$
$$1 \text{ inch} = 2.540 \text{ centimeters}$$
$$1 \text{ meter} = 39.37 \text{ inches}$$

TABLE II

UNITS OF WEIGHT

ENGLISH.

$$1 \text{ pound (lb.)} = 16 \text{ ounces (oz.)}$$
$$1 \text{ ton (T.)} = 2000 \text{ pounds}$$

METRIC.

$$1 \text{ gram (g.)} = 1000 \text{ milligrams (mg.)}$$
$$1 \text{ kilogram (kg.)} = 1000 \text{ grams}$$
$$1 \text{ kilogram} = 2.20 \text{ pounds}$$
1 cubic foot of water weighs 62.4 pounds
1 cubic centimeter of water weighs 1 gram

TABLE III

UNITS OF AREA

ENGLISH.

1 square foot (sq. ft.) = 144 square inches (sq. in.)
1 square yard (sq. yd.) = 9 square feet
1 square rod (sq. rd.) = 30¼ square yards
1 acre (A.) = 160 square rods

METRIC.

1 square centimeter (sq. cm.) = 100 square millimeters (sq. mm.)
1 square meter (sq. m.) = 10,000 square centimeters
1 square kilometer (sq. km.) = 1,000,000 square meters

TABLE IV

UNITS OF VOLUME

ENGLISH.

1 cubic foot (cu. ft.) = 1728 cubic inches (cu. in.)
1 cubic yard (cu. yd.) = 27 cubic feet
1 gallon (gal.) = 4 quarts (qt.) = 231 cu. in.

METRIC.

1 liter (l.) = 1000 cubic centimeters (cm.³)
1 cubic meter (m.³) = 1000 liters
1 liter = 1.06 quarts

MECHANICS OF SOLIDS

MACHINES

A machine is a device used to multiply force or speed or to change the direction of a force. There are three simple machines: (1) the lever, (2) the pulley, and (3) the inclined plane. Other machines are either modifications of one of these machines or combinations of two or more of them.

THE LEVER

A lever consists of a rigid bar which is pivoted at a fixed point called a *fulcrum*. If you lift a weight with a crowbar and use a stone as a fulcrum, you are employing a lever. The weight lifted by a lever is called the *resistance;* the force used at the end of the lever to lift the weight is called the *effort*. The distance of the force from the fulcrum is called the force arm.

There are only three main classes of levers. The lever of the first class is shown in Figure 1. It has the fulcrum between the effort and the resist-

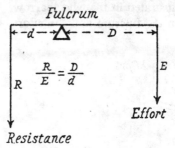

ance. The ordinary balance and the see-saw are examples of this. The longer the distance, or lever arm, between the fulcrum and the effort, the greater the weight that can be lifted. Archimedes once said, "Give me a lever large enough, and I can move the Earth." If he had had a fulcrum on which to rest his lever, he probably could have. By this principle you could lift a house if you had a long enough lever arm. (See Fig. 2.)

FIG. 1. Lever of the first class.

The principle briefly is this: In order to overcome a resistance you must do a certain amount of work. This work which you do is always

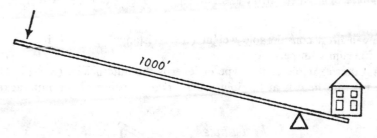

FIG. 2. An application of a lever of the first class.

the product of the force which you exert times the distance through which you move that force. What you lose in distance you gain in power, and

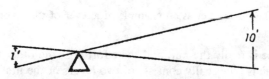

FIG. 3. Distances of effort and resistance in a first-class lever compared.

vice versa. Ten pounds, for example, moving through a distance of one foot is exactly equivalent to one pound moving through a distance of ten feet. So you could lift a ten-pound weight (resistance) one foot with a force (effort) of only one pound, but you would have to exert that force up or down ten feet. (See Fig. 3.)

Other examples of this type of lever, where the fulcrum is between the resistance and the effort, are crowbars, shears, glove stretchers, etc.

The lever of the second class is clearly illustrated in the wheelbarrow. (See Fig. 4.) Here the resistance is between the fulcrum and the effort.

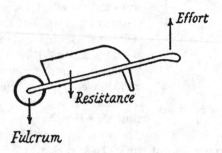

FIG. 4. The wheelbarrow as an example of a lever of the second class.

You can lift a considerable weight (the resistance) and roll it along on this fulcrum with perfect ease.

Another example of this type of lever is the nutcracker. (See Fig. 5.) The fulcrum here is at the joint of the two branches of the nutcracker.

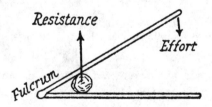

FIG. 5. The nutcracker as an example of a lever of the second class.

The resistance is really the nut, and the effort is at the other extremity at the handles. This type really consists of two levers of the first class joined together. If these two bars were not joined together, then the nut would be the fulcrum.

This second-class lever has the advantage of obtaining a tremendous force for very little effort. The nearer the nut is put to the fulcrum, and the longer the arm of the nutcracker, the greater will be the cracking force on the nut.

The lever of the third class has the fulcrum at one end and the weight at the other, the power being between them. This is shown in an ordinary

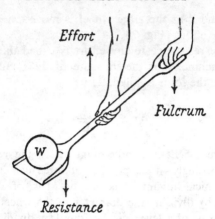

FIG. 6. The use of the shovel as an example of a lever of the third class.

shovel. (See Fig. 6.) Here the load on the shovel represents the resistance at one end, the effort is in the middle, and the handle is the fulcrum.

The slot-machine scales are a combination of levers carefully figured so that when you stand on the platform the platform moves down an exceedingly slight distance which is transmitted, with the aid of these levers, to a pointer which moves over the face of the machine. The typewriter and the piano contain scores of levers.

The law of the lever is: The resistance is to the effort as the effort arm is to the resistance arm, or

$$\frac{R}{E} = \frac{D}{d}$$

where R is the resistance, E the effort, D is the effort arm, and d the resistance arm.

THE WHEEL AND AXLE

The wheel and axle is really a development of the lever; it is a sort of lever revolving around a fulcrum. It consists of a wheel to which is attached a much smaller wheel.

If the large wheel is turned one revolution, the smaller wheel or axle, which also turns a revolution (because it is attached to the large wheel), will not turn so far. Consequently, by the principle of levers, the smaller wheel will have a definite lifting or pulling force greater than the force exerted to turn the large wheel.

If on a wheel six feet in diameter a small wheel one foot in diameter is mounted, and a rope is attached to the smaller wheel in such a way that it winds around it as the large wheel is moved, a great weight can be lifted with little effort (Fig. 7).

The ratio of the resistance to the effort is called the *mechanical advantage* of the machine. It is the measure of the number of times the machine multiplies the force applied. Thus

$$M.A. = \frac{R}{E}$$

where M.A. is the mechanical advantage, R is the resistance, and E is the effort. Accordingly, if 10 pounds of force can lift 60 pounds of weight, the mechanical advantage is 6. The M.A. of a wheel and axle can also be found by dividing the diameter of the wheel by the diameter of the axle. The M.A. of a lever can be found by dividing the effort arm (distance between the point of application of the effort to the fulcrum) by the resistance arm (distance between the fulcrum and the resistance).

Another important application of the wheel and axle—so important that nearly every machine you see is dependent upon it—is the gear wheel. You can easily see how power is produced by gearing (see Fig. 7) be-

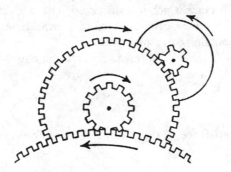

FIG. 7. An arrangement of gear wheels.

cause, by the principle of the wheel and axle, the axle turns more slowly than the rim of the large wheel but has correspondingly more power. This power can be transmitted to other gear wheels, which in turn transmit it to others—as with the familiar coal wagon, where you can watch a man lift a ton of coal by "winding up the wagon."

When you wind a watch it will go for a whole day because the big cogwheel which runs the hour hand, and is very powerful, is geared to the cogwheel which runs the minute hand, and is 1/60 as powerful. This cogwheel is attached to a large cogwheel, which in turn is geared to a smaller cogwheel. This cogwheel runs the second hand and is 1/3600 as powerful as the first cogwheel. What you lose in power you gain in distance, and consequently the second hand must move 3600 times as far as the hour hand, taking 3600 times as long.

THE PULLEY

If you ever visit a factory where heavy machinery is made, you will notice pulleys with numerous chains—perhaps four or six. If you pull on one of these you will observe that the pulley travels upward very, very slowly; but you also observe that you have no difficulty in pulling on it. It moves very easily. If a weight of 600 pounds were put on that end of this pulley, it would take a force of only 100 pounds to pull it up (Fig. 8).

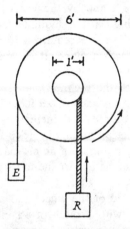
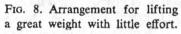

FIG. 8. Arrangement for lifting a great weight with little effort.

FIG. 9. Arrangement for lifting a great weight with application of little force.

There are two kinds of pulleys—the fixed and the movable. The fixed pulley is one with an immovable axis. You pull in one direction in order to make what you are pulling go in the opposite direction. There is no mechanical advantage in such a pulley. It is merely used to lift objects to places where you ordinarily could not lift them; such as, for example, a flag to the top of a flagpole, clothes on a line, etc.

The movable pulley (Fig. 9) is one with an axis free to move. The advantage of such a pulley is dependent on the number of ropes. By pulling with one-pound force, you can lift as many pounds of weight as there are ropes. If there were three pulleys in the system, the advantage would be 3. If there are ten pulleys, the advantage is 10.

Whenever you see a pulley, count the number of supporting chains or ropes which it contains, and you will instantly get the mechanical advantage of that pulley. If it contains six supporting ropes or chains, it means that one pound will lift six; if it contains ten, it means that one pound will lift ten. But naturally the more pounds it will lift per one-pound force, the slower it will move.

THE INCLINED PLANE

Any smooth surface that inclines or goes up is an inclined plane. A hill is an inclined plane. You will recognize that rolling a barrel up an inclined plane requires less force than carrying it up vertically through the same height. The mechanical advantage of an inclined plane can be determined by dividing the length of the plane by the vertical height. Thus an incline 20 feet long and 4 feet high at the summit would have a mechanical advantage of 5. It would therefore require a force of 40 pounds to move a 200-pound barrel up such a plane. It is well to note that in order to lift the barrel vertically up the 4 feet it would be necessary to exert a force of 200 pounds. With the inclined plane, however, a force of 40 pounds is exerted through a distance of 20 feet. The multiplication of the force is obtained at the expense of an increased distance.

Now imagine a road winding around a steep mountain. (See Fig. 10.) Think of this road up a mountain as being a thread of an ordinary screw, for that is exactly what it is like. The *screw* is one of the most powerful machines known.

Understanding the principle of levers and of the wheel and axle, you can readily see that if you have a screw with a pitch of ½ inch (Fig. 11), and you turn it one revolution, you will move the screw up or down (according to the direction you turn it) ½ inch. Now, if an arm 5 feet long is attached to this screw with ½-inch pitch, and the handle of the

FIG. 10. A mountain road as an illustration of the principle of the screw.

arm is moved through one revolution (or 377 inches), the screw would move up or down (according to the direction of the handle) ½ inch, or

1/754 of the distance which the handle moved. This means that if you applied 10 pounds of force to the handle, you could lift a weight of more than 3½ tons. This principle is used in jacks, whereby automobiles

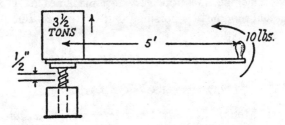

FIG. 11. A screw arrangement for lifting a great weight.

are lifted, houses are moved, and enormous resistances are overcome. The formula for the screw (S = pitch; l = radius turned through; π = 3.1416) is

$$\frac{R}{E} = \frac{2l\pi}{S}$$

The wedge is really a pair of inclined planes back to back. Wedges

FIG. 12. Wedge.

are used to tighten things. The ordinary knife and the chisel are examples of the wedge used as a tool.

To summarize: (1) In any lever the effort times its lever arm (distance from the effort to the fulcrum) always equals the resistance times its lever arm (the distance from the resistance to the fulcrum). For example, a force of 10 pounds over a lever arm of 5 feet is exactly equal to a force of 5 pounds over a lever arm of 10 feet; or a force of 25 pounds over a lever arm of 2 feet, etc. (2) In every machine what you gain in distance you lose in force, and vice versa. (3) Whatever you put into a machine in the way of work (force times distance), you must get out of that machine as work. Allowance must be made for loss of work due to friction in the machine; therefore very few machines have a high efficiency. Perpetual motion is impossible as it contradicts this principle.

DYNAMICS

NEWTON'S LAWS OF MOTION

First Law of Motion: *A body tends to remain in a state of rest or of uniform motion in a straight line unless acted upon by an outside force.* (This is sometimes referred to as the Law of Inertia.)

This means that if you start an object moving, it will keep on moving forever in a straight line until some force stops it. Of course we know that nothing will keep on moving forever, and this law may seem rather absurd. If you will stop to think that friction ultimately brings everything to rest, you will understand this law. A stone set in rapid motion over a frozen lake will come to rest in time, because it is stopped by the force of friction (rubbing of the stone on the ice). Similarly, every other moving object will come to rest in time because of friction. The first part of this law is quite obvious—no object can start of its own free will. Some force must start it.

Second Law of Motion: *A body acted upon by a constant force will move with a constant acceleration in the direction of the force; the amount of acceleration will be directly proportional to the acting force and inversely proportional to the mass of the body.*

Velocity and speed are often confused. *Velocity* has two aspects: size and direction. Speed has only one aspect: size or magnitude. The second law of motion means that a body keeps on increasing in velocity under the influence of a constant force. An automobile to which a constant unbalanced force is applied will go faster and faster, it will gain in *velocity*. The rate of change of velocity is called *acceleration*. Thus an auto which starts from rest and achieves a velocity of 30 miles per hour in 5 seconds is said to have an acceleration of 5 miles per hour per second—usually written: 5 mi./hr./sec. The most common example of acceleration is that of falling bodies. When you drop an object it falls with ever-increasing speed because it is constantly acted upon by a force known as gravity. The acceleration due to gravity is 32 feet per second per second. This means that every second it increases in speed 32 feet per second. The general law of accelerated bodies is given in a simple algebraic formula:

Distance equals ½ the acceleration times the square of the time: or $S = \frac{1}{2}at^2$. The acceleration due to gravity is 32 feet per second per second, so that for falling bodies this formula becomes $S = 16t^2$. For example, in 5 seconds a body will fall 25×16 feet, or 400 feet; in 10 seconds it will fall 1,600 feet.

It is interesting to know that gravity acts independently of outside forces. If a cannon ball, for example, is shot horizontally from a tower 100 feet high at the same time that another cannon ball is merely dropped from the tower, both balls hit the ground at the same instant, even though the first ball traveled some 10 miles while the other ball traveled only 100 feet. The reason for this is simple. At the end of the first second the cannon ball which was shot horizontally is 16 feet nearer the ground re-

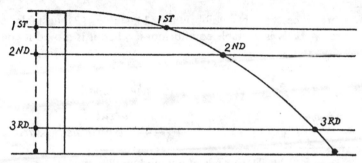

FIG. 13. Newton's Second Law of Motion illustrated by a dropping cannon ball.

gardless of its other position. At the end of the second second it is 48 feet nearer the ground regardless of its position, etc. This is also true of the cannon ball that was merely dropped. Figure 13 explains this more clearly.

Another interesting thing about the acceleration due to gravity is that all bodies fall *with exactly the same speed in vacuum*. A feather and a 10-pound shot, dropped from the same height, would reach the ground at the same time—if it were not for air resistance.

Third Law of Motion: *Action and reaction are equal and opposite.*

This means that when you sit on a chair you are pressing down on it with a force equal to your own weight. The chair, on the other hand, is pressing up on you with exactly the same force. If it were not doing so, you would fall to the ground. If it pushed up on you with a force greater than your own weight, you would go up in the air.

When you say that a floor will sustain a weight of 150 pounds per square foot, it means every square foot of that floor is capable of meeting 150 pounds downward force with 150 pounds upward force.

Newton's Third Law gives us this principle of equilibrium: *For every force pulling one way on a body in equilibrium, there must be an equal and opposite force pulling in the opposite direction.*

Every object has weight or mass, and, while it may not be obvious, the weight of every body acts at a definite point. The weight of a bar, for example, acts at the center point. The weight of a flat disc acts at its center. The weight of an odd-shaped object acts at some point within that object, which can be determined. The point at which the entire weight of a body acts is called the center of gravity, or center of mass; and if an opposing force equal to this weight is applied to that point, the body will be balanced. For example, you can balance a yardstick on a knife edge by putting the knife edge exactly at the 18-inch point, or halfway.

There are three types of equilibrium: (1) stable, (2) unstable, and (3) neutral. A body is in stable equilibrium if when it is moved it comes

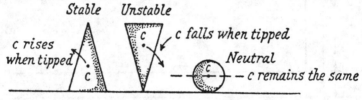

Fig. 14. Three kinds of equilibrium illustrated.

back to its original position. You will note (see Fig. 14) that a wide base, if tipped slightly, will come back to its original position. It can be seen from this that as long as the center of gravity rises when an object is tipped, that object will be in stable equilibrium. In the first figure, C (center of gravity) rises when tipped; in the second figure, C falls when tipped; in the third figure, C remains the same.

A body is in unstable equilibrium if when tipped it does not return to its original position. It falls. In this type of equilibrium the center of gravity is lowered when the object is tipped. Neutral equilibrium takes place only in rolling. The center of gravity is always the same—neither raised nor lowered.

The applications of the principles of equilibrium are numerous. They are the basis of all building and construction as well as mechanical engineering.

THE PENDULUM

The pendulum is a very interesting example of Newton's Laws. A pendulum is a weight hung from a string or stick. When the pendulum is at rest, the string is perpendicular to the ground: it really points to the center of the earth. Here we have action and reaction—equal and opposite in the same straight line (Fig. 15). When the weight is deflected, the action and reaction are not in the same straight line; and if the weight is let go, its tendency is to come back to equilibrium, where it was before it was deflected. Consequently it swings down toward its former position but, by Newton's First Law, continues to swing past its first position. (This is called Inertia.) When it has reached a point on the other side where the downward pull is greater than the swing, it starts back again. The pendulum thus swings from right to left and back again, each time losing a little bit of its inertia, until it finally comes to rest in its original position.

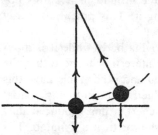

FIG. 15. A swinging pendulum.

The pendulum vibrates to a definite law discovered by Galileo. A pendulum approximately one meter long will swing once a second. This fact is frequently taken advantage of in the pendulum clock. The longer the pendulum the slower it will swing, and vice versa.

FORCE AND WORK

We may define *force* mathematically as mass times acceleration; and *work* as force times distance. In the metric system, the *dyne* is the unit of force, and the *erg* is the unit of work. An erg is the work done by a force of one dyne acting through a distance of one centimeter. A commonly used English unit is the *foot-pound,* which is defined as the work done in raising vertically a weight of one pound through a distance of one foot. Thus an elevator lifting 10 people each weighing 150 pounds, from the bottom to the top of the Empire State Building (1200 ft.), does 1,800,000 foot-pounds of work (disregarding the weight of the elevator). Power is that which connects the important ideas of getting the job done with getting it done in time. The ratio of the work done to the time required to do it is called *power.* The most familiar unit of power is the *horsepower,* which represents 550 foot-pounds of work per second. The *watt* is also a familiar unit of power: it is 1/746 horsepower.

ENERGY

Energy has been defined as the ability to do work. There are two kinds of energy—*potential* and *kinetic.*

Potential energy is stored-up energy. When you wind a clock you are overcoming a certain resistance, and consequently you are doing work.

This work is stored up in the spring of the clock, and the clock is said to have potential energy—it will run for some time, a day or eight days, as the case may be. If you lift an object from the ground, it acquires potential energy because work is done in raising it. This potential energy will quickly be expended if you drop the object.

Kinetic energy is energy possessed by a moving body while it is moving. It is the result of potential energy. It is interesting to note that the sun is our primary source of heat energy. Coal and other fuels have this energy stored up in them in potential form. When we burn fuel, potential energy is liberated in the form of heat. The energy thus produced may be used to generate steam to run a steam engine or turn a dynamo. The dynamo in turn may run an electric railway or light a city, etc. We thus have a continual transformation of energy. Some energy transformations include chemical, mechanical, electrical, magnetic, heat, and light.

In recent years man has learned to unlock the energy in the nucleus of the atom. He is no longer primarily dependent on the sun for his energy. Nuclear energy comes from the conversion of a portion of the matter in the nucleus into energy. Science has discovered that the total amount of matter and energy in the universe is constant, and that one may be converted into the other. Thus we can consider matter as a sort of congealed energy.

MECHANICS OF LIQUIDS

Liquid Pressure

If you fill a glass with water you naturally increase its weight—the water, of course, weighs something. The weight of this water acts on the bottom of the glass. Therefore, the higher the water in the glass, the greater will be the pressure exerted on the bottom of the glass. From

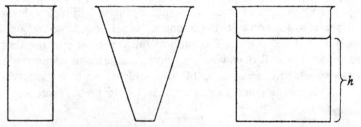

Fig. 16. Three vessels containing the same liquid at the same height.

this we can derive a very simple law: *The pressure of a liquid increases with its depth.*

Suppose a 10-pound weight is resting on a table. It exerts a force of 10 pounds against the table. If the area of the bottom side of the weight is 2 square inches, the force on any one square inch is 5 pounds. The pressure is therefore 5 pounds per square inch. Pressure is the force per unit of area. If two weights of 10 pounds each were standing side by side on the table, a force of 20 pounds would be acting on 4 square inches. The pressure under these weights would still be 5 pounds per square inch. Thus we see that pressure is independent of the area which the force acts upon, since pressure is always referred to a unit of area such as the square foot or square inch.

Liquid pressure therefore depends upon two factors: namely, the *height* and the *density* of the fluid. (Density is the weight per unit volume.) The pressure under any fluid can be found by multiplying the vertical height of the fluid by its density. For example, the pressure under 10 feet of fresh water (density = 62.5 lbs./cubic foot) would be 625 lbs. per sq. ft.

It is interesting to note that regardless of the shape of the vessels, if the height and the density of the liquid they contain is the same, the pressure at the bottom of each container is the same (see Fig. 16).

From what you have read you can understand why water always seeks its own level. Consider two tanks (A and B in Fig. 17) connected by a

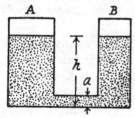

FIG. 17. Two connected tanks.

pipe at the bottom of each. If we pour water into tank A, it flows through the pipe into tank B. When we are through pouring the water we will find that the height of the fluid will be the same in both tanks. This is due to the fact that the pressure at the bottom of both tanks is the same. Adding water to tank A will raise its level, increase the pressure at the bottom, and destroy the balance. Immediately the greater pressure from A will cause a flow to raise the level in B until the two pressures are once again equal. When this happens, the level in both A and B will be the same.

Pascal's Law states that any external force exerted on a unit of area in a confined liquid is transmitted undiminished to every unit of area of the interior of the containing vessel. Thus, assuming we have a huge tank filled with water, at one end of which is an opening one square inch in area, and at the other end there is an opening 100 square inches in area, if we fit each opening with suitable pistons, a one-pound force acting on the one-square-inch piston would cause a pressure of one pound per square inch under the piston. According to Pascal's Law this pressure will be transmitted through the liquid to the bottom of the 100-square-inch piston. With one pound pressing against each square inch of the

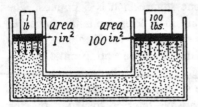

100-square-inch piston, the total force against the piston will be 100 pounds. Thus we have a machine by means of which 1 pound can lift 100 pounds (see Fig. 18). This device is called a hydraulic press and, like any other machine, it gives us a gain in force at the expense of distance, or in this case actually surface.

FIG. 18. The principle of the hydraulic press illustrated by a tank filled with water.

ARCHIMEDES' PRINCIPLE

Archimedes' principle is unquestionably one of the most important laws in physics. Archimedes' principle is that a body immersed in a fluid is buoyed up by a force equal to the weight of the liquid it displaces. When you get into a bathtub filled with water you notice that the water rises—it has to, to make room for your body. You will also notice that your body seems lighter. Its apparent loss of weight equals the weight of water displaced.

When you lift a rock from the bottom of a pool it seems to gain weight as it breaks through the surface. This is due to the fact that the buoyant force (which equaled the weight of the water which the rock displaced) is no longer present when the rock is in the air.

For example, if the rock had a volume of one cubic foot, it would displace one cubic foot of water when submerged, and thus it would appear to lose 62.5 pounds of weight (the weight of one cubic foot of water). If the rock weighed 250 pounds in air, it would weigh 252 − 62.5 pounds, or 187.5 pounds, in water. A body which weighs in air more than the weight of the fluid it displaces will always sink to the bottom of the fluid. However, a body which weighs less than the volume of the fluid it displaces will float. If it is forcibly submerged and then released, the upward or buoyant force will exceed its weight, and it will move upward toward the surface of the fluid. As it breaks through the surface, the volume of fluid it displaces naturally decreases. It continues to rise through the surface until it displaces exactly its own weight in a fluid. A ship which weighs 1000 tons would, when floating, displace 1000 tons of water.

SPECIFIC GRAVITY

The *specific gravity* of a substance is the ratio of the weight of a given volume of that substance to the weight of the same volume of water at 4° C., the temperature at which water is the most dense. When we say a substance has a specific gravity of 1, it means that a cubic foot of that substance weighs exactly the same as a cubic foot of water. If it has a specific gravity of ½, a cubic foot of it weighs half as much as a cubic foot of water.

TABLE OF SPECIFIC GRAVITIES

Platinum	21.5	Hard woods (seasoned)	0.7–1.1
Gold	19.3	Soft woods (seasoned)	0.4–0.7
Mercury	13.6	Ice	0.911
Lead	11.4	Human body	0.9–1.1
Silver	10.5	Cork	0.25
Copper	8.93	Sulphuric acid (conc.)	1.84
Brass	8.4	Sea water	1.03
Iron	7.1–7.9	Milk	1.03
Zinc	7.1	Fresh water	1.00
Glass	2.4–4.5	Kerosene	0.80
Granite, Marble, etc.	2.5–3.0	Gasoline	0.75
Aluminum	2.65	Air	0.0012

According to Archimedes' principle, substances whose specific gravity is less than 1 float in water. Substances whose specific gravity is greater than 1 sink in water. Ice, for example, has a specific gravity of 9/10 and, as a result, floats in water. But it floats in such a way that 9/10 of it is below the surface. This is the reason why only 1/10 of an iceberg is visible. Cork has a specific gravity of about 2/10. The result is that 8/10 of a piece of it in water is above the surface. The specific gravity of a floating substance can usually be determined by the percentage of volume of that substance which is submerged.

When we say that platinum is a very "heavy" metal, we mean that its specific gravity is high (21.5). A cubic foot of platinum weighs 21½ times as much as a cubic foot of water, which weighs 62½ pounds.

SURFACE TENSION AND CAPILLARY ACTION

The best example of surface tension of a liquid is a soap bubble. Here you have an extremely thin film of water in the shape of a sphere enclosing air. This film is on the surface of all water and a similar film is on the surface of all other liquids. This is the result of *cohesion*—the tendency of molecules of the same substance to stick together.

This condition may be illustrated by carefully placing a dry needle or razor blade on the surface of a liquid such as water. The steel, though more dense than water, will rest on the surface and will not sink, because of the cohesion of the water molecules.

The next time you look at a glass of water, notice the rim. You will see that the liquid is drawn up slightly and all around the rim it is slightly concave (see Fig. 19, page 1108). This is the result of *adhesion*—the tendency of molecules of two separate substances to remain in contact. If the glass were a tube 1 inch in diameter, the liquid around the rim having a smaller area would be drawn up considerably higher, and there would be more concavity—because of the adhesion of water molecules to molecules of glass.

Now imagine a tube 1/100 inch in diameter filled with liquid. What would happen? There would be so much surface tension and so little surface that the liquid would actually run up the tube. This is called capillary action, and is familiar to everyone who has used blotting paper or has observed a kerosene lamp wick sucking up oil as the lamp burns. The liquid runs up the tiny fibers of the wick. In a candle the heat melts the paraffin and the melted wax runs up the wick by capillary action.

MECHANICS OF GASES

Suppose you look inside an empty tank in the form of a cylinder. You see that there is nothing in it. But if you were to fit a piston (which would *exactly* fit the tank) that would push down into it, you would soon find out that what you thought was an empty tank had something in it of considerable resistance. Air, when confined in a vessel and compressed, exerts terrific pressure on the sides of the vessel. If the quantity is unchanged and the temperature remains constant, the smaller the volume of air in the vessel, the greater will be the pressure on the sides of the vessel.

This principle is true of any gas, and is made use of in the steam engine, in which enormous quantities of steam are forced into a little box with a piston, the pressure being so great that the piston is pushed out and drives a wheel. The law of pressure is that when we decrease the volume we increase the pressure.

Let us look into this a little more thoroughly. The air in our original tank contains billions and billions of molecules, which are moving with great speed in all directions. These molecules in moving exert a certain amount of pressure on the walls of the tank in bumping against them.

There are a definite number of molecules which are moving in this way. Now suppose we reduce the space by half. There are the same number of molecules in half the original space. Consequently, in traveling the same speed as before, they bump more often on the sides of the vessel, which gives us an increased pressure. If the volume (space) is reduced further, the pressure will be increased proportionately.

Air has weight. The reason you do not feel the weight of the air is because it acts on you equally from all sides. You can raise or lower your arm without the slightest difficulty, and when you put your hand over an empty glass you have no trouble removing it. The reason for this is that the air exerts equal pressure on all sides of your hand. If you place your hand flat on a table the same thing is true. The air under your hand, which seems negligible, is pressing up with just as much force as all the air above your hand.

If, however, you place your hand over the tube attached to a vacuum cleaner and turn on the vacuum cleaner, your hand will be sucked right up against the tube, and you will find it difficult to draw it away. The reason for this is that the air in the tube is pumped away and nothing remains but vacuum when one end of the tube is closed (by your hand). The air on the outside pushes against your hand with the full force of its own weight. There being no air in the vacuum tube, there is consequently no reverse pressure. Air exerts a pressure of 15 pounds on each square inch. The total force against your hand is considerable.

Of course this all refers to air at sea level. The higher up we go, the less the air weighs. That is why climbing a high mountain is so difficult; the pressure up there is only a few pounds per square inch, and human beings are constructed for a pressure of 15 pounds (exactly 14.7 pounds per square inch at sea level). Effects of high-altitude flying are well known. Nose bleeding, difficult breathing, and unconsciousness result from the exceedingly low air pressure. For this reason pressure cabins and oxygen helmets are required for high flying.

If a tube about a meter long is filled with mercury and inverted in a dish of mercury (Fig. 20), the mercury will drop until it is 76 centimeters (30 inches) high, and there it will remain. What keeps the mercury in the tube? Why does it not run out into the dish? The answer is that the atmosphere presses down with a weight of about 15 pounds per square inch all over the surface of the mercury in the dish, and this is enough to support the column of mercury in the tube 30 inches high. In other words, a tube of mercury 1 square inch in diameter and 30 inches high weighs about 15 pounds. The space in the tube above the mercury is almost a vacuum.

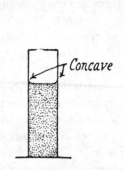

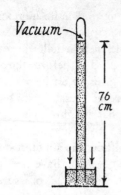

FIG. 19. Concavity of the   FIG. 20. Mercury in a tube
surface of water.   a meter long.

If this apparatus were taken to the top of a very high mountain, the
mercury would be much lower in the tube, because of the reduction in
atmospheric pressure. That is how aviators tell altitude. They have an
instrument which records the decrease in atmospheric pressure as they
go higher, and from this their altitude is determined. This instrument is
an altimeter.

Inasmuch as mercury weighs about 13.6 times as much as water, it
follows that the atmosphere will push water up a pipe 13.6 times as high as
30 inches, or about 34 feet. When we pump water in a well which is less
than 34 feet below the surface, we are really making the atmosphere push
the water up the pipe and out the spout, for that is exactly how a pump

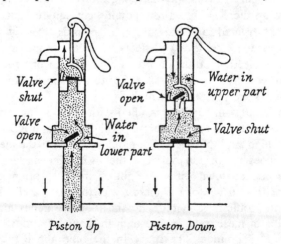

FIG. 21. The operation of a water pump.

works. The simplest kind of a pump consists of a cylinder into which fits a piston with a valve in it (Fig. 21). When the piston is pushed down the piston valve opens, and when it is pulled up the valve closes. There is also a spout in the upper portion of the cylinder, and from the bottom of the cylinder a pipe runs to the water. When the piston is pulled up it sucks the air out of the cylinder by way of the spout. This causes a vacuum, with a consequent rush of water up the pipe, because of atmospheric pressure on the water outside the lower end of the pipe. The water fills the cylinder under the piston.

When the piston is pushed down, the piston valve opens again and water pours into the upper part of the cylinder. When the piston is pulled up again, the valve closes and lifts this water to the spout through which it passes. This is briefly the principle of the pump.

The medicine dropper works on the same principle. You squeeze air out of it when you squeeze the bulb, and when you put it in the liquid, the liquid rushes up into it—pushed up by atmospheric pressure. The same is true when you drink anything through a straw. You first suck all the air out of the straw and up comes the liquid to take the place of the air.

EXPANSION OF LIQUIDS

Liquids, like solids, expand with almost irresistible force when they are heated. Water, like most substances, expands when heated, except near the freezing point. There is a point just slightly above the freezing point at which water will expand whether it is heated or whether it is cooled. Naturally, when water expands, it becomes lighter—steam is lighter than water and so is ice. It follows then that this point, which is 4° C., is the point at which water is the most dense. Thus one cubic centimeter of water weighs exactly one gram at 4° C. If it is cooled to zero degrees C. or below, it expands, and one cubic centimeter then weighs less than one gram (floats on water). If it is heated, it weighs less than a gram and keeps on getting lighter until the boiling point is reached, when it goes off in steam.

When the water in a lake freezes, a very curious phenomenon takes place. When the water at the surface reaches 4° C. it becomes heavier than the water beneath it, and consequently it goes to the bottom, and the water underneath comes up to the surface to be cooled in its turn to 4° C. This keeps up until the entire depth of the water in the lake has reached an even 4° C.; at that point the surface water becomes chilled further, with the result that ice is formed. Ice, being lighter than water, remains at the top.

HEAT

EXPANSION OF METALS

We all know that when brakes are applied to the wheels of a locomotive, or a knife is applied to the grindstone, numerous sparks result. Where do these sparks come from, and why do the locomotive brakes and the knife become hot? To understand this, we must know something about the nature of heat.

Heat is a form of energy. Heat arises from the rapid motion of molecules. When you rub your hands together the heat which results from the friction is due to the setting in rapid motion of molecules. When you light a candle, heat is produced by what is known as rapid oxidation, and it takes the form of rapid motion of the molecules making up the products of combustion. Let us imagine a hollow sphere about an inch in diameter. Inside this sphere there are millions of tiny molecules of air. All these molecules are moving about helter-skelter and bumping repeatedly against the sides of the sphere. If the air inside the sphere were heated, the molecules would move faster and consequently would bump against the sides of the sphere more frequently. The result would be a tendency to stretch or expand the sphere, because of this terrifically swift bombardment of molecules and the heat which it produces. Whenever you heat anything it expands for this reason. You heat a piece of iron and set its molecules into rapid vibration, causing the iron to expand in proportion to the amount you heat it.

The amount a metal will expand depends upon its nature and the intensity of the heat applied to it. For example, if we were to heat ten different metals to the same temperature, we would find that each one expands differently, some considerably more than others. The fact that mercury expands a great deal when heated is taken advantage of in the making of thermometers. On the other hand, the negligible expansion of invar (nickel steel) is made use of in the manufacture of precise and accurate instruments which can operate in almost any temperature.

The amount which a metal expands per degree of heat is called the *coefficient of linear expansion,* and is always figured as a percentage of its size. When we say that the coefficient of linear expansion of zinc is .000029 per degree of heat, we mean that a bar of zinc one foot long will expand 29/1,000,000 of a foot when heated one degree. The table following gives you the coefficient of expansion of a number of metals. Notice the extremely small coefficient of expansion of invar; zinc expands more than thirty times as much as invar.

Table of Coefficients of Expansion

Zinc	0.000029	Cast iron	0.000011
Lead	0.000029	Steel	0.000010
Aluminum	0.000023	Platinum	0.000009
Tin	0.000022	Glass	0.000009
Silver	0.000019	Pyrex glass	0.0000032
Brass	0.000019	Invar	0.0000009
Copper	0.000017		

What is the use of all this explanation about expansion? What practical value has it? If we did not know exactly how much different metals expand, all of our railroads, modern buildings, and machinery would be in a sad state.

For example, the cables in the huge George Washington Bridge over the Hudson River are capable of enormous expansion, and this must be allowed for in the design and construction. It may seem trivial to you that steel expands only 1/100,000 of its length for each degree of heat, but when you consider this mass of steel, thousands of feet long, and the variations of temperature which it is subjected to, from zero in the winter to between 90° and 100° in the summer, you will realize that this apparently trivial matter has assumed large proportions. This same principle must be taken into account in laying railroad tracks, and in making all kinds of machinery.

In any experiments in the physical or chemical laboratory which require accuracy, the temperature is nearly always considered, and every effort is made to maintain an even degree of heat.

You know that when you pour boiling water into a glass vessel, the vessel will break. This is because glass does not conduct heat rapidly, and the inside of the vessel expands while the outside does not, and something must give way to this irresistible force. If you have trouble opening a container fitted with a metal screw cap, the obvious thing to do is heat the cap and it will come off easily.

Thermometers

There are three thermometer scales. One you are undoubtedly familiar with. It fixes the freezing point of water (or the melting point of ice) at 32 degrees, and the boiling point of water (or the condensing point of steam) at 212 degrees. This thermometer is called the Fahrenheit, after its inventor.

A scale with which you are perhaps less familiar is the Centigrade. The freezing point of water (or the melting point of ice) on the Centigrade thermometer is zero, and the boiling point of water (or condensing point of steam) is 100 degrees. Because of its extreme simplicity, this scale is always used in chemistry and physics.

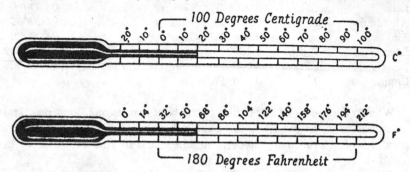

FIG. 22. Centigrade and Fahrenheit thermometer scales compared.

The third scale is used almost entirely for gases, and is called the Absolute thermometer. We have already learned that when you heat a gas it expands. As a matter of fact, it has been definitely proved that all gases expand 1/273 of their volume for every degree Centigrade that they are heated. It is also true that they shrink or contract 1/273 of their volume for every degree Centigrade that they are cooled. Thus if we had a volume of gas at a temperature of 0° C. and cooled it 10°, it would contract 10/273 of its volume. Theoretically, if we cooled it 273°, its volume would vanish. This hypothetical temperature, 273° below zero C., is known as the *absolute zero*. At this temperature all molecular motion would cease. So far, scientists, in their experiments, have not succeeded in reaching it, although some gases have been liquefied at temperatures as low as 272° below zero C.

Since 100 divisions of the Centigrade scale are equivalent to 180 divisions of the Fahrenheit scale (the interval between freezing point and boiling point of water on both scales), 1° Centigrade is equal to 180/100, or 9/5 of a degree Fahrenheit. To change Centigrade to Fahrenheit, we must therefore multiply each degree Centigrade by 9/5 and add 32 degrees.

For example, 20° C. is 20° above the freezing point on the Centigrade scale. Applying our formula, 20° C. is 20 × 9/5, or 36 degrees above the freezing point Fahrenheit. Therefore we see that 36 degrees above freezing is 68° (since the freezing point on the Fahrenheit scale is 32°).

To change Fahrenheit to Centigrade, we perform this computation in reverse—that is, we subtract 32 degrees and take 5/9 of the resulting number. For example, 212° F. equals 212° minus 32°, or 180° × 5/9, which equals 100° C.

CONVECTION

Hot-water heating systems operate on the basis that a given fluid is less dense when warm. As warm water rises to the top it is constantly replaced by cold water. Thus circulation of the water continues so long as heat is applied.

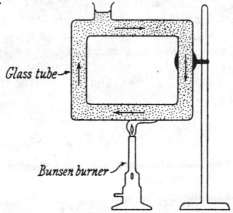

FIG. 23. The warm water rises and is replaced by cool water; thus there is constant circulation.

This principle can be illustrated by filling a glass ring with water, applying heat, and then dropping a few colored crystals of potassium permanganate through the opening at the top. The path taken by the colored water is indicated by the arrows.

The same principle is applied to ventilation and tells why windows are opened from top and bottom.

CONDUCTORS

Metals are good conductors of heat. This means that they become hot quickly when subjected to heat. If you put a silver teaspoon into a cup of boiling water, it is not long before the handle of the teaspoon becomes very hot. It would be very foolish indeed to attempt to use an old-fashioned flatiron after the bottom had been heated without putting an asbestos cloth over the handle. It is because metals are good conductors of heat that coffee percolators, electric irons, pokers, etc., usually have wooden handles, or handles made of some material that is a poor conductor of heat. Silver and copper are the best-known conductors of heat. Glass and wood, on the other hand, are poor conductors. A vacuum is an extremely poor conductor, and this fact is t   advantage of in the thermos bottle, which is so constructed that a liquid can be kept hot in a vessel which is insulated from the outside air by a vacuum. The vacuum prevents the heat from penetrating the outside wall of the bottle and escaping into the air. It also keeps the outside air, which is much cooler than the liquid within the bottle, from chilling the contents of the vessel.

Thermo-equilibrium occurs at the point where two substances of different temperatures become equal in temperature. How often have you heard people say, "Drink your coffee before it gets cold"? What is really meant by this is, "Drink your coffee before it has lost heat to the air, and the air has gained heat accordingly." In other words, "Drink your coffee before it becomes the same temperature as the air." The same is true, of course, of cold substances, and in summer we must hurry and eat our ice cream before it all melts and becomes the same temperature as the air in the room.

RADIATION

A hot object radiates heat in all directions. The radiation emitted from such a body travels at the amazing speed of 186,000 miles per second. This heat is fundamentally the same thing as light, except that you feel it instead of seeing it. If you heat a piece of iron slightly, it will give off heat which you can feel but cannot see. We speak of this as infrared radiation. When infrared strikes opaque objects, it sets the molecules of the object into motion, thus producing heat. If you heat the piece of iron long enough, the amount of radiation which comes from it becomes greater and greater, until it reaches the point where it is visible as a dull red, then as a lighter red, then yellow, and finally white (whence our expressions "red hot" and "white hot"). At white heat, of course, there is a considerable amount of light. As we continue to heat an object, it begins to radiate light to which our eyes are not sensitive. This is ultraviolet light. We shall also learn, under the subject of light, that radiation is a wave motion, and the number of vibrations per second determines whether we can see the radiation or merely feel it. Heat from the sun comes to us by radiation. Heat radiation is a wave process similar to light and radio waves but involves waves of different wave lengths.

Radiation can be reflected and transmitted in the same way that light can. The ordinary electric heater is an example of the reflection of radiation. The heater has a hot piece of metal in the center, and a reflecting surface. The metal glows with red heat set up by electricity running through it, and the rays are thrown out from the reflecting surface. If the reflecting surface were lacking, the radiation would be dissipated in all directions instead of in one direction.

A reading glass brings all the rays of the sun to one point. When the rays of the sun are concentrated in such a small area they are greatly increased in power, and it is possible to set fire to a paper or burn dry leaves merely by holding a reading glass in one place with the sun shining upon it.

Heat Engines

Heat is a form of energy, and as such can do work. Man has devised several types of engines which transform heat energy into the energy of mechanical motion.

In the *steam engine,* steam under pressure is led into a cylinder where it pushes a piston back and forth as it expands. In the double-acting steam engine, steam is admitted alternately to opposite sides of the piston by means of a slide valve operated by the shaft of the engine itself. The used steam is pushed out of the cylinder into the exhaust pipe.

In the *steam turbine,* expanding steam flows against the blades of a series of wheels, causing them to turn at high speed. After passing through the vanes of a movable wheel, the steam is redirected by vanes on a fixed wheel to strike the vanes of the next movable wheel.

The *gasoline engine* used in modern automobiles and airplanes is called an *internal-combustion* engine because the fuel is burned inside of the cylinder. (In the steam engine, the fuel is burned outside of the cylinder, and it is called an *external-combustion* engine.) In one type of gasoline engine, called the four-stroke-cycle internal-combustion engine, hot gases produced by the rapid burning of the fuel and air mixture drive a piston down the length of the cylinder. If intake and exhaust valves are placed in each cylinder, exhaust gases may be pushed out and a new charge sucked in.

The *diesel engine* is similar to the gasoline engine except that pure fuel is sprayed into the cylinder, where it ignites on contact with air, because the air has been previously heated by compression. Thus the diesel engine uses a fuel injector and it does not require a spark-plug ignition system.

The *rocket engine* operates according to Newton's Law of Action and Reaction. When a bullet is fired from a gun, the gun has a kick backward as the bullet fires forward. In the same manner, as gas streams from an opening at the rear of the rocket, the rocket itself is pushed forward. The thrust is produced by the constant burning of the fuel in an atmosphere of pure oxygen. The main difference between a rocket and a jet lies in the fact that a rocket carries its own supply of both fuel and oxygen, while the jet carries only the fuel and depends upon atmospheric oxygen for its burning.

The *turbo-jet,* which is the most common form of jet engine for aircraft, operates in this fashion: A compressor wheel (Fig. 24) is attached by shaft S to a turbine wheel. In starting, the shaft is rotated rapidly. The vanes on the rotating compressor force air at high speed into the combustion chamber beyond. Fuel is injected into this chamber, mixed with the air, and exploded. The explosion proceeds toward the rear faster than toward the front, since the wall of incoming air limits

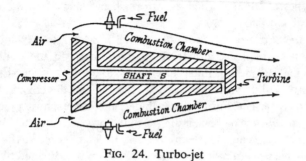

FIG. 24. Turbo-jet

the spread of the explosion in that direction. Gases passing over the turbine wheel on their way out of the exhaust pipe cause the compressor wheel to turn more rapidly and thus continue to feed air for the explosion and to act as a solid wall against the force of expansion. Thus considerable thrust backward is developed, and the engine is pushed forward. Once started, ignition of the fuel is sustained by the high temperature of the walls of the combustion chamber.

SOUND

Sound is caused by vibrating matter. If you strike a bell, it gives off a metallic sound. What you really do is to set the metal in very rapid vibration. This rapid vibration "moves" the air all around the bell in exact accordance with the way it vibrates. Waves of air set up which travel from the bell with a velocity of about 1,100 feet per second in all directions. These waves beating against our eardrums cause the sensation we know as sound.

Any vibrating object will produce a musical note provided it vibrates uniformly and fast enough. If you could take a metal bar and move it up and down in the air forty times per second, you would hear a very low note. If you could increase the motion and move it, say, one hundred times per second, the note would become clearer and higher. The more rapidly this metal bar is vibrated, the higher would be the resulting note. When we strike a tuning fork, we set the prongs in very rapid vibration, with the result that a musical note is given off. The rate of vibration of most tuning forks is known, and when you have your piano tuned, you will notice that the first thing the tuner does is to take out his fork and test a certain note on the piano with the note of his fork. The violinist "tuning up" is adjusting the tension of his strings until the vibration of each strikes the required note.

If you put an electric bell in a jar and send a current through it, you will hear the bell ring through the jar. If you exhaust the air from that jar and send a current through the bell, you won't hear a sound. Without air there can be no sound, so that if it were possible to visit the moon, no such thing as conversation or music could take place there, because there is no atmosphere.

We find, on examination, that sound waves arise from the condensation and rarefaction of air. The air is normally "even." When a sound wave passes through air, we get a series consisting of condensed areas followed by rarefied areas. These correspond to the crests (high points) and troughs (low points) of a water wave. The distance between crest and crest or trough and trough is the *wave length*. Sound waves travel with great speed. Thus, if we strike middle C on the piano, the air around us is set in vibration 256 times per second; 256 little waves of condensation and rarefaction reach our eardrums every second, setting them in motion and producing a tone which we recognize as middle C. If C an octave higher is struck, the air is set in vibration 512 times per second—that is, twice as many little waves reach our eardrums per second

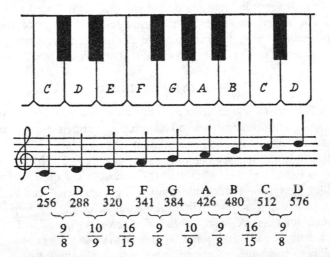

FIG. 25. The relationship between the notes that comprise an octave on the musical scale.

as before. If C an octave lower is struck, 128 or half as many vibrations are sent out. The whole musical scale is a series of vibrations in definite ratio to one another. This is given on page 1117: the first row of numerals gives the frequency per second of vibrations; the second row, the ratio of the frequency of vibrations of each note to the one following it.

These ratios determine the musical character of the intervals. When the ratio of two frequencies is 9/8 or 10/9 they are said to differ by a whole tone, while those whose ratio is 16/15 are said to be a half tone apart.

VELOCITY OF SOUND

The velocity of sound in air varies with the temperature. At 0° C. sound travels 1090 feet per second, increasing two feet per second for every degree rise in temperature. It is an interesting experiment to determine how far away a thunderstorm is by counting the number of seconds between the lightning and the resulting thunder. We know that they both take place simultaneously. We also know that the velocity of light is almost instantaneous for distances on the earth (186,000 miles per second). Therefore all we need to do is count the number of seconds and multiply by the velocity of sound and the approximate distance of the storm is instantly found.

Sound travels in water about four and one half times as fast as it does in air. Devices for testing the depth of the ocean are based on this fact. A huge gong is sounded under water and the interval between the sound and its echo is recorded and multiplied by 4820 (the speed of sound in water). The sound travels from the gong to the bottom of the ocean and is reflected back to the surface. The distance it travels is timed, and divided by two. The depth of the ocean at that point is readily obtained.

REFLECTION OF SOUND

The reflection of sound is known as the *echo,* which is familiar to everyone. As children we have all shouted in tunnels or against stone walls and heard our own echo come back at us.

Sound shadows are very common. They are very much like ordinary shadows of light. A cliff or a building will suddenly cut off a sharp sound. Sound, like light, is best reflected from hard, polished surfaces, and consequently, in gauging acoustics in building, it is obviously important to avoid such surfaces. A highly polished marble wall, or hard, bare expanse of wall, is undesirable for acoustic purposes unless it is so constructed as to focus the reflecting sound in the right direction.

Carnegie Hall, in New York, is one of the best examples of excellent acoustics in the world. High above the stage, in the ceiling, there is a huge hollowed spherical section, so gauged that sound coming from the stage is reflected to the audience throughout the entire hall. It is a remarkable thing that in the top gallery, some 200 feet from the stage, one can hear clearly the lightest notes of a pianist on the stage.

Draperies absorb sound. The more draperies in a room, the less the sound will be reflected. This is only natural when you stop to think that these tiny air waves which vibrate so rapidly are smothered as soon as they hit heavy cloth. They are absorbed, as it were, and all possible chance of reflection is eliminated. Long wave lengths have much more penetrating power than short ones. The low notes of a piano or violin can be heard more distinctly in the next room, with the door closed, than the high notes. The ticking of a watch, which sends out extremely high frequency waves, cannot be heard at all if you put a thin board between it and your ear.

Have you ever noticed how a grand piano or harp is constructed? If you have, you observed that the wires which produce the low notes in the bass are very long compared with the short wires in the high treble. That is what gives the piano and harp their characteristic shape. What is true for the piano is also true for the organ, in which there are pipes varying from several feet to several inches in length and with varying widths. Have you ever noticed a trombone player—how he is constantly changing the length of the trombone? If he wants a low note, he makes the instrument longer; if the note is high, the instrument is short. Cellos are really overgrown violins, and bass viols are even larger.

All this merely means one thing: namely, that the longer the wire in a string instrument, or the air column in a wind instrument, the lower will be the frequency of vibration, and the lower will be the note.

REPRODUCTION OF SOUND

Sound may be reproduced in various ways. The telephone, the radio, and the phonograph are examples. We shall discuss the first two later, under the subject of electricity; we describe phonographic reproduction of sound here briefly. In recording sound on a phonographic record, a microphone picks up the sound, electronic circuits amplify it and cause the needle to vibrate, which then impresses lines of varying characteristics on the wax record, according to the needle vibration. This original record is then treated by a process which enables thousands of copies to be made. In the playing of a copy—the regular phonograph disk used in homes—a needle passes over the grooves and picks up the vibrations.

These vibrations are transmitted to a crystal or magnetic cartridge. This in turn changes them into electrical charges which activate a loud-speaker, thus reproducing the sound originally recorded on the disk.

MUSICAL SOUNDS

A musical sound is different from a noise. When we hear a musical note and compare it with the rattling of a motor truck or an elevated train, we realize that there is a tremendous difference. The difference lies in the fact that in a musical tone the frequency of vibration is uniform and regular. The vibrations pour out at the rate of exactly so many per second. In a noise the vibrations are irregular. They have no system, and they come from the source to your ear helter-skelter.

There are three fundamental characteristics of musical tones, as follows: (1) *Pitch* has to do entirely with the frequency of vibration—the higher the frequency, the higher the pitch. (2) *Intensity* has to do entirely with the volume of sound and the energy of vibration and varies with the amplitude of the sound wave. A loud note on the piano results when you hit the note hard. If you hit the same note gently, the tone will not be so loud. This is due entirely to the energy with which the string vibrates, and has nothing to do with the pitch. (3) *Quality* or *timbre,* a rather complex characteristic, enables us to distinguish one instrument from another. When you strike a note—for example, E—on the piano, and play the same E on the violin, both strings vibrate with the same frequency and their intensity may be exactly the same, yet the quality is entirely different, and you can easily tell which is the violin and which is the piano note. This difference is due to overtones which produce changes in wave shape.

Some definite laws of vibrating strings are:

(1) The frequency of vibration of a string is inversely proportional to its length. The longer the string, the less its vibration and the lower the note. The shorter the string, the more its vibration and the higher the note.

(2) The vibration frequency is directly proportional to the square root of the tension. This merely means that the greater the tension or pull on the string, the greater will be the frequency and the higher will be the note.

(3) The vibration frequency is inversely proportional to the square root of the density. In other words, the thinner the string, the greater the frequency and the higher the note.

All these laws can be easily demonstrated by examining the strings of a grand piano and noting the long, heavy coils in the base, the varying length of the strings through the middle part, and the short, thin, extremely tight strings in the high treble.

Almost the same laws apply to columns of air. In other words, the frequency of vibration of an air column, such as an organ or any other wind instrument, is inversely proportional to its length. The longer the pipe in an organ, the deeper the note. The shorter the pipe, the higher the note.

LIGHT

Light, like sound, is caused by wave motion. It differs from sound, however, in the nature of its motion and its velocity. Sound waves are a series of condensations and rarefactions—they are longitudinal vibrations. Sound waves can exist only in solids, liquids, or gases. Light, on the other hand, is a transverse wave motion and does not necessarily need a solid, liquid, or gas to conduct it. The light from the sun penetrates 93,000,000 miles of space which is practically a vacuum, for there is no atmosphere between the earth's atmosphere and the sun. It is thought that this wave motion is transmitted through the vacuum, sometimes called the ether, which fills all the space in the universe not otherwise occupied. Sound travels about 1,100 *feet* per second. Light, on the other hand, travels at the amazing speed of 186,000 *miles* per second.

We see most things by reflected light—that is, some definite source of light shines upon them and the reflection penetrates the retina of the eye and causes the sensation of sight. We never see by direct light unless we happen to stare at the sun, or at a brilliant incandescent bulb or some other luminous object. Nearly all reflection that we see is diffused; that is, the light is scattered. The powerful light of the sun shines through the atmosphere, lighting it up in the soft, beautiful sky blue which we call daylight. On a cloudy day the sky is white and we see everything by this light. The white of the sky is merely diffused reflection.

When a beam of light strikes a highly polished surface, its direction is immediately changed—it is reflected. If the beam of light strikes the surface at an angle, it will be reflected from that surface at the same angle. The most familiar reflecting surface is a plane mirror. It may be proved very easily by plane geometry that an object is as far in front of a plane mirror as the image appears to be behind it; in other words, the mirror is halfway between object and image. Eye doctors with small offices frequently make use of this fact by placing the eye chart above the patient and making him look in a mirror at the other end of the room. The effect is as though the room were twice as long.

A spherical mirror is one in which the reflecting surface is a portion of a sphere. The amount of curvature of the mirror depends upon the radius of the sphere of which it is a section. When the reflecting surface is *outside* the sphere, the mirror is *convex*. When the reflecting surface is *inside* the sphere, the mirror is *concave*.

When parallel light rays strike a conca e spherical mirror, the rays are brought down to a common point of intersection known as the principal focus. This is shown in Figure 26. Notice how the rays of light are all parallel to one another until they strike the concave surface of the mirror.

When a beam of parallel light strikes a plane mirror, the rays of light are all reflecting parallel to one another, both before and after the beam strikes the mirror. When a beam of light strikes a white surface such as snow, the reflected rays are not parallel—they are sent out in every direction. To make this a little clearer, imagine a small piece of ice whose highly polished surface reflects a beam of light to your eye. You see this by direct reflection because its rays commonly are reflected to your eye in the same parallel way that they struck the reflecting surface of the ice. If now you crush the ice into millions of tiny pieces, the reflected rays are sent out in all directions and the ice appears white. This is precisely the reason that snow appears white.

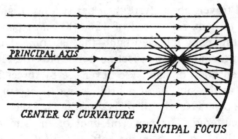

FIG. 26. A concave mirror focusing rays of light at a single point.

REFRACTION OF LIGHT

The velocity of light is diminished when it travels through a medium denser than air; *e.g.*, the velocity of light in glass, quartz, or water is less than the velocity of light in air. The light is, in a manner of speaking, retarded. It is very much like an army of soldiers marching eight abreast with a definite speed on a smooth pavement. As soon as they come to a rough pavement they slow up, and as you can see in Figure 27, the first man of the eight reaches the rough pavement first and starts traveling slower than the eighth man; then the second man reaches the rough pavement and keeps abreast of the first man while the other six are marching with the original speed on the smooth pavement. The result is a bending

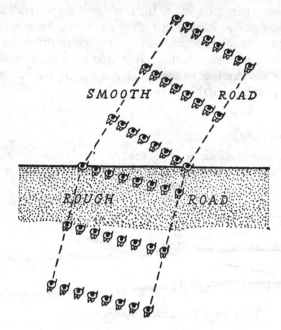

FIG. 27. The refraction of light compared to a line of marching soldiers.

of the line. This is exactly what happens when a beam of light penetrates water, glass, or other media denser than air. This phenomenon is known as refraction—the light is bent. That is why an oar will look bent when it is half out of water, or a spoon in a glass of water will appear bent. Some interesting illusions result from this.

Let a beam of light penetrate a glass jar of water from below (in Fig. 28a). According to the law of refraction it will emerge from the water

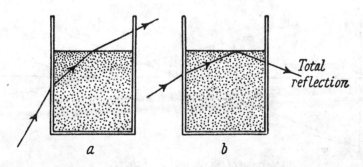

FIG. 28. A beam of light in a glass jar of water.

bent away from a perpendicular to the surface of the water. There will be a point, however (Fig. 28b), at which the reflected beam will be so far bent away from this perpendicular that it will be in the water itself, and the result will be internal reflection. Just hold up a glass of water above your eye: the undersurface of the water is a mirror and you will see the reflection of your hand in this surface.

LENSES

There are two main kinds of lenses. A *convex* lens is thicker in the middle than it is at the edges. A *concave* lens is thinner at the center

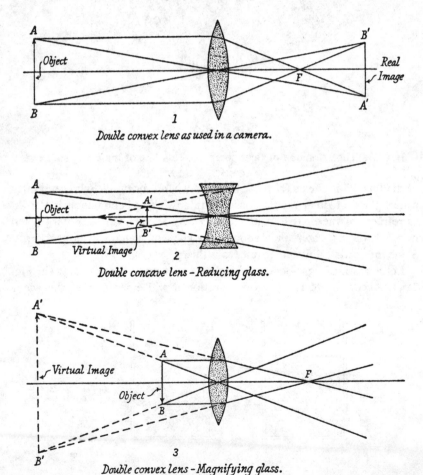

Double convex lens as used in a camera.

Double concave lens – Reducing glass.

Double convex lens – Magnifying glass.

FIGS. 29, 30, 31. Various kinds and uses of lenses.

than at the edges. Parallel rays of light passing through a convex lens are refracted in much the same way as they are reflected from the concave mirror. They all come to a point called the principal focus. There is, however, a point in the lens through which a ray of light passes without any refraction whatever. This is called the optical center. Bearing all this in mind, you can see with the aid of Figures 29, 30, and 31, how images are formed by means of a lens. (F is the principle focus of the lens.)

THE TELESCOPE

The principle of the telescope is extremely simple. Light from a distant object passes through two convex lenses. The first lens produces a small inverted image which is then enlarged by the second lens. In the terrestrial telescope a lens is placed between the two to re-invert the image as shown in Figure 32.

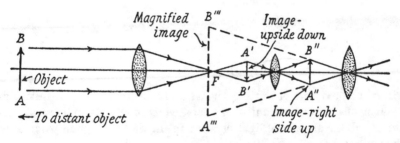

FIG. 32. The arrangement of lenses in a telescope.

THE CAMERA

The camera is a black box on the inside of which is a ground-glass screen. A movable lens is placed in such a way that the outside objects may be clearly pictured upon the ground-glass screen by adjusting to the proper focal length. By sliding a sensitized plate between the ground glass and the lens and exposing it, a permanent picture or negative results.

THE HUMAN EYE

The eye is essentially a camera in which the cornea (C in Fig. 33), a liquid known as the aqueous humor (A), and the crystalline lens (L) act as one single lens and form on the retina or back of the eye an image of whatever we look at. This retina is made up of thousands of little nerves connected with the optic nerve, which transmits the sensation to our brain.

Unlike the camera, in which the lens is moved back and forth in accordance with the varying focal length, the distance from the crystalline lens to the retina remains fixed. Nature takes care of the adjustment for distances by a muscular variation in this lens. Thus, for near-by objects the muscles automatically make the lens thicker; and for distant objects they automatically make it thinner. This variation in the thickness of this marvelous little lens (which is a gelatin composition and clearer than any manufactured lens) takes care of the varying focal length in exactly the same way as the moving back and forth of the lens of a camera. The

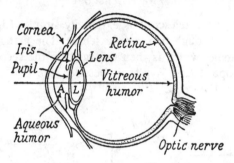

FIG. 33. The human eye.

iris, or colored part of the eye (usually brown or blue), is a little diaphragm of muscles in front of the lens which contracts or expands according to the amount of light present. In the dark, the pupil is large; in the light, it is small.

Sometimes it happens that the crystalline lens is slightly out of adjustment—that the image is formed either in front of or behind the retina; and when it strikes the retina, it is blurred. This may be remedied by placing before the retina a corrective pair of lenses, commonly known as eyeglasses.

COLOR

When a beam of white light is sent through a prism (Fig. 34), a rainbow or spectrum results. As the white light passes through the prism and is dispersed, it is broken into its component colors. The red light, which vibrates slowest and has the longest wave length, is bent the least, while the violet light, which has the highest frequency and consequently the shortest wave length, is bent the most. Other colors appear in between the red and the violet, depending on their frequency. The band of color composed of red, orange, yellow, green, blue, indigo, and violet light is called a spectrum.

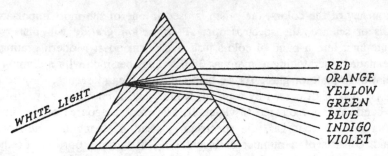

FIG. 34. White light as broken up by a prism.

The visible spectrum is only a small portion of the waves sent out by the light into which white light breaks up. There is a long extended portion beyond the violet, known as the ultraviolet, and a long portion beyond the red, known as the infra-red, neither of which the eye can see.

When we say that the spectrum is made up of seven colors we must remember that we do so merely for convenience. The spectrum consists of these colors and all the gradations (wave lengths) between them. White light is made up of all the colors. If we shine a beam of white light on a red tie, the tie appears red because the material absorbs all colors except red, and it reflects the red light to our eye. A purple tie (purple, you will note, is not a color in the spectrum) appears purple in white light because all colors except red and blue are absorbed. When the reflected red and blue light strikes our retina we get the sensation of seeing purple.

A blue tie in green light will appear black, since all the light which strikes the tie is absorbed and none reflected to our eye. Black is the absence of all light.

PIGMENTS

When we mix various colors of light, the color which results comes from the *addition* of the colors. When we mix paints or pigments, however, the resulting color comes from *subtracting* colors. For example, a blue paint generally reflects violet, blue, and green though it appears blue to the eye. A yellow paint generally reflects red, yellow, and green. Mixing the blue with the yellow paint results in green because green is the only color reflected by both pigments.

THE SPECTROSCOPE

Because a glass prism will arrange the light passing through it into a definite pattern which corresponds to the scale of increasing wave-length frequency of the colors, the prism is used in one of the most important tools of science, the spectroscope. A *diffraction grating* will disperse white light into a band of colors just as a prism does. Modern gratings are made by scratching as many as 30,000 lines per inch with a diamond point on a plate of glass. As we heat solids to incandescence, they emit light which, if dispersed by a prism, would yield a continuous spectrum or band ranging from red to violet. If, however, the source of the light is an incandescent gas, the spectrum, instead of being a continuous band, consists of a number of bright lines in various portions of the spectrum with no light between them. In fact, a particular gas, when incandescent, always emits the same lines regardless of where it may be. For example, if the light from a neon sign were analyzed by a spectroscope we would see that it always produces a spectrum consisting of many lines in the red region, several in the orange and yellow, and a few in the blue and violet. This same combination of lines is found in the spectra of certain stars. We can thus be sure that they contain neon. By means of the spectroscope we can analyze the various components of gaseous materials and even determine the presence of minute amounts of impurity.

WAVE MOTION IN GENERAL

The nature of wave motion is best understood if we use, as an example, water waves which appear on the surface of a pond when we throw in a small stone. The point at which the stone hits the water is the center of disturbance, and waves appear in circles around this center. It is important to note that it is the energy of the disturbance which causes the waves, and that the water itself does not move outward from the center. This is seen clearly if a twig or leaf is floating on the pond. The twig or leaf merely bobs up and down at right angles to the direction of wave movement, and does not move outward from wave to wave.

Certain kinds of waves need a physical medium for their transmission, while others do not. Mechanical waves, such as sound, require a physical medium; the medium may be solid or liquid or gas. Electromagnetic waves, such as heat and light, do not; they travel primarily in the vacuum between particles of matter.

All waves are characterized by wave length, velocity, and frequency. *Velocity* refers to both the rate and direction of movement. *Wave length,* as we have seen, is the distance between two crests of a wave. *Frequency* may be described as the number of crests passing a given point per unit of time. The velocity is equal to the frequency multiplied by the wave length.

The velocity of a wave depends upon the nature of the medium through which the wave travels. For mechanical waves, like sound, the velocity increases as the rigidity of the medium increases, and decreases as the density of the medium increases. For example, sound travels in air at about 1,100 feet per second (at ordinary room temperature); in water, at about 5,000 ft./sec.; in ice, at about 10,500 ft./sec.; and in cast iron, at about 15,000 ft./sec. Although air is less dense than water, sound travels through water much faster because water has more rigidity than air. Ice is less dense than water, but is far more rigid—hence sound travels through ice twice as fast.

For electromagnetic waves, the opposite situation exists. Light travels through a diamond—a substance of high density and high rigidity—only about half as fast as through air. In a vacuum, however, all electromagnetic waves travel at a speed of approximately 186,000 miles per second.

The frequency of a wave governs an important characteristic of sound and light waves. In sound, this is *pitch*—the higher the frequency, the higher the pitch. Middle C on the piano has a frequency of 256 vibrations per second; E in the same octave has 320 vibrations per second. In the case of light, the corresponding characteristic governed by frequency is *color*. Lower frequencies give us *red* light; higher frequencies appear as *blue* or *violet* light.

MAGNETISM AND ELECTRICITY

Everyone is familiar with the old horseshoe magnet. We all played with it when we were children. We watched it pick up small bits of steel, needles, nails, etc., without really knowing the theory behind it. Here we shall study very briefly the theory of magnetism as an introduction to electricity.

MAGNETISM

Every magnet has two poles: a north pole and a south pole. In the case of a horseshoe magnet, one side is the north pole and the other side is the south pole. If you place two horseshoe magnets together, so that the north pole of one is in contact with the north pole of the other, and consequently their south poles are in contact—there will be absolutely no attraction. If, now, you place them so that the unlike poles are in contact with one another, there will be a great attraction. We thus have the law of magnetism that states: *Unlike poles attract; like poles repel.*

When you bring either pole of the magnet near a piece of steel, the steel is immediately magnetized with the opposite pole. Thus the north pole of the magnet near the end of a needle causes the appearance of a magnetic south pole at that end of the needle. The result is an attraction.

It is an interesting fact that if a bar magnet with a north and south pole is cut in half, the result is two bar magnets each with a north and a south pole. This can be done indefinitely—no matter how many times they are cut up, the resulting pieces will always be independent magnets with north and south poles. This leads us to believe that the atoms of all magnetic substances such as iron, cobalt, and nickel are themselves magnets, each with its north and south pole.

The earth is a huge magnet. It has a north magnetic pole in the northern part of North America (Latitude 70° 30′ North, Longitude 95° West) and a south magnetic pole at a point considerably south of Australia.

If a light needle is delicately pivoted so that it is free to swing, it will align itself with the two poles, one end pointing to the North Pole and the other to the South Pole. This fact is used in the compass. A compass does not give true north; it merely points to the north magnetic pole. The difference between the north magnetic pole and the North Pole is known and tabulated for all points in the northern hemisphere. The number of degrees by which at a given point on the earth the needle varies from the true north is called its declination at that point. Inasmuch as these declinations are all known, the compass proves a very useful guide to ships at sea, because the true north can easily be figured from it.

STATIC ELECTRICITY

There are two kinds of electricity: *static* electricity and *current* electricity. Static electricity is known to everyone who combs his hair with a hard rubber comb on a cold day. Almost every one of us has at some time surprised a friend with a "shock" by rubbing our feet on a carpet and touching that friend. This is static electricity. It exists in positive and negative charges. Bodies charged with the same kind of electricity repel each other; bodies charged with opposite kinds of electricity attract each other. Charges are produced whenever two unlike materials are rubbed together.

To understand the nature of charge, we must recall the structure of the atom. The atom consists of a nucleus containing positive charges (protons), around which electrons, which are negatively charged, move in orbits. There are usually the same number of positive as negative charges in each atom. By applying energy in such forms as friction, heat, or light, we can remove some of the electrons from an atom. The atom is thus left with a positive charge. When we rub a hard rubber rod with a piece of cat's fur, the fur loses electrons and becomes positively charged. The negatively charged electrons removed from the fur are now lodged on the rubber, thus giving it a negative charge.

During the summertime, when air becomes heated as it contacts the surface of the earth, the warm, moist air rises with considerable force, and as it cools in the upper atmosphere, a thunderhead cloud forms. When precipitation begins, the raindrops from the cloud pass through the violent updrafts of warm air and they become charged positively while the cloud accumulates a negative charge. The negatively charged cloud induces a positive charge in the ground below in very much the same manner that a south pole of a magnet induces a north pole in a near-by piece of iron. The result is a huge spark of electricity as electrons surge from cloud to ground and back to cloud several times. This discharge we call lightning. The heating effect of the huge current in the lightning creates a detonation known as thunder. Sometimes it happens that near-by clouds are charged oppositely, in which case lightning takes place between one cloud and another.

THE CONDENSER

A *condenser* is used to store electrical charge in much the same manner as charges of static electricity are stored in a cloud and on the earth. The condenser consists of two metallic plates separated by an insulator. As one plate is filled with charge it induces an opposite charge in the other. The charge in the first plate crowds toward the induced opposite charge in the other plate and allows us to put additional charge on the first plate.

CONDUCTORS AND INSULATORS

Anything which transmits electricity is called a conductor. In other words, any substance through which electrons may move freely is a conductor. Anything which does not transmit electricity is called an insulator.

Metals are excellent conductors, particularly silver and copper. Rubber is an excellent insulator. So is glass.

CURRENT ELECTRICITY

The general accepted theory of electricity explains it as a rapid flow of billions and trillions of electrons, always flowing from where they are in excess to where they are lacking—from negative to positive. It should be kept in mind that the negative charge results from an excess of electrons, because an electron has a negative charge. A current in a wire is somewhat like the flow of water in a tube. Imagine two tanks of water, one high above the other. If we connect these two tanks with a rubber tube, the water will flow from the upper to the lower tank. The rate of flow depends upon the difference in elevation of the tanks, just as the rate of flow or current in an electric wire depends upon what is known as the difference of potential: that is, the difference of charge between two bodies.

To return to the analogy of the tanks: if we wish to keep a continual flow of water in the rubber tube, we must keep the upper tank always filled with water. In the same way, if we wish to maintain a continuous current, we must maintain a continual difference of potential. This is accomplished by the use of a voltaic cell, which consists of a strip of zinc which acts as a constant source of electrons and is thus negatively charged, and a strip of copper which becomes positively charged and is therefore a place to which electrons are attracted. The charges on the plates are produced when the plates are immersed in a solution of sulphuric acid. The function of the sulphuric acid is to transfer the electrons which arrive at the copper back to the zinc.

When the zinc and copper are connected, we have a continual flow of current, because of the chemical action of the sulphuric acid on the zinc and copper. This current will flow—that is, there will be a difference of potential between the zinc and copper—as long as the sulphuric acid acts upon the zinc and copper.

This principle is applied to all batteries, and there are a number of different types, such as the dry-cell battery, the storage battery, the Daniel Cell, the galvanic cell, etc.

In every electric current three factors are important:

(1) The number of electrons flowing past a given point in the circuit. If 6 billion billion electrons pass in one second, we say that the "current" is one *ampere*.

(2) The "electron-moving-force" (E.M.F.) behind each electron, which is measured in *volts*.

(3) The "resistance" which the conductor offers to the flow of electrons, which is measured in *ohms*.

The practical definitions of these three factors are as follows:

An *ampere* is 6 billion billion electrons flowing past a given point on a wire in one second.

The *volt* is the amount of force which will cause a current of one ampere to flow through a resistance of one ohm.

The *ohm* is that resistance which will allow one ampere to flow through it on a voltage of one volt. It is approximately the resistance offered to a steady current by a thread of mercury $106\frac{3}{10}$ centimeters long and one square millimeter in cross-sectional area.

There is one other factor which is important: the *watt*. It is defined as the amount of power required to keep a current of one ampere flowing under a potential difference of one volt. The watt, of course, is always a measure of power.

OHM'S LAW

Ohm's Law states that the current passing through a conductor is directly proportional to the electromotive force and inversely proportional to its resistance. Thus, if I is the current, E is the electromotive force, and R the resistance: $I = \frac{E}{R}$. This is a very important formula in electricity. To give one application: the average light bulb passes ½ ampere on a 120-volt circuit. What is its resistance? According to Ohm's Law it would be $\frac{120}{\frac{1}{2}}$ or 240 ohms. The applications of this law are very far-reaching.

MAGNETIC EFFECTS OF THE ELECTRIC CURRENT

When an insulated wire is wound around a piece of soft iron a number of times and a current is sent through the wire, the iron immediately becomes a magnet. The magnetic field of the wire induces the iron to become magnetic.

When the current is stopped, the iron loses its magnetism. This is known as an *electromagnet,* and is unquestionably one of the most useful and valuable instruments in modern civilization. The electromagnet is basic to the construction and operation of electric motors and electric dynamos. A few other applications of the electromagnet will be studied here. These are: the telegraph, the electric bell, and the telephone.

THE TELEGRAPH

The telegraph consists essentially of a battery, a key, and a sounder (Fig. 35). The key is used for making and breaking the circuit. When the button is pushed down, a contact is made and the current flows through the wires. When the button is released, the circuit is broken and no current flows through the wire. At the other end of the line—it may be a mile or it may be a thousand miles away—is the sounder. This consists merely of an electromagnet over which a soft iron bar is placed. This iron bar is connected with a spring. On the iron bar is an iron crosspiece. When the button of the telegraph key is pushed down, a current flows through the circuit into the electromagnet of the sounder miles away.

The electromagnet attracts the iron crosspiece to it and this makes a click. When the button of the telegraph key is released, no current flows through the wire and the electromagnet loses its magnetism. The spring pulls the bar and crosspiece away from the magnet. It can readily be seen that every time you press the button of the telegraph key, the contact is formed, the electromagnet of the sounder becomes magnetized and the

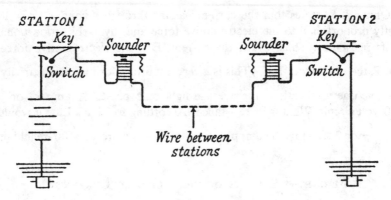

FIG. 35. Telegraph system.

crosspiece is drawn down to it with a click. When the button is released, the crosspiece is pulled up again. In this way a regular code (such as the Morse Code) of clicks—some long and some short—known as dots and dashes, can be tapped out on the button of the telegraph key in one place and the corresponding clicking will be heard in the sounder of another place thousands of miles away.

THE ELECTRIC BELL

The circuit of the electric bell (Fig. 36) consists of a battery, a push button, and the bell itself connected by wires. When the button is pushed, the current flows through the wire into the electromagnet of the bell. The magnet then attracts the little bar on which is attached the hammer. As soon as the bar strikes the magnet, the circuit is broken at the adjusting screw, with the result that the magnet loses its magnetism and the bar is pulled back to its original position by a spring. When the bar is back to its original position, it closes the circuit again and the magnet again becomes magnetic. The same thing takes place all over again. As long as the button is pushed, the bar will go back and forth between the electromagnet and the contact screw. The hammer which is attached to the bar will consequently hit the bell many times per second and we get a steady ringing of the bell.

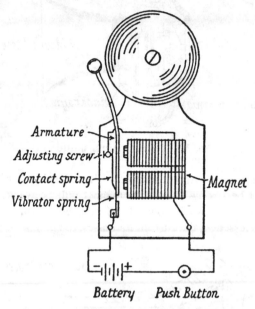

FIG. 36. Electric bell.

THE TELEPHONE

The transmitter of a telephone (Fig. 37) is essentially a carefully designed microphone. It contains a little box which is filled with tiny bits of carbon. The tiny bits of carbon form a contact between the front and back of the box in such a way that the current has to flow in through the front, through the carbon granules, and out through the back. It so happens that the resistance of carbon to an electric current is proportional to the pressure, so that when carbon is compressed, its resistance decreases and the current gets stronger. When someone talks into the mouthpiece of the transmitter, the diaphragm is vibrated, with the consequent compressing of the carbon granules. The result is that the current varies according to the sound waves of speech. Now let us follow these varying currents to the receiver (Fig. 38) at the other end of the line. The receiver consists of a permanent magnet at the end of which is a tiny electromagnet. In front of the electromagnet and very close to it is a soft iron diaphragm which is attracted to the electromagnet in exact accordance with the vary-

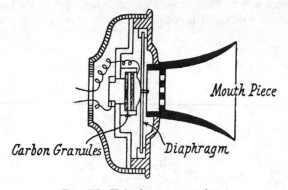

FIG. 37. Telephone transmitter.

ing currents sent up by the transmitter. If the resistance is great, the current will not be strong, the electromagnet will be weak, and the diaphragm will not be drawn in toward the magnet. If, on the other hand, the resistance is lessened, the current increases, the magnet is strengthened,

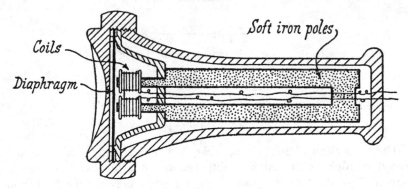

FIG. 38. Telephone receiver.

and the diaphragm will be drawn toward the magnet. In this way the diaphragm is made to vibrate the way the diaphragm of the transmitter vibrated when spoken into. The result is a reproduction of one's speech.

THE ELECTRIC MOTOR

The electric motor takes advantage of the fact that between two magnets there is an attraction between the unlike poles and a repulsion between the like poles. If we pivot a bar magnet freely on its center so that it may rotate in a horizontal plane and present the north pole of another magnet to the like pole of the pivoted magnet, there is immediately a repulsion between the two like poles. The north pole of the pivoted magnet swings away. Its south pole, attracted by the north pole of the stationary magnet, moves toward it—thus helping to complete a half-circle motion. Suppose, however, that just as the south pole of the pivoted magnet moves opposite the north pole of the stationary magnet, this magnet's position is reversed so as now to present a south pole to the moving magnet. The two south poles now repel and the pivoted magnet continues to swing another half-circle, returning to its original position. If the polarity of the stationary magnet is switched at the right moments, the pivoted magnet will rotate continuously. This is the principle of the electric motor. Instead of employing two permanent magnets, however, the motor uses two electromagnets. One electromagnet, called the field

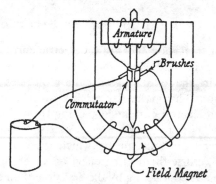

Fig. 39. A direct-current motor.

magnet, is stationary and has a constant polarity. Mounted between the poles of the field magnet is a moving, pivoted electromagnet, called the armature. By reversing the current through the armature at the right moments, the magnetic field of the armature constantly repels that of the field magnet and the armature rotates continuously. The device which switches the current in the armature is mounted directly on the shaft of the armature and consists of commutator segments and brushes. Figure 39 shows a diagram of a simple electric motor.

The Electric Generator

Michael Faraday, a nineteenth-century English scientist, discovered that whenever a wire moves across a magnetic field a current is induced to flow in the wire. We speak of this as electromagnetic induction.

If an armature similar to that of the electric motor is rotated in a magnetic field, a current is induced to flow in the armature coil. In order to get the current out of this generator without twisting the wires attached to the armature coil, we use a device similar to that used in the commutator of the motor. The design of this device determines whether the generator produces alternating (A.C.) or direct (D.C.) current.

A coil rotating in a magnetic field first cuts the field in one direction and then, as it turns, cuts the field in the other direction. This induces a current which first flows one way and then the other. This is an alternating current, and it is the type of current which an armature always produces. If we use a commutator consisting of two separate rings, alternating current flows from the brushes. If, however, we use a split-ring commutator similar to the one used in the motor described above, the split ring switches the brush connections at exactly the moment the alternating current switches direction, and the result is that direct current is sent out of the brushes.

HEATING AND CHEMICAL EFFECTS OF ELECTRIC CURRENT

In addition to the magnetic effect of an electric current, electricity has two other effects: a heating effect and a chemical effect. As electrons move through a wire they strike against the molecules of the wire and set them into motion. This molecular motion we recognize as heat. The heating effect of an electric current in passing through a conductor depends largely on the current and to a lesser extent on both the resistance of the conductor and the time during which the current flows. Fuses, toasters, irons, etc., utilize the heating effect of the electric current.

When water is made conducting by the addition of an acid, a base, or a salt, and a current of electricity is passed through the solution, we find that the water will break up into the elements of which it is composed, hydrogen and oxygen. This process is called *electrolysis*. If a metallic salt such as copper sulphate is used in the solution, and a sheet of copper is attached to the submerged positive terminal (anode) of a battery, copper will be transferred from this copper sheet into the solution and from there onto a metallic object attached to the negative terminal (cathode). The metal attached to the cathode will become completely coated with copper deposits if the current is allowed to flow for a sufficient time. This process is called electroplating and is used to coat objects with silver, gold, nickel, chromium, copper, etc.

ELECTROMAGNETIC RADIATION

ELECTROMAGNETIC WAVES

Whenever visible light is produced, radiant heat is also produced. This observation led physicists to the conclusion that radiant heat (infrared) and light have properties in common. They are both electromagnetic waves and, as we now know, they are only two of a number of varieties of this type of wave. Electromagnetic waves include radio waves, infrared, visible light, ultraviolet, X rays and gamma rays, all of which travel at 186,000 miles per second and differ from one another only in frequency of vibration.

RADIO WAVES

In any metallic conductor such as a wire there are always many unstable electrons—electrons which are held loosely by the nuclei of atoms. If we can make these electrons move rapidly back and forth through the wire, the wire becomes the center of a disturbance which moves out into space with the speed of light—186,000 miles per second. These waves which come from the agitation of the electrons are commonly called radio waves. If the back-and-forth motion of the electrons is relatively slow (let us say 60 vibrations or cycles per second), waves of very little energy result. If, however, we force the electrons to move back and forth 500,000 times in one second (500 kilocycles per second, a kilocycle being 1000 cycles), a radio wave is produced that can be detected within a 150-mile radius. Thus, in the antenna of a radio station broadcasting at 560 kilocycles per second, the electrons are made to surge up and down 560,000 times in one second. The standard broadcast band will have stations broadcasting from about 500 kilocycles to 1.6 megacycles (a megacycle is one million cycles).

As we go higher in frequency we enter the so-called short-wave band. Since the higher we go in frequency the more energetic are the waves, waves of short-wave frequency will cover great distances. Moreover, we

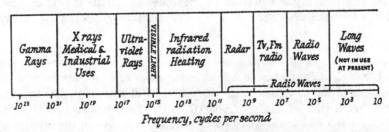

FIG. 40. The electromagnetic spectrum.

find that these waves bounce off of a layer of ionized air about 70 to 150 miles above the surface of the earth. This reflection of the waves greatly extends the distance of communication. The frequencies of short-wave transmitters range from about 2 megacycles to 30 megacycles.

If we employ waves of even higher frequency, we find that these waves behave very much like light in that they travel in straight lines. They are so energetic, however, that they travel through the ionosphere into the space beyond. Such waves, with a frequency of 30 megacycles to 1000 megacycles, have been reflected from the moon. These waves are used for commercial television broadcasts.

ULTRAVIOLET LIGHT

Heating an object makes the molecules move more rapidly; as the temperature rises and the energy of molecular collisions increases, the object first gives off invisible infrared radiation (see page 1114) and then visible light. Continued heating produces a frequency too high for us to see. This is ultraviolet light. The frequency of vibration of electrons which produces light is of the order of 10 to the 15th power (10^{15}) cycles per second.

X RAYS

Radio waves and ultraviolet light waves result from a disturbance of the outer electrons in the atom. If we disturb the electrons near the nucleus, we can produce even higher frequencies than ultraviolet. An extremely energetic radiation which can penetrate matter is produced by bombarding a metal target with high-speed electrons. In this manner, what we call X rays are produced. The electrons are given their great speed by the high voltage placed across the terminals of the X ray tube. The electrons crash through the outer electron layers of the atoms of the target and strike the electrons near the center of the atom. These are then sent into rapid vibration in the order of 10 to the 18th power (10^{18}) vibrations per second. The radiations thus produced are X rays.

GAMMA RAYS

The highest frequency of all, called *gamma rays,* results from a disturbance of the electrons in the very nucleus of the atom. Gamma rays have frequencies of the order of 10 to the 23rd power (10^{23}) vibrations per second. Scientists cannot produce these rays in the laboratory, but they are among the rays emitted by radioactive substances. Radium, uranium, thorium, etc., have been used for many years as sources of gamma rays. Today, however, by bombarding certain elements with neutrons (in an atomic pile), we can make a large number of artificially radioactive varieties of elements. One such, cobalt 60, produces gamma rays many times more powerful than those produced by radium.

ELECTRONICS

In the relatively short time since the discovery of electrons, man's ability to control these tiny bits of negative electricity has had a tremendous effect on the development of science, particularly in the field of communication. The story of electronics began in 1883 when Thomas Edison found that the filament of his newly invented electric lamp threw off negatively charged particles. It was not until several years later that these were identified as electrons.

It was established that a piece of metal which is heated within gives off electrons. A heated filament, however, cannot continue to throw off electrons indefinitely, unless the ones which leave are replaced. Furthermore, rather than allowing the electrons to escape at random into the space around the filament, scientists were looking for a way of attracting them to a single place. Sir Ambrose Fleming, an English physicist, solved both problems by the use of a high-voltage "B" battery. (The battery used to heat the filament is called the "A" battery.) By connecting the positive terminal of the "A" battery to a plate placed inside the tube with the filament, Fleming caused the released electrons to be attracted to this plate. The negative terminal of the "B" battery was attached to the filament to supply it with electrons. Thus there was a continuous flow of electrons from the negative filament to the positive plate, as though a conductor were placed between the two. Note, however, that if the terminals of the "B" battery were reversed so that the plate became negative and the filament positive, no such current could flow. Here, for the first time, we see a circuit in which electrons can flow in one direction but not in the other.

Vacuum Tubes. Such a *vacuum tube* containing a heated filament and a plate is called a *diode*. It can be used to rectify an alternating current; that is, change it to pulsating direct current, as it allows the electrons to flow from filament to plate but not the other way.

Shortly after 1900 the American scientist Lee De Forest added another feature, called the *grid,* to the diode, thus making it a *triode*. The grid is a meshwork or screen between the filament and the plate. With the negative filament and the positive plate, electrons pass through the grid and a flow of current appears in the plate circuit. If now the grid is made negative, electrons leaving the filament will be repelled and few if any will arrive at the plate. On the other hand, if the grid is made positive, it aids the positive plate and the current to the plate increases. The prime function of the triode is *amplification:* a very small change in the charge on the grid will greatly vary the current to the plate. Thus, even a weak signal placed on the grid will cause a strong signal to appear at the plate.

TRANSISTORS. If two adjustable fine wires are placed together on a crystal (usually of germanium), the crystal functions as a crystal triode amplifier, giving signals great amplification. This device is known as a *transistor*. Transistors are tiny, need no warm-up period since they have no heated filaments, and can operate on very small voltages and currents. They can be used to replace vacuum tubes in hearing aids, portable radios, guided missiles, and space vehicles.

RADIO TRANSMITTERS AND RECEIVERS

A radio wave is produced, as we have said, whenever electrons surge rapidly back and forth in a wire. In the radio transmitter a triode is used to cause oscillation of electrons in the antenna. Oscillation having frequencies of about a million cycles per second is used. The frequency of the oscillation is determined by a coil and a condenser in the oscillating circuit. The oscillation produces radio waves which can travel great distances through space. They are, however, too rapid in vibration to be heard at the receiver. They are used only to *carry* the sound waves. We must impress on these radio waves the much slower frequencies of sound waves if we wish to transmit sound. We can accomplish this in one of two ways. 1) We can vary the strength or swing of the radio waves according to the pattern of the sound waves which are to be broadcast; this is *amplitude modulation*. 2) In *frequency modulation* the radio or carrier wave keeps a constant amplitude but its frequency changes according to the pattern of the sound waves. Frequency modulation has one advantage over amplitude modulation. In a receiver sensitive to changes in frequency rather than amplitude, static (which is an amplitude-modulated disturbance) is not picked up. At the broadcasting station a microphone changes the pattern of the sounds to be broadcast into a corresponding electrical pattern, which is then impressed on the radio wave to produce the modulated wave which is then broadcast.

As radio waves sweep past any metallic conductor they induce a surging of electrons in a rhythm corresponding to that of the electrons in the transmitting antenna. This surging is picked up by the receiving antenna and brought down into a coil and a condenser which has selected out the desired station. The high-frequency wave, having served its purpose in carrying the sound wave to the receiver, is stripped from the sound wave by a diode rectifier or a crystal detector which allows current to flow in only one direction. The weak sound signal is received as electrical impulses and then amplified in other vacuum tubes and appears in the headphones or a loud-speaker, which function exactly as the tele-

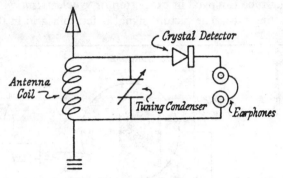

FIG. 41. A simple receiver

phone receiver in converting varying electrical currents into sound waves.

TELEVISION

The heart of the television transmitter is the *iconoscope* or *image orthicon*. It is a bottle-shaped tube which contains an *electron gun* in the neck. The electron gun is a heated filament from which a controlled stream of electrons is emitted. This stream of electrons can be directed to any spot on a *mosaic plate* within the tube. The direction of the beam is regulated by two pairs of plates on which charges are placed. One pair of the plates makes the beam move rapidly across the mosaic plate at regular intervals, while the other jerks it down a short distance after each sweep. The motion is like that of your eyes as you read a page of print. The mosaic plate consists of many tiny droplets of a material sensitive to light, usually the element cesium. Each droplet is actually a tiny photoelectric cell. The scene to be televised is focused on the mosaic plate by a lens, and the electron beam scans the images and converts them into a succession of electrical impulses. These impulses are then impressed on the carrier radio wave through amplitude modulation. Thus, line by line, the image is converted into a series of electrical waves. In American television there are 525 lines of scanning to each picture, and a full picture is scanned in 1/30 of a second. The sound wave is transmitted at a slightly different frequency and is frequency modulated so that the receiver can separate out the picture wave (video) from the sound wave (audio).

In the receiver the TV picture tube, or *kinescope,* converts the video signals back into light. The kinescope contains an electron gun whose stream of electrons is directed against a phosphorescent screen. Wherever the electrons strike the screen they cause a splash of light. The beam in the receiving tube is moved in exact step or *synchronization* with that in the transmitting tube. The picture signal is fed to a grid in the receiving

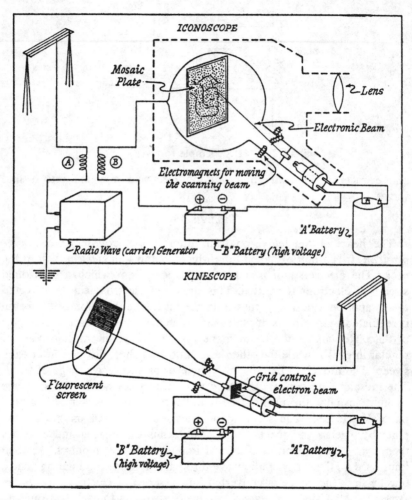

FIG. 42. Diagram of a television transmitter (above) and receiver (below).

tube which acts like a gate. When the transmitter is scanning a light image, the grid in the receiver is positive and the electrons go through to the screen and produce light. When a dark area is scanned, the grid is made negative by the signal and few or no electrons reach the screen, which remains dark. Thus a picture is painted out. As in viewing motion pictures, the rapid series of still pictures gives the illusion of continuous motion.

RADAR

Just before World War II it was discovered that objects, particularly metallic ones, reflect radio waves. Since we know that radio waves travel with the velocity of light (186,000 mi./sec.), by timing the interval between the sending and the return of radio waves, we may determine the distance to any object which reflects them back to the sender. This is the basic principle of radar, which gets its name from the first letters of its original title, "Radio Detection and Ranging."

The transmitter sends out regular, short pulses of very high frequency radio waves. During the intervals between pulses, a receiver near by listens for reflections of these pulses from various objects. The initial and the reflected waves are both fed to a picture tube in which an electron beam is moving across a screen. The distance between the two bumps or "pips" can then be used to determine the distance of the object. By directing the beam downward from an airplane and varying the method of scanning used in the receiving tube, a rough, actual picture of the ground below appears on the face of the tube.

Radar can penetrate fog and rain. It can guide and locate airplanes and ships. It can even detect icebergs and show the position of storm centers. Recently, astronomers have used radar to track the paths of meteors and man-made earth satellites.

NUCLEAR PHYSICS

NUCLEAR ENERGY

Before December 2, 1942, practically all of the energy used by mankind was derived directly or indirectly from the energy of sunlight. On that day, however, man had accomplished the task of releasing the energy locked away in the atom, and thus a limitless amount of energy was made available to him to be used as he desired. This was the day that the first "atomic pile" went into operation.

ATOMIC STRUCTURE

The most important scientific event in the f   half of the twentieth century was the release of atomic energy locked away in the nucleus of atoms. To understand the source of this energy, it is first necessary to understand something of atomic structure. It is suggested that the material in the section following on Chemistry be read and the following points kept in mind.

(1) There are 92 naturally occurring elements of which all things in the universe are made.

(2) Atoms consist of protons, neutrons, and electrons; and differences between atoms are differences in the number of these particles.

(3) Protons and neutrons clump together to form the nucleus of the atom, while a number of electrons equal to the number of protons circle the nucleus.

(4) The number of protons in the nucleus is the atomic number. The total number of protons plus neutrons is the atomic weight. For example, radium, atomic number 88, atomic weight 226 (written $_{88}Ra^{226}$) consists of a nucleus of 88 protons and 138 neutrons surrounded by 88 electrons.

ISOTOPES

Physicists have discovered that not all atoms of the same element have the same atomic weight. It has been found, for example, that at least two kinds of hydrogen atoms exist in nature. They are H^1 and H^2. The H^1 consists of 1 proton and 1 planetary electron. The H^2 consists of a nucleus made of 1 proton and 1 neutron surrounded by 1 planetary electron. Chemically, both hydrogens are identical, since the chemical properties

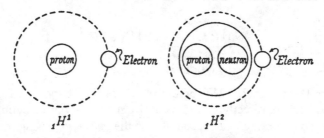

FIG. 43. Isotopes of hydrogen.

depend only on the outer electron shell. The H^2, however, weighs twice as much as the H^1. These atoms which have the same atomic number but different atomic weight are called isotopes. Almost all elements have one or more isotopes, and the figures given in most charts for the atomic weights of the various elements show an average atomic weight for all the naturally occurring isotopes.

Natural Radioactivity

In general, the atoms of elements with atomic numbers over 82 (the element with atomic number 82 is lead) seem to be too large to stay together. These heavy elements (radium, uranium, etc.) are unstable; their atoms have a strong tendency to expel fragments of their nuclei, thus being transformed into lighter, more stable elements. How these heavy atoms were ever formed in the first place has been the source of much speculation by scientists.

A heavy element becomes simplified into a lighter one through either of two processes. The atom may eject from its nucleus a unit of particles consisting of 2 protons and 2 neutrons. Such a unit is equivalent to the nucleus of a helium atom. The other process of simplification of a heavy atom is to convert a neutron in its nucleus into a proton by ejecting one electron. (This conversion results from the fact that a neutron is composed of a proton and an electron in close association.) Whenever an ejection of a helium nucleus or an electron from a heavy atom occurs, the process is usually accompanied by a radiation of gamma waves. From the earlier discussion of gamma waves, you will remember that they have a higher frequency than X rays and are consequently more penetrating. The emission of helium nuclei or electrons by heavy atoms and the resulting radiation is called *natural radioactivity*.

When Mme. Curie first discovered radioactivity, she identified three different things coming from the radioactive pitchblende. Not knowing anything about their nature, she called them rays and named them after the first three letters of the Greek alphabet—alpha, beta, and gamma rays. Today we know that the alpha and beta rays are not rays at all but streams of particles. The alphas are helium nuclei, the betas are electrons, but the gamma ray is a true ray.

Radioactive elements shoot off their rays and particles at different rates. As they do so, the elements are simplified until they are transformed usually into lead, with an atomic weight of 82. Lead is a stable element. Half of any sample of uranium will become lead in about four billion years. Radium, on the other hand, has a "half-life" of 1,650 years; that is, half of any sample is simplified into lead in 1,650 years. Some man-made elements like francium have a half-life of only about a millionth of a second.

Artificial Radioactivity

Nitrogen has two naturally occurring isotopes. They are $_7N^{14}$ and $_7N^{15}$. Scientists wondered whether it could be possible to make $_7N^{16}$. By bombarding the $_7N^{15}$ with neutrons in a cyclotron, they were able to produce $_7N^{16}$. The $_7N^{16}$ was found to be radioactive. It emitted a beta particle (electron), becoming oxygen.

By bombarding elements with neutrons in an atomic pile or with charged particles from a cyclotron, scientists have produced isotopes which do not exist in nature. All such isotopes are radioactive and emit beta particles and gamma rays. These artificially made radio-isotopes or "labeled atoms" are useful in industry and medicine as "tracers." For example, if a plant is grown in an atmosphere containing carbon dioxide (CO_2) "labeled" with radioactive carbon atoms, we can track the carbon into the plant and learn more about how plants can manufacture starch from CO_2, water, and sunlight.

DETECTION OF RADIATION

The most convenient device for the detection of radiation is the Geiger counter. The heart of the counter is the Geiger tube, which consists of two conductors in a glass envelope containing gas under low pressure. A voltage is passed across the two conductors which are separated by the gas, and the voltage is adjusted to just below the sparking potential. If a particle or ray enters the tube, it makes the gas a conductor and there is a momentary spark. The sudden surge of electricity between the two wires may be used to produce a click in a pair of earphones or flash a light.

Photographic film is also sensitive to radiation; the radiation causes the film to darken on development. From the degree of darkening we can estimate the intensity of the radiation. The film badges worn by workers who are exposed to radiation are an application of this type of detection.

To record the path of individual particles in radiation, we employ the *cloud chamber*. If the moisture content, the pressure, and the temperature within a confined space are properly adjusted, the track of each particle passing through it becomes visible as a cloud, much as the vapor trails which define the path of high-altitude airplanes.

NUCLEAR FISSION

Uranium is the heaviest element which occurs naturally. By adding particles to uranium atoms, scientists have succeeded in creating artificial elements which are heavier than uranium and do not exist in nature. Bombarding uranium with neutrons has produced elements 93 and 94, neptunium and plutonium. In the process, scientists stumbled on a new and remarkable phenomenon. When the uranium isotope 235 was bombarded with neutrons, the final result was not a heavier, radioactive element, because the complex nucleus produced split into two fragments. These were nuclei of medium atomic weight. In addition, several independent neutrons were also ejected. This process of breaking down a large nucleus into two of comparable size is called *fission*. Two features of this process make it of great importance. First, the total weight of the two atoms and the neutrons which result from fission is less than the total weight of the original uranium atom plus that of the neutron which caused the fission. In other words, somehow in this process an infinitesimal amount of matter is completely annihilated or destroyed. Einstein had predicted, as long ago as 1905, that if matter could be annihilated, it would be transformed into energy. In fact, Einstein developed an exact formula for the transformation, which is:

$$E = mc^2$$

or, energy equals mass times the square of the speed of light. This is exactly what happens in fission. The two nuclei and the neutrons are ejected with an accompaniment of terrific energy and heat, light and gamma radiation resulting as by-products.

The second feature of fission which makes it of great interest is that fission is caused by neutron bombardment, and in the process neutrons are produced. This means that if a single atom of uranium 235 were struck by a neutron and underwent fission, it would produce other neutrons which in turn could cause fission in other atoms. Thus a *chain reaction* would be initiated. It is the application of these principles that has made possible the production of the atomic bomb—with its unprecedented destructive power.

NUCLEAR FUSION

Energy can also be released if we take the very light elements and fuse them to form heavier ones. If hydrogen gas is heated to a temperature of some 100 million degrees Centigrade, the molecules move so rapidly that their nuclei collide and are united. Four hydrogen atoms contain all the parts needed to unite into one helium atom, but one helium atom weighs slightly less than four hydrogen atoms. So, in the process of fusing hydrogen into helium, there is a loss in matter, and according to the Einstein mass-energy relation, energy is liberated. Since the process of *fusion* of light elements into heavier ones is initiated under high temperature, we speak of this type of reaction as a *thermonuclear reaction*. The thermonuclear reaction is the basis of the fusion bomb, sometimes called the H bomb.

We believe that the origin of the sun's energy lies in the thermonuclear reaction which fuses hydrogen into helium. Each second, 564 million tons of hydrogen are fused to form 560 million tons of helium. Even though the sun loses mass into energy at the rate of 4 million tons per second, the sun is so large that it would take 150 billion years for it to lose one per cent of its mass.

Nuclear fusion requires such a high temperature to start the reaction that at present the only way we can supply this temperature is by using an A bomb as a fuse. Thus we are not able to control the fusion, but in the very near future science is sure to solve the problem of controlling thermonuclear reactions and then mankind will have at its disposal an unlimited supply of energy which will be inexpensive and free from any problems of radioactive contamination. This energy can be used to transport water for irrigation, to provide industry with unlimited power, and for numerous other purposes which increase prosperity and raise the standard of living.

EXAMINATION QUESTIONS

1. What is physics?
2. What is the internationally used scientific system of measurement?
3. Name the three simple machines.
4. What statement by Archimedes showed complete confidence in the lever?
5. What principle of mechanics does a nutcracker illustrate?
6. What is a fixed pulley?
7. What governs the mechanical advantage of a movable pulley?
8. How can the mechanical advantage of an inclined plane be determined?
9. What is a wedge?
10. What does Newton's First Law of Motion mean?
11. What does Newton's Second Law of Motion mean?
12. What is the acceleration of a falling body?
13. If a cannon ball is shot horizontally from a tower 100 feet high at the same time that another cannon ball is dropped from the tower, which ball will hit the ground first?
14. How does a vacuum affect the speed of falling bodies?
15. What does it mean when you say that a floor will sustain a weight of 150 pounds per square foot?
16. What principle of equilibrium does Newton's Third Law give us?
17. What are the three types of equilibrium?
18. How does the length of a pendulum affect its swing?
19. Name the two kinds of energy.
20. On what two factors does liquid pressure depend?
21. What does Pascal's Law state?
22. What is Archimedes' principle?
23. What is specific gravity?
24. What principle in physics does the use of blotting paper illustrate?
25. If we reduce the volume of a given amount of gas, what is the effect on the pressure?
26. What is the weight of air?

27. What is heat?
28. Do all metals expand the same under the same heat?
29. Why does glass break when boiling water is poured into it?
30. What is the freezing point of water on the Centigrade thermometer?
31. What temperature is known as absolute zero and why?
32. Convert 59° Fahrenheit to Centigrade.
33. What are the best-known conductors of heat?
34. At what speed does heat radiate?
35. What is the most common form of jet engine for aircraft?
36. By what is sound caused?
37. What is the number of vibrations of middle C on the piano?
38. How fast does sound travel?
39. What is the reflection of sound called?

40. What phenomenon occurs when a beam of light penetrates water, glass, or other media denser than air?
41. Which color light vibrates slowest and has the longest wave length?
42. Name two kinds of electricity.
43. List some applications of the electromagnet.
44. List some kinds of electromagnetic waves.
45. When is a radio wave produced?
46. What is the basic principle of radar?
47. What is natural radioactivity?
48. How have scientists produced isotopes which do not exist in nature?
49. What is the heaviest element which occurs naturally?
50. What is Einstein's formula for the conversion of mass into energy?

FOR FURTHER STUDY

FROM GALILEO TO THE NUCLEAR AGE, by H. B. Lemon. (University of Chicago Press, Chicago.)

INTRODUCTION TO PHYSICS, by Frank M. Durbin. (Prentice-Hall, Englewood Cliffs, N.J.)

NEW PRACTICAL PHYSICS, by N. H. Black and H. N. Davis. (The Macmillan Co., New York.)

PRIMER OF ELECTRONICS AND RADIANT ENERGY, by Don Caverly. (McGraw-Hill Book Co., New York.)

XXV

Chemistry Self Taught

THE IMPORTANCE OF CHEMISTRY

CHEMISTRY IS the science which deals with the composition of matter. It is concerned with the properties of substances and the conditions under which they are transformed into other substances. As we mentioned at the beginning of the Physics section of this book, Chemistry and Physics supplement one another. Chemistry, in its applied form, studies the uses to which materials can be put and seeks to create new and formerly unavailable or nonexistent materials for specific uses.

Many of the applications of chemistry are extremely useful. It is no exaggeration to say that everything you see around you that is manufactured is produced with the aid of chemistry. The books you read are printed on paper made from wood pulp by means of a chemical process. The ink which prints the reading matter is produced by chemical means. The type could not be produced without the aid of the chemist. Photography is almost entirely chemical in nature. Artificial silk is a triumph of modern industry. So are aniline dyes, and cellophane, and quick-drying paints and enamels, and imitation leather, synthetic flavorings for use in cooking, and preserved foods of all kinds. The chemist not only improves and tests old products, but he is constantly developing new ones.

THE BASIS OF CHEMISTRY

Very likely it has not occurred to you that every second of the day almost everything you touch and see is undergoing a slow change. Iron rusts, fruit decays, wood rots. You yourself are continually undergoing chemical changes. You must, or you could not live. In breathing, you inhale a gas (air), allow it to pass into your body, and exhale a gas of different composition. And this you do continually, at the approximate rate of 18 times per minute.

Plant life also breathes. It takes in the very gas which we and other animals breathe *out,* while we breathe *in* the gas that plants give *out.* That is one of the reasons we find the air in the country so fresh and pure.

A chemical change like respiration, the rusting of iron, or the decaying of fruit takes place whenever a solid, liquid, or gas is transformed by a change of composition into something of an entirely different nature.

If you heat a piece of copper for a long time in a very hot flame, you will see that a fine powder forms on it. Scrape off this powder with a knife. Keep doing this for a long enough time, and the entire piece of copper will eventually be transformed into this powder. What has happened? The heat has made the copper combine with something in the air to form a new substance. In chemical terms, the copper has combined with oxygen in the air to form copper oxide. This is an example of a simple chemical change.

Consider the gases, oxygen and hydrogen. They are both invisible; they are both odorless. You cannot feel them; you cannot taste them. If these gases are mixed in a certain proportion, and a lighted match is applied to them, there is an explosion, and water is produced. Water is a liquid—two gases have been transformed into a liquid. This is another chemical change. Water does not resemble either oxygen or hydrogen, yet it is a combination of these two elements. Chemistry makes a study of the composition of the various substances found in the universe, and of the changes in their composition which are constantly taking place.

ELEMENTS

Oxygen and hydrogen are called elements, because, though they can be combined with each other and with other elements, neither in itself can be broken up into any substance simpler in composition. An *element* is a substance that cannot be separated into other substances by ordinary chemical means. The break-up of the atoms of an element produces particles—protons, neutrons, and electrons—which do not have the characteristics of the substance. There are 92 naturally occurring elements, many of which are very rare. The eight elements most abundant in the earth are oxygen, silicon, aluminium (commonly spelled "aluminum"), iron, calcium, magnesium, potassium, and sodium; these together make up nearly 98% of the earth's crust, mostly in chemical combination with other elements. The bodies of water, of course, contain large quantities of hydrogen; and the earth's atmosphere has very large amounts of nitrogen.

Some elements are more active than others. Oxygen readily combines with most metals to form *oxides.* If the metal mercury is heated in a test tube for any length of time, little red particles collect on the sides of the tube. If the heating is kept up long enough, all the mercury will change to this red powder. The red powder is a compound of mercury and oxygen, called mercuric oxide. If this red powder is heated to a higher temperature, it will ultimately break down into mercury and oxygen. Similarly, zinc oxide results if the metal zinc is heated in oxygen.

Everyone is familiar with burning. Every day we light matches to ignite cigarettes, we burn gas in cooking, or we start the furnace in late autumn. Burning, or combustion, is a common and very important chemical phenomenon. The light, or luminous quality, of the flame is due to inconceivably minute particles of a substance (usually carbon) heated to incandescence. Some flames, such as that of burning hydrogen, are almost invisible, due to a lack of such incandescent particles.

If a lighted match is applied to a piece of paper, the paper at once catches fire. But the same lighted match applied to a piece of wood or a piece of coal will not ignite it. Why? This is due to difference in *kindling temperature,* which is determined by the readiness with which a substance combines with the oxygen in the air. As soon as any substance is heated to a sufficiently high temperature, known as its kindling temperature, it bursts into flame. As a rule, the more intimately the substance is in contact with oxygen, the lower will be its kindling temperature.

A piece of paper has oxygen distributed loosely among its tiny fibers, and oxygen completely surrounding it, in the air. Hence its kindling temperature is very low: it is easily ignited when brought into contact with a flame. Wood requires a little more time than paper to catch fire; it must be heated longer because it is more compact than paper and oxygen is not so free among its fibers. Hence the kindling temperature of wood is higher than that of paper. Coal requires a still greater amount of heat because it is tremendously compact, and the oxygen inside of it (not in combination with it, of course) is very small in quantity. To start a coal fire it is necessary to begin with burning paper, which ignites wood, the burning wood finally igniting the coal. Each kind of fuel in turn heats the other to its respective higher kindling temperature.

Burning or combustion (in air or in oxygen) is very rapid *oxidation,* the combining of a substance with oxygen. This is clear because substances will burn, with the liberation of light and heat, only when oxygen is present. A fire may be smothered and put out by shutting off its supply of air. A candle will burn only briefly in a tightly closed jar.

Notice at this point that the *combining* of chemical elements or substances is quite different from a *mixing* of them. Carbon in the form of charcoal may be mixed with pure oxygen and remain unchanged as long as heat is not present; as soon as the mixture is heated, or the carbon is ignited, the carbon *combines* chemically with the oxygen, forming the *compound* known as carbon dioxide. The carbon dioxide is quite unlike either carbon or oxygen; it has its own form and properties.

OXYGEN

Oxygen is necessary for ordinary burning or combustion. Oxygen is necessary for all forms of life, too; it is the part of the air we utilize when we breathe air into our lungs, where the oxygen loosely combines with the red coloring matter (hemoglobin) of the blood and is carried thereby to the various parts of the body.

The earth's atmosphere, or "air," is made up of about 78% nitrogen, 21% oxygen, and 1% a mixture of other gases. If the air were entirely composed of nitrogen, burning would be impossible, for nitrogen does not support combustion. If the air were entirely oxygen, a fire would burn very fiercely and would be extremely difficult to extinguish. Even iron will burn in pure oxygen: if a rod of iron, preheated to a glowing red, is plunged into a container of pure oxygen, it will burn brightly, giving off brilliant sparks. Slow oxidation of iron takes place in the open air, forming what we call rust; non-rusting metal compounds, notably "stainless steel," are products of modern chemistry.

Oxygen is so much a part of the earth that everywhere man may dig he finds oxides, compounds of oxygen. Oxygen, as a matter of fact, is the most abundant element on the earth, forming nearly half of the total composition of the earth's crust.

Liquid air is a good source of oxygen when desired in quantity, but the apparatus required is too expensive for laboratory purposes.

The most common way of preparing oxygen in the laboratory is to heat potassium chlorate and manganese dioxide in a test tube. (A test tube is a glass tube closed at one end; it is used in scientific laboratories

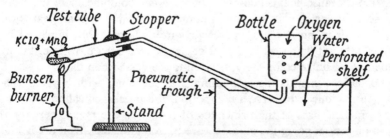

FIG. 1. Laboratory method of collecting oxygen.

as a convenient container for heating or otherwise treating substances experimentally.) Potassium chlorate requires only a slight amount of heat to liberate a large amount of oxygen. Potassium chlorate is a powder composed of three elements: potassium, chlorine, and oxygen, the latter forming an exceptionally large proportion. The presence of manganese dioxide helps the process of obtaining the oxygen from the potassium chlorate, but, curiously enough, the manganese dioxide remains unchanged; the part it plays is not yet clearly understood. Substances such as manganese dioxide, which facilitate a desired reaction but which are not themselves changed by the reaction, are referred to as *catalysts*.

Oxygen is an odorless, colorless, and tasteless gas, slightly heavier than air. In the pure state it has many uses. Doctors use it in the treatment of some diseases, particularly in severe cases of pneumonia, and during the administration of an anesthetic if the patient needs reviving suddenly. In the oxyhydrogen blowpipe, pure oxygen is mixed at the nozzle with pure hydrogen and ignited; the mixture burns with an intense heat, melting or vaporizing most metals; the flame of this blowpipe reaches a temperature as high as 5000° Fahrenheit. When this flame is projected against lime, the lime glows very brightly, a fact which is made use of in limelight or Drummond light.

The most striking property of oxygen is its tendency to support combustion. As a result of chemical combination with other elements, oxides are formed and energy is released. Indeed, oxygen combines with all the elements except fluorine, bromine, and five or six others (all very rare). Oxygen has a tremendous attraction or chemical affinity for two elements in particular: carbon and hydrogen. Oxygen will forsake many other compounds if heated in the presence of carbon or hydrogen, to combine with the carbon or hydrogen. The product of the combustion of hydrogen with oxygen is always water; that resulting from the combination of oxygen and carbon is carbon dioxide (sometimes carbon monoxide also, but this burns rapidly, in air, into carbon dioxide). Common substances used for fuel—because heat is liberated when oxygen combines with the carbon in them—are principally carbon in content, as coal, charcoal, peat, wood, etc. The diamond is almost pure carbon in crystal form; if placed in a sufficiently hot flame, as in the jet of an oxyhydrogen blowpipe, the diamond will oxidize completely, becoming the gas carbon dioxide.

Oxidation, then, is the combining of a substance with oxygen. When oxygen is induced to leave a compound, the process is called reduction. The practical uses of the principles of reduction are many, perhaps the most important being the manufacture of iron and steel. Iron ore is really iron oxide mixed with various impurities. The ore is heated in a huge furnace together with carbon (usually in the form of coke); the oxygen forsakes the iron oxide to unite with the carbon, leaving the iron, the impurities passing off as gases or remaining as slag. Iron, one of the metallic elements, is thus obtained, but it is not pure since much of the carbon remains in the iron. Cast iron contains much carbon and other substances (silicon, phosphorus, sulphur, etc.); wrought iron contains the least carbon of the commercial forms of iron. Steel is intermediate in carbon content between cast and wrought iron, and is made in various forms, depending on its composition.

Ozone is a curious form of concentrated oxygen. It has been humorously described as an "oxide of oxygen." Ozone is pure oxygen, for it always breaks down into nothing but oxygen; it seems to be made up of particles or molecules of oxygen more closely knit, in a manner of speaking, than the molecules of oxygen are. Electricity in the air causes the formation of ozone, as during thunderstorms or near electrical machines. The gas is colorless, but it has a peculiar odor (oxygen, it will be remembered, is odorless). Ozone is very unstable in composition, for it breaks down almost immediately into oxygen when it is liberated in the air. It is commonly thought that ozone is present in sea air and in the air of rural districts, but the presence of ozone in the air, to any large or permanent extent, has never been proved.

HYDROGEN

Hydrogen does not occur free in the air in any appreciable quantity, except near active volcanoes and natural gas wells, where it is present in the escaping fumes. Like oxygen, pure hydrogen is colorless (invisible), odorless, and tasteless; when somewhat impure, however, hydrogen has a distinct odor. Hydrogen is unique in being the lightest in weight of all the elements: 2,500 gallons of hydrogen weigh only a little over two pounds. Because of its lightness, the gas is used in balloons and dirigibles (illuminating gas, which contains hydrogen, has often been used in balloons). Hydrogen has one undesirable property for use in dirigibles: it is highly inflammable. (For this reason helium, a very light but non-inflammable gaseous element, is used where possible; helium is comparatively rare, and consequently very precious.) Hydrogen may be produced in the laboratory by placing some metal such as zinc in contact with hydrochloric or sulphuric acids and collecting the gas by displacement of water in a bottle.

Hydrogen burns in air or oxygen with a very pale, almost invisible blue flame. This flame is extremely hot, much hotter than an ordinary bright flame. Though pure hydrogen burns calmly in air, a mixture of hydrogen and air is highly explosive when ignited, the combustion being instantaneous; for this reason, hydrogen must be handled with extreme care in the laboratory and in commercial use. Hydrogen also "burns," in a special kind of combustion (oxygen not being present), in chlorine gas, with a bluish-white flame, forming hydrochloric acid gas. The product of hydrogen burning in oxygen is always water; the drops of water which sometimes gather on the bottom of pans over gas flames, in cooking, are formed from the combustion of hydrogen in the gas flame. The oxyacetylene torch, used to cut steel beams and other metals, works much like the oxyhydrogen blowpipe. Acetylene, a hydrocarbon gas, is burned in the presence of pure oxygen, giving a dazzling flame of tremendous heat.

Hydrogen is an essential component of all acids. It is combined with carbon in the great group of hydrocarbons, so called, which include kerosene, gasoline, naphtha, illuminating gas, etc. It is combined with carbon and oxygen in sugar, wood, paper, and other organic substances. It forms 1/9 (by weight) of water.

ACIDS, BASES, AND SALTS

An *acid* is a substance that releases hydrogen gas when it reacts with a metal. Lemon juice and vinegar both contain acids; acids generally taste sour.

A *base* (or *alkali*) is chemically the opposite of an acid. Examples of bases are ammonia and lye.

A *salt* is produced when acids and bases interact. Water is formed at the same time as the salt. Common table salt is the best-known example.

There are certain substances known as *indicators* which chemists use to distinguish between acids and bases. Very common for this purpose is *litmus* paper. Acids turn blue litmus red; whereas bases turn red litmus blue. *Methyl orange* is turned red by an acid solution. A third indicator is *phenolphthalein,* which is decolorized by acids.

The composition of acids, bases, and salts is often complex, since all are composed of two or more chemical elements. All acids contain hydrogen and some other element or elements. Hydrochloric acid, for example, is composed of hydrogen and chlorine in the proportion of one atom of hydrogen to one atom of chlorine. When *hydrogen chloride gas* (HCl) is dissolved in water, *hydrochloric acid* (same formula, HCl) is formed. However, the acid differs from the hydrogen chloride gas in that the HCl molecule of the acid has broken into two electrified particles when put into water. Such charged particles are called *ions,* and consist of atoms or groups of atoms from which electrons have been removed or to which electrons have been added. A characteristic of acids is the presence of hydrogen ions in water solutions of the acid.

The base called lye or *sodium hydroxide* contains one atom of the metal sodium to one atom each of oxygen and hydrogen. Curiously, the oxygen and hydrogen in bases unite, one atom of each, and act as a unit, as though they were one element. Any group of atoms which acts as a unit in chemical combination is called a *radical*. The combination of an atom of oxygen with an atom of hydrogen (OH), which acts as a unit of bases, is known as the *hydroxyl* radical. In water solutions, this radical becomes the *hydroxyl ion* and accounts for the characteristic properties of bases.

Acids are composed of hydrogen atoms plus an atom or atoms of non-metallic elements. Typical formulas are: HCl (hydrochloric acid); H_2SO_4 (sulphuric acid); and HNO_3 (nitric acid). Note the SO_4 and NO_3 radicals in the second and third examples.

Bases are composed of an atom of a metal combined with one or more hydroxyl radicals. Examples are: NaOH (sodium hydroxide); $Ca(OH)_2$ (calcium hydroxide, or whitewash); $Mg(OH)_2$ (magnesium hydroxide). An interesting example of a base is ammonia water (NH_4OH), for instead of a metal atom, its molecule contains the ammonium radical (NH_4).

When an acid acts on a base, one neutralizes the other, and in the process a salt is formed, with the liberation of water. This reaction may be described thus:

$$acid \ + \ base \ = \ salt \ + \ water$$
hydrochloric acid + sodium hydroxide = sodium chloride + water.

The water is formed from the hydroxyl radical of the base plus an extra atom of hydrogen from the acid, for water consists of hydrogen and oxygen in the proportion of two atoms of hydrogen to each atom of oxygen (HOH). The nonmetal part of the acid is then left to combine with the metal of the base to form a salt.

The most common acids are sulphuric acid (hydrogen, oxygen, and sulphur), hydrochloric acid (hydrogen and chlorine), nitric acid (hydrogen, nitrogen, and oxygen), and acetic acid (carbon, hydrogen, and oxygen). Usually acids are thought of as liquid in form; sulphuric and nitric acid are naturally liquid. Citric acid is a solid; citrus fruits contain citric acid. Any solution of an acid in water is commonly called an "acid," in popular usage. Sulphuric acid is commercially known as "oil of vitriol," and hydrochloric acid as "muriatic acid."

Bases, particularly the stronger ones, are also known as alkalies. Most bases occur naturally as solids, but solutions of them (in water) are commonly called bases. Sodium hydroxide, a common base, is popularly called caustic soda, the word "caustic" referring to its corrosive property; potassium hydroxide is similarly called caustic potash. Slaked lime is the base calcium hydroxide. Ordinary ammonia is the base ammonium hydroxide in solution. Bases, or alkalies, are used in cleaning because they dissolve greases; they also interact with fats to form soaps—sodium hydroxide is largely employed in the manufacture of soap. Since bases contain hydrogen and oxygen as hydroxyl radicals, they are called hydroxides. In inorganic chemistry, bases are always hydroxides of metals.

Salts are compounds formed by the substitution of a metal for the hydrogen of an acid, or by the substitution of a nonmetal for the hydroxide radical of a base. The usual method of the formation of a salt is by the action of an acid on a base. A salt may also be formed by the action of an acid on an oxide (of certain metals), or by the action of an acid on a metal. Sulphuric acid acting on zinc gives zinc sulphate; sulphuric acid on magnesium gives magnesium sulphate; nitric acid on zinc gives zinc nitrate; carbonic acid on sodium gives sodium carbonate; etc.

Most nonmetals form oxides which, when united with water, form acids. Most metals form oxides which, when united with water, form hydroxides (bases). Thus, sulphur trioxide plus water forms sulphuric acid, and calcium oxide plus water forms calcium hydroxide.

WATER

Water is the most abundant liquid on the earth's surface. It occurs naturally as a gas (water vapor), a liquid, and a solid (ice). Water vapor is always present in the air, though in varying quantity; its presence causes the humidity which may be oppressive in hot weather. The phenomena of rain, hail, and snow concern the meteorologist; the geologist makes a study of the action of water in wearing away rocks and cutting valleys through hills; water power is of great importance to industry. The chemist is primarily concerned with the composition of water and its action in combining or mixing with various substances; the chemist is also called upon to purify public drinking water, just as the engineer is called upon to ensure its plentiful supply throughout the year.

Water does not exist pure in nature, but always contains a varying amount of dissolved substances. A substance is said to be dissolved in a liquid when it disappears and becomes apparently (so far as the eye can see) a part of that liquid, without having been altered chemically. Thousands of substances are varyingly soluble in water; many others may be held in suspension in fine particles in water. Pure water can be obtained by distillation, as follows: Water is heated in a closed vessel, the escaping water vapor being led by a tube to a cooling chamber, in which the hot vapor condenses to water again—the latter is distilled water, free of all nonvolatile impurities (provided that the container is clean). Water vapor should not be confused with what is popularly called steam; water vapor is invisible, but when suddenly cooled it condenses quickly into tiny drops of water which float in the air in clouds of steam. The mineral substances in solution in natural water are often beneficial to health, though the medicinal value of some mineral springs has been much exaggerated; good drinking water always contains some dissolved substances. Distilled water lacks these important minerals. When water contains considerable quantities of dissolved calcium or magnesium compounds, it is difficult for soap to form a lather. Such water is described as "hard water."

The amount of a substance that water will dissolve varies with the temperature. A hundred pounds of water at 20° C. will hold in solution only about 42 pounds of copper sulphate; the same amount of water at 100° C. will hold in solution more than 200 pounds of copper sulphate. When a solution will dissolve no more of a dissolved substance, the solution is said to be *saturated.* A solution containing only a small amount of the dissolved substance is *dilute.* As a solution is cooled, it will hold less and less in solution, for solubility usually decreases with lower temperature. As a solid begins to separate from the solution, it often takes form in crystals. A solid can be separated by cooling the liquid; by evaporating the liquid, thus leaving the solid free; and by *precipitation,* a process which results when liquid in which the solid is not soluble (or is only slightly soluble) is added to the solution. A solid may also be brought out of solution by changing it chemically into an insoluble substance; this may be done by the addition of a substance which reacts with the solid in solution to form an insoluble compound.

Water is a compound of hydrogen and oxygen. This can be demonstrated in various ways; one proof is that when hydrogen is burned in oxygen, water is formed. A laboratory proof is called the *electrolysis of water.* Sulphuric acid is added to some water, to make it a conductor of electricity. The solution is placed in a special apparatus so that a direct electric current can be passed through the liquid. The electricity decomposes the water into two gases, one gathering in one tube, the other in another. It is found that one is oxygen, the other hydrogen, and that there is just twice as much hydrogen (by volume) as oxygen; it is also found that the weight of the two gases together is equal to the weight of the water decomposed. Several other chemical proofs of the composition of water are known, and all agree in this result.

THE STRUCTURE OF MATTER

MOLECULES AND ATOMS

Matter is composed of millions and millions of inconceivably small units called *molecules.* These are so small that an enormous number could fit on the head of a pin. Picture to yourself a marble an inch and a half in diameter. The marble is as many times larger than a molecule as the earth is larger than the marble, and the earth is about 8,000 *miles* (or more than 500,000,000 inches!) in diameter. Molecules are known to exist, and their existence is proved by complicated physical and chemical demonstrations, upon which all scientists are agreed. Certain large molecules have been seen through the electron microscope.

Although a molecule is a basic small unit of matter, it is not the smallest particle of a substance. Each molecule is made up of one or more *atoms*. A molecule of an element is composed entirely of its own atoms; molecules of compounds contain atoms of two or more elements. The word "atom" comes from the Greek, meaning "indivisible." Modern study of the structure of atoms shows that an atom of any substance is made up of still smaller particles. The breakup of the atom cannot, however, be accomplished by chemical means; therefore, in the study of chemistry, atoms function as fundamental units of elements.

A molecule of water is composed of two atoms of hydrogen and one atom of oxygen—three atoms in all. You will recall that in the electrolysis of water a volume of hydrogen twice as great as the volume of oxygen was derived from an equal weight of water. This proves that water contains twice as many atoms of hydrogen as of oxygen, for, according to a fundamental chemical hypothesis, equal volumes of all gases (at the same temperature and pressure) contain an equal number of molecules.

Chemical symbols are used to record and explain chemical action. Each element has a symbol, usually the initial letter or the first and another letter of its name (sometimes the English and sometimes the Latin name). The symbol of hydrogen is H, that of oxygen is O—the chemical *formula* of water is therefore H_2O, which means that a molecule of water contains two atoms of hydrogen to one of oxygen. The symbol of carbon is C. The composition of starch, an organic substance, may be represented by the formula $C_6H_{10}O_5$, which means that a molecule of starch contains six atoms of carbon and ten atoms of hydrogen to five atoms of oxygen.

THE CHEMICAL ELEMENTS

The factor in chemistry which makes elements combine in different ratios is called *valence*. The valence of an element is the power of its atoms, expressed by a number, to hold a certain number of atoms of other elements in combination. The valence of hydrogen is 1, and all elements which combine with hydrogen in the atomic proportion of one to one have the valence 1. Since oxygen combines with hydrogen in the proportion of one atom of oxygen to two of hydrogen, oxygen has a valence of 2. The following table lists all the known chemical elements, with the chemical symbol, atomic weight, valence, and atomic number of each, where known.

TABLE OF CHEMICAL ELEMENTS

Name	Symbol	Atomic Weight	Valence	Atomic Number
ACTINIUM	Ac	227	3	89
ALUMINIUM	Al	26.98	3	13
AMERICIUM	Am	243?	3, 4, 5 & 6	95
ANTIMONY	Sb	121.76	3 & 5	51
ARGON	A	39.944	0	18
ARSENIC	As	74.91	3 & 5	33
ASTATINE	At	211	?	85
BARIUM	Ba	137.36	2	56
BERKELIUM	Bk	245?	3 & 4	97
BERYLLIUM	Be	9.02	2	4
BISMUTH	Bi	209.0	3 & 5	83
BORON	B	10.82	3	5
BROMINE	Br	79.916	1 & 5	35
CADMIUM	Cd	112.41	2	48
CALCIUM	Ca	40.08	2	20
CALIFORNIUM	Cf	246?	3	98
CARBON	C	12.01	2 & 4	6
CERIUM	Ce	140.13	3 & 4	58
CESIUM	Cs	132.91	1	55
CHLORINE	Cl	35.457	1, 5 & 7	17
CHROMIUM	Cr	52.01	2, 3 & 6	24
COBALT	Co	58.94	2 & 3	27
COPPER	Cu	63.54	1 & 2	29
CURIUM	Cm	243?	3	96
DYSPROSIUM	Dy	162.5	3	66
EINSTEINIUM	E	253?	?	99
ERBIUM	Er	167.2	3	68
EUROPIUM	Eu	152.0	2 & 3	63
FERMIUM	Fm	255?	?	100
FLUORINE	F	19.0	1	9
FRANCIUM	Fr	223	1	87
GADOLINIUM	Gd	157.26	3	64
GALLIUM	Ga	69.72	3	31
GERMANIUM	Ge	72.6	4	32
GOLD	Au	197	1 & 3	79
HAFNIUM	Hf	178.50	4	72
HELIUM	He	4.003	0	2

Holmium	Ho	164.94	3	67
Hydrogen	H	1.0080	1	1
Indium	In	114.82	3	49
Iodine	I	126.91	1, 5 & 7	53
Iridium	Ir	193.1	3, 4 & 6	77
Iron	Fe	55.85	2 & 3	26
Krypton	Kr	83.80	0	36
Lanthanum	La	138.92	3	57
Lead	Pb	207.21	2 & 4	82
Lithium	Li	6.94	1	3
Lutetium	Lu	175.0	3	71
Magnesium	Mg	24.32	2	12
Manganese	Mn	54.94	2, 3, 4, 6 & 7	25
Mendelevium	Mv	256?	?	101
Mercury	Hg	200.61	1 & 2	80
Molybdenum	Mo	95.95	3, 5 & 6	42
Neodymium	Nd	144.27	3	60
Neon	Ne	20.183	0	10
Neptunium	Np	237	3, 4, 5 & 6	93
Nickel	Ni	58.71	2 & 3	28
Niobium	Nb	92.91	3 & 5	41
Nitrogen	N	14.008	3 & 5	7
Nobelium	No	258	?	102
Osmium	Os	190.2	2, 3, 4 & 8	76
Oxygen	O	16.0	2	8
Palladium	Pd	106.4	2 & 4	46
Phosphorus	P	30.975	3 & 5	15
Platinum	Pt	195.09	2 & 4	78
Plutonium	Pu	242?	3, 4, 5 & 6	94
Polonium	Po	210.0	2, 4 & 6	84
Potassium	K	39.100	1	19
Praseodymium	Pr	140.92	3	59
Promethium	Pm	145?	3	61
Protactinium	Pa	231	5	91
Radium	Ra	226.05	2	88
Radon	Rn	222.0	0	86
Rhenium	Re	186.22	1, 4 & 7	75
Rhodium	Rh	102.91	3 & 4	45
Rubidium	Rb	85.48	1	37
Ruthenium	Ru	101.1	3, 4, 6 & 8	44
Samarium	Sm	150.35	3	62
Scandium	Sc	44.96	3	21
Selenium	Se	78.96	2, 4 & 6	34
Silicon	Si	28.06	4	14
Silver	Ag	107.88	1	47

SODIUM	Na	22.991	1	11
STRONTIUM	Sr	87.63	2	38
SULPHUR	S	32.06	2, 4 & 6	16
TANTALUM	Ta	180.95	5	73
TECHNETIUM	Tc	99	6 & 7	43
TELLURIUM	Te	127.61	2, 4 & 6	52
TERBIUM	Tb	159.2	3	65
THALLIUM	Tl	204.39	1 & 3	81
THORIUM	Th	232.05	4	90
THULIUM	Tm	168.94	3	69
TIN	Sn	118.7	2 & 4	50
TITANIUM	Ti	47.9	3 & 4	22
TUNGSTEN	W	183.86	6	74
URANIUM	U	238.07	3, 4 & 6	92
VANADIUM	V	50.95	2, 4 & 5	23
XENON	Xe	131.3	0	54
YTTERBIUM	Yb	173.04	2 & 3	70
YTTRIUM	Y	88.92	3	39
ZINC	Zn	65.38	2	30
ZIRCONIUM	Zr	91.22	4	40

Those elements with zero valence are *inert;* that is, they do not combine chemically with any other elements. The fact that helium is an inert gas is of importance in aeronautics (as we have already pointed out), for its lightness makes it desirable for use in dirigibles, and since it does not combine with any other element, it is not inflammable (as hydrogen is). The United States has the principal source of the world's supply of helium; the gas is commonly used in American dirigibles.

The ninety-two naturally occurring elements are roughly divided into *metals,* which form compounds known as bases, and *nonmetals,* which form compounds known as acids; some, however, form both basic and acid compounds. Only about twenty are nonmetals, but among these are such important elements as oxygen, hydrogen, nitrogen, sulphur, carbon, silicon, and chlorine. Mercury is the only metal which is not solid at ordinary temperatures; mercury occurs naturally as a liquid, commonly called quicksilver. Ten or so of the nonmetals are gases. Bromine is a liquid. The rest of the nonmetals are solids.

When the elements are arranged in the order of their ascending atomic weights, they group themselves in series conforming to the *periodic law.* (The order is more exactly indicated by the *atomic numbers* of the elements, which are derived independently of the atomic weights.) Each series consists of seven (sometimes nine) elements. The corresponding members in all the series form families of elements with similar valences and similar chemical properties.

Another factor in the description of an element is its density. The density of an element (or a compound) is generally given in *grams* per *cubic centimeter*. The gram and centimeter are units of measure in the so-called *metric system* of weights and measures, which is used in scientific work throughout the world. A cubic centimeter of water at 4° C. weighs one gram; therefore these density figures also indicate the ratio of the weight of each element to the weight of an equal volume of water; that is, zinc, with a density of 7.14, weighs 7.14 times as much as an equal volume of water at 4°. A gram is equal to 15.432 grains; there are 7000 grains in a pound avoirdupois. To convert density to pounds per cubic foot, it is only necessary to multiply the density of a given element in grams per cubic centimeter by 62½ (more exactly 62.4, the weight in pounds of a cubic foot of water).

THEORY OF ATOMIC STRUCTURE

Elements are substances which cannot be broken into anything simpler by ordinary chemical means. The physicist, however, using the cyclotron and atomic pile, is able to break down the atoms of elements; and when he does, all atoms seem to break down into the same basic particles—protons, electrons, and neutrons. The *proton* is a positive unit of electricity, while the *electron* has an equal but negative charge. The proton weighs about 1,847 times more than the electron. The *neutron* seems to be a proton and electron in such close association that their charges cancel each other, and thus the neutron shows no charge. A neutron weighs about the same as a proton, since the relative weight of the electron is negligible. The total number of protons in an atom is naturally the same as the total number of electrons, the atom therefore having a neutral charge.

Since the atoms of all elements apparently are made up of protons, neutrons, and electrons, the difference among the atoms of the various elements must consist of the relative number and structure of such particles. This first supposition is borne out by the fact that, since very ingenious and indirect methods have been devised to weigh atoms, scientists have found that the atoms of different elements have different weights.

The lightest and therefore the simplest of all atoms is the hydrogen atom. Experimentation has demonstrated that it is made of one proton and one electron. We picture the lighter particle, the electron (– charge), as circling around the proton (+ charge), the two particles being held in association by their electrical attraction—much as the moon is held in a circular orbit around the earth by gravitational attraction. In order to have a convenient unit for expressing the weights of atoms, physicists developed a scale based on the weight of the oxygen atom as 16 units. These units were called "atomic mass units" (a.m.u.). On this scale the weight of the hydrogen atom is approximately one atomic mass unit (1 a.m.u.), a proton and a neutron each weighing 1 a.m.u. The weight of an electron is, as we said earlier, negligible.

The atom just heavier than hydrogen is helium. It was presumed that helium contained 2 protons and therefore, to be electrically neutral, also 2 electrons. Measurements of its weight, however, indicate that it weighs 4 a.m.u. We reason that there must also be 2 neutrons in the atom. (A neutron is actually, as we said, an electron and a proton in very close association.) The helium atom, therefore, consists of 2 protons, 2 electrons, and 2 neutrons.

The protons and neutrons in any atom seem to clump together to form the *nucleus* of the atom, which contains almost the entire weight of the atom. The electrons (negligible weight) circle around the nucleus in orbits. Diagrams of the hydrogen and helium atoms are pictured in Figures 2 and 3.

The number of protons in an atom (or the number of electrons) is called the *atomic number* of the atom. The total number of protons and neutrons in the nucleus is called the *atomic weight*. If we arrange the

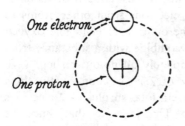

Fig. 2. Hydrogen atom, atomic weight 1.

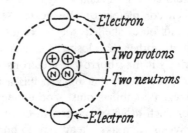

Fig. 3. Helium atom, atomic weight 4.

atoms in order of increasing atomic weight, we shall find that each element differs from the one preceding it in that it has one more proton in its nucleus (and therefore one more electron outside the nucleus). The number of neutrons also increases. For example, helium has 2 outer or planetary electrons and a nucleus consisting of 2 protons and 2 neutrons. Helium has an atomic number of 2 and an atomic weight of 4. The physicist usually writes it thus: $_2\text{He}^4$—putting the atomic number in the lower left and the atomic weight in the upper right.

Lithium ($_3Li^7$) has 3 electrons revolving about a nucleus consisting of 3 protons and 4 neutrons. Beryllium ($_4Be^9$) has 4 planetary electrons and a nucleus consisting of 4 protons and 5 neutrons. The atomic number tells us the number of protons (and, consequently, also the number of planetary electrons) while the atomic weight tells us the total number of particles in the nucleus (protons and neutrons). Thus uranium ($_{92}U^{238}$), the heaviest naturally occurring element, is composed of 92 planetary electrons and a nucleus of 92 protons and 146 neutrons ($92 + 146 = 238$).

In the picture of atomic structure which modern science proposes, the chemical properties of atoms (particularly valence) depend upon the number and arrangement of the electrons. The electrons circle about the nucleus of the atom in a number of orbits or rings. No more than two electrons can fit into the ring which is nearest the nucleus. The next two rings (farther from the nucleus) can each hold 8, then 18, and then 32— the maximum capacity of the rings increasing as they are farther from the nucleus, except that the *outermost shell,* which determines the valence, never can have more than 8. The oxygen atom ($_8O^{16}$), for example, has a nucleus consisting of 8 protons and 8 neutrons, which is surrounded by 8 electrons; the electrons are arranged in two shells, with 2 electrons in the ring nearest to the nucleus and 6 in the next. When an atom combines chemically with other atoms, it must either lose its outer shell completely or else borrow enough electrons from other atoms to fill its outer shell to the maximum for the outer shell (8). The oxygen atom, rather than losing 6 electrons, will combine with a substance from which it may borrow 2 electrons to completely fill its outer shell. (We say, therefore, that oxygen has a *valence* of 2.) The atoms with which oxygen combines must, consequently, have a total surplus of 2 electrons for each atom of oxygen in combination. That is to say that, since the oxygen atom has a tendency to borrow electrons, it combines with atoms which have a tendency to lose electrons. If hydrogen (which has but 1 electron in the outer shell) is to combine with oxygen, it would require 2 atoms of hydrogen to yield the 2 electrons necessary to fill the vacancies in the outer electron shell of the oxygen. This is why we write the formula for this compound of oxygen and hydrogen (which you will probably recognize as water) as H_2O, indicating that there are two atoms of hydrogen for each atom of oxygen.

It is interesting to note that those atoms whose outermost shells are entirely filled have an 0 valence and do not combine with any known element. They are stable in themselves. These include He, Ne, A, Kr, Xe, and Rn.

SOME IMPORTANT ELEMENTS AND THEIR COMPOUNDS

CHLORINE (Cl)

Chlorine is prepared in the laboratory by *oxidizing* hydrochloric acid. (You will recall that oxidation means adding oxygen to a substance.) If we oxidize hydrochloric acid, which is hydrogen chloride, we get water and chlorine; that is, the hydrogen of the hydrogen chloride is oxidized into water. To do this, we must add an oxidizing agent: manganese dioxide.

The equation for oxidizing HCl is as follows:

$$4HCl + MnO_2 \rightarrow 2H_2O + MnCl_2 + Cl_2$$

| hydrochloric acid | manganese dioxide | water | manganese chloride | chlorine (liberated as a gas) |

Each symbol in the equation represents an atom of an element. Thus H = 1 atom of hydrogen, Cl = 1 atom of chlorine. HCl = 1 molecule of hydrochloric acid. The coefficient 4 before the HCl means four molecules of hydrogen chloride (four atoms of hydrogen and four of chlorine). The small 2 below the O in MnO_2 means two atoms of O in the molecule of MnO_2. The 2 is used as a subscript rather than as coefficient because there is only one atom of Mn in MnO_2.

As you can see from the equation, the "4HCl," or four molecules of hydrochloric acid (hydrogen chloride), have been distributed among the three compounds on the right-hand side of the equation (the part to the right of the arrow). You will notice that here we have used up 2H in the water, Cl_2 in the manganese chloride, and Cl_2 in free chlorine. This is what happened to the 4HCl when it reacted with MnO_2.

MnO_2, the compound which reacted with the 4HCl, breaks up into 2O, which combines with the hydrogen to form the water, and Mn, which becomes part of the manganese chloride.

This *balancing of equations* will become more clear as you proceed. Here we were confronted with the problem of how to prepare chlorine. We knew that hydrochloric acid contains hydrogen and chlorine. We knew that if we could get the hydrogen out of hydrochloric acid, chlorine would be left. We knew that the best way to get hydrogen out of a compound was to oxidize it—that is, unite it with oxygen to form water. We did this with the aid of manganese dioxide—a compound which is rich in oxygen, having the formula MnO_2. As a result, we get a water solution of manganese chloride and free chlorine which is liberated and caught in a receptacle. The equation is *balanced* because there is exactly the same number of each kind of atom on each side of the equation—that is, before and after the chemical reaction—although they are arranged differently. If the equation did not balance, it would be false; it would describe an impossible reaction.

Chlorine is a greenish-yellow gas, heavier than air, with a heavy, noxious odor. It is used in small quantities as a disinfectant in swimming pools. However, in large quantities, the gas is highly poisonous.

Just as oxygen combines with carbon and hydrogen to form carbon dioxide and water, so chlorine combines with hydrogen to form hydrogen chloride. If hydrogen and chlorine are mixed and ignited we get hydrogen chloride (the gas of hydrochloric acid), thus:

$$H_2 \quad + \quad Cl_2 \quad \rightarrow \quad 2HCl$$

hydrogen   chlorine   hydrogen chloride

So great is the tendency of chlorine to combine with hydrogen that if a piece of paper is wet with turpentine (a compound of hydrogen and carbon) and put in a jar of chlorine, there is a violent action followed by a cloud of smoky soot. The chlorine combines instantly with the hydrogen in the turpentine, leaving soot (carbon) on the sides of the jar.

The molecules of hydrogen, nitrogen, oxygen, and chlorine contain two atoms each. Hence these molecules are written H_2, N_2, O_2, Cl_2. Before the atoms combine into molecules, the gas is nascent. A nascent gas is always very active, because its atoms must find the second atom to complete its molecules. Nascent oxygen is the most common nascent gas.

Nascent oxygen (O) is extremely active. It "runs around trying to find another atom of itself," so to speak. If it cannot find another atom of itself, it "takes hold of whatever it can." That is why hydrogen peroxide is a disinfectant. When you cut your finger and put hydrogen peroxide on the cut, the hydrogen peroxide breaks up into water and nascent oxygen, thus:

$$H_2O_2 \quad \rightarrow \quad H_2O \quad + \quad O$$

hydrogen peroxide   water   nascent oxygen

This nascent oxygen, for want of something else to combine with, takes hold of the poisonous matter in the wound. That is why we call it a disinfectant—no germs can remain near nascent oxygen. Nascent oxygen also combines with the color in hair or dye in cloth, and bleaches it. Hence peroxide is often used for bleaching.

When chlorine is dissolved in water, we get hydrochloric acid and nascent oxygen, thus:

$$Cl_2 \quad + \quad H_2O \quad \rightarrow \quad 2HCl \quad + \quad O$$

chlorine   water   hydrogen chloride   nascent
                                (hydrochloric acid)   oxygen

This nascent oxygen is used commercially in bleaching. Raw cotton is bleached entirely by this very means. Laundries bleach or whiten washings with bleaching powder which contains chlorine. This powder, when put in the water, liberates nascent oxygen.

Hydrochloric acid is the water solution of hydrogen chloride. We have already learned that hydrogen chloride is produced by uniting hydrogen with chlorine, and consequently it would seem that this would be an easy way to prepare hydrochloric acid. Unfortunately, when hydrogen and chlorine combine, the action is very violent and difficult to control.

The most common way to prepare any acid is by the use of sulphuric acid. If you want to prepare hydrochloric acid, put sulphuric acid on a chloride. The most common chloride is table salt—sodium chloride. If sulphuric acid is put on sodium chloride, we immediately get sodium bisulphate and hydrochloric acid, thus:

$$NaCl + H_2SO_4 \rightarrow NaHSO_4 + HCl$$

sodium chloride   sulphuric acid   sodium bisulphate   hydrochloric acid

Before discussing the uses and properties of hydrochloric acid, let us summarize what we have learned about acids and apply it here. We learned that an acid and a metal when combined always give the metallic salt of that acid and hydrogen. We then learned that an acid and a metallic salt always give a new acid and a new salt.

Another acid and a nitrate give nitric acid plus a salt. Sulphuric acid and a chloride give hydrochloric acid plus a salt. Sulphuric acid and a carbonate give carbonic acid plus a salt.

Sulphuric acid, because of its high boiling point, is used to prepare other acids. Therefore the way to prepare hydrochloric acid would be to mix sulphuric acid with a chloride; the way to prepare nitric acid would be to mix sulphuric acid with a nitrate.

The most important use of hydrochloric acid is in the preparation of chlorides. There are only four common metals with which hydrochloric acid does not react to any great extent; these are mercury, silver, copper, and lead. Many other metals react to form chlorides and liberate hydrogen.

Hydrochloric acid and zinc give zinc chloride; hydrochloric acid and iron give iron chloride; hydrochloric acid and tin give tin chloride.

Sodium (Na) and Potassium (K)

Sodium and potassium are usually grouped together because they are very similar. They both exhibit chemical properties such as those found in the more familiar metals. They are rarely seen in metallic form—you have never seen sodium or potassium kitchenware, because these metals are unsuitable for such use. You naturally think of a metal as something which is hard, shiny, or heavy. Actually, potassium and sodium are neither hard nor heavy. They are so soft that you can cut them with a knife, and so light that they float in water. Not only that, but both sodium and potassium react violently even to the point of minor explosion when put on water. When a small piece—the size of a pea—of either sodium or potassium is put in a pan of water, it goes hissing and sputtering over the surface, expending itself as it goes along, and eventually bursts into a flame. Both sodium and potassium conduct heat and electricity, and combine with acids in exactly the same way that other metals do. Because of their extreme activity, sodium and potassium must be stored in kerosene, with which they do not combine.

Sodium and potassium cannot be used as ordinary metals. However, the salts of sodium and potassium are so numerous and so useful that it is a question whether life could exist without them. A great many of them are used in medicine, the commercial names of the most common being soda and potash. All the salts of sodium and of potassium are soluble in water.

Sulphur (S)

Sulphur is, of course, an essential element in sulphuric acid. This chemical has innumerable uses. It is necessary in the manufacture of fertilizers, explosives, kerosene, storage batteries, drugs, dyes, and many other commodities, and in the production of many other acids. These acids, in turn, or their salts, are necessary every minute of our lives.

Sulphur is found in nature either free or in combination with other elements. It is found in its natural state in great abundance in Louisiana and Texas, hundreds of feet below the surface of the earth. It is found also in volcanic regions. Few other elements have as many varieties of form as sulphur. There is, for example, rhombic sulphur—small crystals, yellowish in appearance and somewhat octagonal in shape. Then there is prismatic sulphur, which is more of a powder than rhombic and not quite so heavy. Then there is amorphous sulphur, which has the consistency of rubber and can be poured. There are a number of other varieties also. The commercial form of sulphur is roll sulphur, which consists almost entirely of the rhombic variety (small crystals).

Sulphur burns readily in oxygen, forming sulphur dioxide, thus:

$$S + O_2 \rightarrow SO_2$$

Sulphur also combines with metals to form what are known as sulphides. For example, copper plus sulphur gives copper sulphide; zinc plus sulphur gives zinc sulphide; hydrogen plus sulphur gives hydrogen sulphide. (This last-named compound is given off by rotten eggs; the bad odor is partly due to this gas.)

As we have seen, sulphur combines with oxygen to form sulphur dioxide (SO_2). This sulphur dioxide also combines with oxygen, forming sulphur trioxide (SO_3), thus:

$$S + O_2 \rightarrow SO_2$$
$$2SO_2 + O_2 \rightarrow 2SO_3$$

Sulphur trioxide (SO_3), when dissolved in water, instantly gives the heavy, oily liquid known as sulphuric acid, thus:

$$SO_3 + H_2O \rightarrow H_2SO_4$$
$$\text{sulphuric acid}$$

Sulphuric acid and a metal or a salt produce sulphates. Thus sulphuric acid and zinc produce zinc sulphate and hydrogen; sulphuric acid and iron produce iron sulphate and hydrogen; sulphuric acid and sodium produce sodium sulphate and hydrogen; etc. Sulphuric acid on copper has a slightly different reaction. Copper ordinarily does not react to cold sulphuric acid, but when the acid is heated, copper and sulphuric acid give copper sulphate, water, and sulphur dioxide.

Sulphuric acid and a base give water and a salt, as any acid and base do. For instance, sulphuric acid and potassium hydroxide produce water and potassium sulphate; sulphuric acid and sodium hydroxide produce water and sodium sulphate; sulphuric acid and calcium hydroxide produce water and calcium sulphate.

Sulphides result from the direct union of sulphur with a metal. The sulphides are salts of hydrosulphuric acid (H_2S), often called hydrogen sulphide. When we put sulphuric acid on metals, we get sulphates. The difference between a *sulphate* and a *sulphide* is that a sulphide never contains oxygen, whereas a sulphate always does. A *sulphite* contains oxygen in lesser quantity than a *sulphate*.

Thus we have three distinct groups: sulphides, identified by S; sulphites, identified by SO_3; and sulphates, identified by SO_4. Sulphites are usually produced by the action of sulphur*ous* acid, which has the formula H_2SO_3. It is extremely important to note these three groups carefully. Note, first, the sulph*ides,* and the lack of oxygen in that group. Note, secondly, the sulph*ites,* and the characteristic SO_3. And note, lastly, the sulph*ates,* with the ending SO_4. Whenever you see these endings in a formula you will recognize their identity instantly. Note a corresponding similarity in other groups of salts as shown in the table on pages 1178–79.

NITROGEN (N)

We have already seen that the air is about four-fifths nitrogen. This being so, you might naturally expect to find an abundance of nitrates in the earth, just as you find an abundance of oxides. Nitrates are indeed very plentiful, being essential to fertile soil, as every farmer knows.

Nitrogen is prepared in a number of ways. The simplest way is to get it from the air. This is done by passing air through a tube in which copper gauze is placed, and heating the tube. The air, in passing over the heated copper, loses its oxygen to the copper, forming copper oxide. The remaining gas is nitrogen. Of course it is not entirely pure nitrogen, because air contains traces of carbon dioxide and very slight amounts of some other gases. But for practical purposes air from which the oxygen has been removed may be regarded as pure nitrogen.

Nitrogen is slightly lighter than air. It is odorless, tasteless, and colorless, and does not support combustion. Nitrogen unites with oxygen, in various proportions, to form nitric oxide, nitrous oxide, and nitrogen peroxide, thus:

$$NO \qquad N_2O \qquad NO_2$$
nitric oxide   nitrous oxide   nitrogen peroxide

Nitrogen unites with hydrogen to form a very familiar gas known as ammonia, with the formula NH_3. The common household ammonia with which we are familiar is the water solution of this gas ($NH_3 + H_2O$), known as ammonium hydroxide (NH_4OH).

There are five oxides of nitrogen, some of which have already been mentioned. The most common is nitrous oxide (N_2O), which has an anesthetic effect and is known as laughing gas.

Nitric acid (HNO_3) is prepared by mixing sulphuric acid with a nitrate. Either sodium nitrate (saltpeter) or potassium nitrate is ideal for the purpose.

The action of sulphuric acid on sodium nitrate is as follows:

$$2NaNO_3 \quad + \quad H_2SO_4 \quad \rightarrow \quad Na_2SO_4 \quad + \quad 2HNO_3$$
sodium nitrate   sulphuric acid   sodium sulphate   nitric acid

Nitric acid (HNO_3) is a very powerful acid. It is unique in one respect—namely, that whereas it reacts with a great many metals to form nitrates, hydrogen is *not* liberated.

Nitric acid is used extensively to make nitroglycerine, guncotton, and many drugs, dyes, etc.

All explosives contain nitrogen. Dynamite is pure nitroglycerine mixed with a certain kind of earth known as infusorial earth. Nitroglycerine, the main constituent of dynamite, is prepared by mixing nitric acid and glycerine. Nitroglycerine is a thick, heavy oil which burns slowly. When it is heated to a certain temperature it explodes with terrific violence. Nitroglycerine can also be exploded by sending an electric charge through it, or by percussion. By mixing this oil with infusorial earth to make dynamite, we have it in a form that is not so sensitive and can be handled with more ease and safety than in the pure form.

Gunpowder is a combination of potassium nitrate, sulphur, and charcoal. It burns with extreme rapidity. If a pile of gunpowder is spread out and lighted, it will flare up in a bright flame, and in a fraction of a second the whole pile will be burnt up. This is due to the fact that there is a quantity of oxygen present in the nitrate which is unstable—ready to leave the nitrogen. Compressed gunpowder burns as fast as when in open space and produces nearly 2,000 times its own volume of gases. Hence it explodes violently.

Air

Air is neither an element nor a chemical compound. Air is a mixture of gases; though they are thoroughly mixed, these gases are not in chemical combination. This explains why, when you send air through a tube containing hot copper gauze, the oxygen of the air remains behind to combine with the copper and lets the nitrogen pass through. The composition of air is as follows:

> 78.02% nitrogen
> 21.00% oxygen
> .93% argon
> .04% carbon dioxide
> .01% traces of other gases

Varying amounts of water vapor are also present in air.

Plants utilize carbon dioxide, which human beings eliminate in breathing. Carbon dioxide is always present in the air, though in very small quantities. Nevertheless, it is sufficient for the plant life, which takes it in and changes it to carbon and oxygen, using the carbon for food and giving off the oxygen into the air.

Ammonia (NH_3)

Ammonia is prepared by uniting nitrogen with hydrogen and is also obtained as a by-product of the destructive distillation of soft coal. Ammonia gas is easily produced, and its odor is well known to anyone who has used the household form of it.

Ammonia is readily soluble in water—it is one of the most soluble gases. Ammonia in solution forms a typical base, called ammonium hydroxide. It will react with acids to form water and an ammonium salt. If the acid is sulphuric, the result is water and ammonium sulphate; if the acid is hydrochloric, the result is water and ammonium chloride; and so on.

The chief use of ammonia is in the manufacture of ice. The principle is very simple. It is based on the fact that when a gas is liquefied, heat is set free; and when a liquid is made into a gas, heat is absorbed. You can see how true this is, because it is necessary for water to absorb an enormous amount of heat in order to become steam. Ammonia gas is pumped through a series of pipes. This gas is then condensed; that is, it is cooled and liquefied. The liquid ammonia is run through another series of pipes which are submerged in a solution of salt water. In this solution of salt water there are also a number of cans of pure water. The liquid ammonia circulating in the pipes has a marked tendency to go back to the gaseous state in which it was originally produced. It does this readily, but in order for it to do so, something must supply the heat, because to transform liquid into a gas, heat is needed. The salt-water solution in which the liquid-ammonia pipes are submerged has to supply the heat to turn this liquid back into ammonia gas. This it does with a decided and inevitable drop in temperature. In a short time the temperature of the salt solution drops to a point far below freezing. The cans of pure water submerged in this terrifically cold salt solution are naturally chilled below the freezing point, as is the pure water in them. In a short time the water in these cans is brought down to the freezing point and ice is formed.

PHOSPHORUS (P)

Phosphorus is found in the bones and teeth of animals in the form of calcium phosphate. To secure phosphorus, calcium phosphate is ground up into a fine powder and put in an electric furnace together with sand and coal. Phosphorus exists in two forms, white phosphorus and red phosphorus. White phosphorus is a waxy, translucent solid which must always be kept under water because the instant it is exposed to air it bursts into flame. The reason for this is that it has an extremely low kindling temperature and when it is exposed to air it begins to oxidize immediately. The heat which is generated in the process of oxidation raises the phosphorus to its kindling temperature almost immediately, and a brilliant flame results. The reaction is

$$4P + 5O_2 \rightarrow 2P_2O_5$$

White phosphorus is extremely poisonous: the slightest quantity taken internally causes instant death. Red phosphorus is the result of heating white phosphorus to about 250° C. in a vessel from which air has been extracted. Red phosphorus is a soft reddish powder, much less poisonous than white phosphorus, and does not burn until heated by friction or other means.

A common match consists of a stick of wood which has been dipped in melted wax. The head of the match is composed of phosphorus sesquisulphide, a high oxidizing agent such as potassium chlorate, and glue. (Sometimes other chemicals are used; the composition of patented matches is likely to be a trade secret.) The glue in the head of the match holds the potassium chlorate and the phosphorus together. When you strike the match, the heat generated by friction ignites the tip. The result is immediately a bright flame. This is helped along by the oxygen in the potassium chlorate. If the potassium chlorate were not present, the match would light and go out almost immediately. After the burst of flame which results upon first striking the match, you will notice a more gradual burning. This is the potassium chlorate, which helps to raise the stick to its kindling temperature, and in less than a second the stick has caught fire and burns slowly, owing to the wax in which it was dipped. When the match is burned out, it does not glow after the flame is gone. This is due to a certain chemical with which the wood has been treated in order to lessen the danger of fires from carelessly discarded matches that have merely been blown out.

THE HALOGENS

The halogens consist of five elements, as follows: fluorine, chlorine, bromine, iodine, and astatine. These elements belong to the same group when all elements are arranged in accordance with the periodic law already mentioned. They react to acids in a similar way and are very much alike chemically in other respects. Chlorine has been fully discussed above.

The word *halogen* means salt former. These elements are so called because the first four unite directly with a large number of metallic elements to form salts. The salts thus formed containing bromine are called bromides; those containing chlorine, chlorides (as we have already seen); those containing fluorine and iodine, fluorides and iodides, respectively.

Bromides occur in nature along with chlorides. Large deposits of crude salt (sodium chloride) also contain sodium and magnesium bromide. Bromine is easily prepared from magnesium bromide. Magnesium bromide plus chlorine gives magnesium chloride and bromine.

Bromine is a dark, brownish-red liquid, much denser than water. An interesting characteristic of bromine is that it is the only nonmetallic element which exists in a liquid form. It has an odor resembling chlorine, and vaporizes very quickly. It is poisonous, 1   not so destructive as chlorine. Just as we had hydrochloric acid from chlorine, so we have hydrobromic acid (HBr) from bromine.

Iodine is obtained from seaweed: when seaweed (kelp) is burned, the remaining ashes contain potassium and sodium iodides. By heating a mixture of sulphuric acid, manganese dioxide, and potassium iodide, we obtain potassium sulphate, manganese sulphate, water, and iodine.

Iodine is a blackish-gray solid, slightly soluble in water and extremely soluble in alcohol. The alcohol solution, known as tincture of iodine, is what you paint your cuts and bruises with to prevent infection. Even a very small amount of pure iodine will turn common starch blue.

Fluorine differs in some properties from chlorine, bromine, and iodine. It is a pale, greenish-yellow gas with an extremely poisonous odor, much more poisonous than chlorine. Fluorine has a greater tendency to form salts than any of the other halogens.

Hydrofluoric acid is prepared by mixing sulphuric acid and calcium fluoride. The preparation is made in a lead dish, and hydrofluoric acid is kept in wax bottles, because it attacks glass and dissolves it. Nearly all etching on glass is done with hydrofluoric acid. This acid is extremely dangerous.

Astatine is the radioactive product of man-made elements which have high atomic weight and high atomic number. Although it falls in the halogen group under the arrangement indicated by the periodic law, it differs from the other members which we have just discussed, and behaves more as though it were a metal. However, it can be displaced from certain of its compounds by chlorine, thus showing a halogen characteristic.

TABLE OF COMMON SALTS

All chlorates and nitrates are soluble in water. All K (potassium), Na (sodium), and NH_4 (ammonium) salts are soluble in water. All carbonates, oxides, and hydroxides are insoluble in water except those of K, Na, and NH_4.

For symbols used in the following list, see the Table of Chemical Elements, page 1163.

BROMINE forms *bromides* (example: KBr, potassium bromide), all soluble in water except AgBr and HgBr salts.

CARBON forms *carbides* (example: CaC_2, calcium carbide); and *carbonates* (example: $CaCO_3$, calcium carbonate), latter insoluble in water except K, Na, and NH_4 salts.

CHLORINE forms *chlorides* (example: NaCl, sodium chloride), all soluble in water except AgCl and HgCl; and *chlorates* (example: $KClO_3$), all soluble in water.

IODINE forms *iodides* (example: HI, hydrogen iodide), all soluble in water except Pb, Hg, and Ag salts.

NITROGEN forms *nitrites* (example: KNO_2, potassium nitrite); and *nitrates* (example: $AgNO_3$, silver nitrate), latter all soluble in water.

OXYGEN forms *oxides* (example: CuO, copper oxide), all insoluble in water except K, Na, and Ba oxides.

SULPHUR forms *sulphides* (example: H_2S, hydrogen sulphide); *sulphites* (example: Na_2SO_3, sodium sulphite); and *sulphates* (example: Na_2SO_4, sodium sulphate), all the latter soluble in water except Ba and Pb salts.

HYDROXIDES (example: KOH, potassium hydroxide) are all insoluble in water except K, Na, Ba, and NH_4 hydroxides.

SOME COMMON ELEMENTS AND THEIR BEST-KNOWN SALTS

ALUMINIUM (Al), metal—*properties:* gray color, extremely light, reacts with HCl and H_2SO_4; used for kitchenware; forms aluminium oxide (Al_2O_3) and aluminium hydroxide ($Al[OH]_3$); salts used in welding and dyeing.

BROMINE (Br), liquid—*properties:* dark brown color, combines with metals; forms silver bromide (AgBr) and potassium bromide (KBr); salts used in photography and medicine.

CALCIUM (Ca), metal—*properties:* silver-white color, very light; forms calcium oxide (CaO), calcium hydroxide ($Ca[OH]_2$), and calcium carbonate ($CaCO_3$); salts used in making lime, mortar, and cement.

CHLORINE (Cl), gas—*properties:* greenish color, poisonous odor; used in bleaching and sterilizing, especially drinking water and swimming pools; forms sodium chloride or common salt (NaCl), chlorides of most of the metals, potassium chlorate ($KClO_3$); salts used in medicine, gunpowder, matches.

COPPER (Cu), metal—*properties:* yellow metal with reddish tinge, very good conductor of heat and electricity; used in wiring and photoengraving; forms copper sulphate ($CuSO_4$), used in electroplating and in electric batteries.

FLUORINE (F), gas—*properties:* very poisonous; forms hydrofluoric acid (HF), used in etching on glass.

GOLD (Au), metal—*properties:* yellow color, heavy, slow in combining with other elements, good conductor of heat; used in coins and jewelry.

HYDROGEN (H), gas—*properties:* lightest gas known, highly inflammable; used in inflating balloons and dirigibles; compounds are mostly acids; used in preparations of other chemicals.

IODINE (I), solid—*properties:* gray color, crystalline in form, soluble in alcohol and in water; used in solution as an antiseptic; forms potassium iodide (KI); salts used in medicine, dyeing, and photography.

LEAD (Pb), metal—*properties:* gray color, dull luster, heavy and very soft; used for pipes and printers' type (in alloys); forms lead carbonate ($PbCO_3$); salts used in making paints.

MAGNESIUM (Mg), metal—*properties:* silvery white color, burns readily; used in flashlight photography; forms magnesium sulphate ($MgSO_4$) and magnesium carbonate ($MgCO_3$); salts used in medicine and in making talc and face powders.

MERCURY (Hg), liquid metal—*properties:* silvery color, bright luster, expands and contracts readily with variations of temperature; used in thermometers and barometers; forms mercury chloride (HgCl) and mercury bichloride ($HgCl_2$); salts used in medicine and as a disinfectant.

NICKEL (Ni), metal—*properties:* silvery white color, will not rust; used in plating iron.

NITROGEN (N), gas—*properties:* invisible, tasteless, odorless, forms about ⅘ of the earth's atmosphere; forms nitrous (N_2O) and nitric (NO) oxides; the chief constituent of laughing gas; salts used in making fertilizers and explosives.

OXYGEN (O), gas—*properties:* invisible, odorless, tasteless, forms about ⅕ of the earth's atmosphere; used in pure state in blowpipes and pulmotors (for resuscitation); has hundreds of useful compounds.

PHOSPHORUS (P), solid—*properties:* white and red (two kinds), burns (oxidizes) readily in air; used in making matches, and as fertilizer in the form of phosphates (phosphorus combined with oxygen and metal).

PLATINUM (Pt), metal—*properties:* silvery white color, very heavy, slow in combining with other elements; used in jewelry and electrical instruments.

SILICON (Si), nonmetal—forms silicon dioxide (sand, SiO_2), used in making glass.

SILVER (Ag), metal—*properties:* shiny, silvery color, best conductor of heat known; used for making jewelry, coins, mirrors; forms silver nitrate ($AgNO_3$) and silver bromide (AgBr); salts used in medicine and photography.

ZINC (Zn), metal—*properties:* bluish-white color; used for galvanizing iron and in photoengraving; forms zinc oxide (ZnO); salts used in white pigment and in medicine.

METALS AND THEIR COMPOUNDS

Two important *metals,* sodium and potassium, have been discussed under the preceding main heading "Some Important Elements and Their Compounds." This was particularly desirable not only because they are important, but the knowledge of sodium and potassium makes it easier to present the compounds of the other elements discussed. However, it should be noted that except for sodium and potassium, all the other elements which are topics under "Some Important Elements and Their Compounds" are *nonmetals.* We turn now to the other important metals.

CALCIUM (Ca)

Metallic calcium is an active metal which releases hydrogen from acids and forms salts.

Thus:

$$Ca + 2HCl \rightarrow CaCl_2 + H_2$$

Metallic calcium finds but few uses. Its compounds, however, are quite useful.

Calcium carbonate ($CaCO_3$), the most common salt of calcium, occurs in nature almost as frequently as sodium chloride—ordinary salt. We are all familiar with it as limestone or marble—sometimes a whole mountain range is made up of limestone and marble. Pure calcium carbonate is a white solid which is frequently transparent. The color of marble, with its various streaks of blacks and grays, is due entirely to the impurities in the calcium carbonate.

Quicklime is calcium oxide, which is obtained by heating calcium carbonate to a red heat, thus:

$$CaCO_3 \rightarrow CaO + CO_2$$

Calcium oxide is a white powdery substance which, when heated to very high temperatures, gives a dazzling light called limelight.

When calcium oxide is mixed with water, we get another compound, known as slaked lime, the chemical name of which is calcium hydroxide. This substance is perhaps one of the most useful that Nature has given us. Slaked lime mixed with sand gives us mortar, which is necessary in the construction of brick buildings.

The reaction of mortar is very interesting. It is a pasty white mass consisting of calcium hydroxide, sand, and water. When it is allowed to stand in the air for any length of time, it draws carbon dioxide from the air (you will remember that air is a mixture and not a compound) to form calcium carbonate and water.

$$Ca(OH)_2 \quad + \quad CO_2 \quad \rightarrow \quad CaCO_3 \quad + \quad H_2O$$

mortar   carbon dioxide   limestone   water

Calcium carbonate, or limestone, is always a hard, brittle substance. That is the reason mortar hardens when exposed to the air.

There are three other important compounds of calcium: namely, calcium sulphate, which is commonly known as plaster of Paris; chlorinated lime, a disinfectant, known as bleaching powder; and calcium phosphate, an important fertilizer.

MAGNESIUM (Mg)

Magnesium is a very light, silvery white metal. It burns with a brilliant white light to which photographic plates are extremely sensitive. Magnesium is sometimes used in flashlight photography. The most common salts of magnesium are magnesium carbonate, magnesium citrate, and magnesium sulphate. The magnesium carbonate and hydroxide are used in face powders. Talcum powder contains a considerable amount of talc, which is magnesium silicate. Magnesium citrate, or citrate of magnesia, and sulphate of magnesia (Epsom salts) are used as laxatives.

ZINC (Zn)

Zinc is found combined with other elements in ores. Zinc oxide, or zincite (ZnO), is used in the preparation of pure zinc. The process involves reduction. The zinc oxide is heated with coal dust (carbon), and the carbon reduces the zinc oxide to zinc and carbon monoxide (carbon monoxide is a deadly gas with the formula CO).

Zinc is a bluish-white metal which is used extensively in making alloys such as brass, German silver, and bronze, in galvanizing iron to prevent rust, and in photoengraving. The last-named use gives us nearly all line-drawing reproductions in books, newspapers, and magazines.

Zinc readily unites with acids, forming zinc salts and hydrogen. Zinc oxide (ZnO) is an extremely white powder which is used as the basis of white pigment for paints. It is used also in the preparation of rubber. Zinc chloride ($ZnCl_2$) is used for preserving wood; wood soaked in a solution of zinc chloride resists decay.

MERCURY (Hg)

Mercury is found in an ore known as cinnabar or mercuric sulphide. It is obtained very simply by heating mercuric sulphide with oxygen, giving us mercury and sulphur dioxide:

$$HgS \quad + \quad O_2 \quad \rightarrow \quad Hg \quad + \quad SO_2$$

mercuric sulphide   oxygen   mercury   sulphur dioxide

At ordinary temperature, mercury is a liquid—the only liquid metal—with a brilliant luster. It is commonly known as quicksilver, and seems heavy for its bulk because it has a comparatively high specific gravity or density.

An interesting property of mercury is that it forms what are known as amalgams with gold and silver. If you dip a five-dollar gold piece into a vessel containing mercury, it is instantly turned to the color of mercury; the mercury has amalgamated with the gold—that is, the mercury dissolves the gold and forms an alloy on the surface of the coin. Silver amalgam is used by dentists in filling teeth.

Mercury combines readily with halogens and sulphur. It is not acted on by acids in general. Of course the most common use of mercury is in barometers and thermometers. The chloride ($HgCl$) and the bichloride ($HgCl_2$) are useful compounds; mercurous chloride ($HgCl$) is a white powder known in medicine as calomel. Mercuric chloride (bichloride of mercury), or corrosive sublimate ($HgCl_2$), is a splendid disinfectant and a violent poison.

IRON (Fe)

Iron occurs in great abundance as an ore in the form of iron oxide (Fe_2O_3). The Latin name for iron is *ferrum;* the symbol is Fe; and compounds of iron are called ferric or ferrous, depending upon whether the valence is 3 or 2, respectively.

Iron has a number of forms commercially, including cast iron, wrought iron, and pig iron.

Cast iron is produced in a blast furnace by reducing ferric oxide with carbon, thus:

$$Fe_2O_3 \quad + \quad 3C \quad \rightarrow \quad 2Fe \quad + \quad 3CO$$

ferric oxide   carbon   iron   carbon monoxide

The terrific heat necessary for this melts the iron, which is drawn out minus the slag at the bottom of the furnace. This molten iron, if cooled suddenly, becomes brittle and is called cast iron. It is used in stoves, plates upon which building columns rest, and in other places where it is not subject to tension. Because of its brittleness, it is of little use for beams and the like. It is excellent under compression. A great many molds, forms, and pipes are cast iron. Because of the fact that carbon is used in the manufacture of cast iron, there is a little excess carbon in cast iron. This carbon helps to make the iron even more brittle. There are also other impurities in cast iron, such as sulphur, phosphorus, and silicon, which were present in the original iron ore and not separated in the refining process.

A much purer form of iron is called wrought iron. It contains usually less than .15% of carbon, 1% to 2% of slag, and is practically free from sulphur and phosphorus.

Steel is made by removing most of the carbon, silicon, and impurities from cast iron. In the process of manufacturing steel, samples are constantly tested to determine how much of the various impurities have been removed and how much carbon it contains. The percentage of carbon in steel varies from .2% in soft steel to 2% in hard steel. Steel can be tempered according to the amount of carbon it contains. Tempered steel is used in tools.

There are many compounds of iron, the most common, of course, being ferric oxide (Fe_2O_3). Ferric oxide is a bright red powder used in pigments like Venetian red, Indian red, and sometimes scarlet.

Iron forms two classes of salts, the fer*ric* and the fer*rous,* the difference being in the number of atoms required for the combination. Thus while ferric chloride's formula is $FeCl_3$, ferrous chloride's formula is $FeCl_2$.

There is another group of iron salts called the ferric and ferrous cyanides. The salts containing the cyanide group (CN) consist of carbon and nitrogen, and are violently poisonous. (Potassium cyanide is one of the most deadly poisons in existence. All the cyanide salts are poisonous.)

Iron and potassium together unite with the cyanide group to form potassium ferricyanide, with the formula $K_3Fe(CN)_6$. This potassium ferricyanide acts on ferrous chloride to produce ferrous ferricyanide, an intensely blue compound, thus:

$$3FeCl_2 + 2K_3Fe(CN)_6 \rightarrow 6KCl + Fe_3[Fe(CN)_6]_2$$

This is made use of in blueprints. The paper is coated with ferric ammonium citrate and potassium ferricyanide. When exposed to light, the paper serves as a reducing agent and the ferric salt is reduced to a ferrous salt. If this exposed paper is covered with water, the parts of the paper which have been reduced to the ferrous salt will turn an intense blue. The potassium ferricyanide acts as a developer.

Copper (Cu)

Copper is another extremely useful metal. It occurs free in nature. Because of its high conductivity of heat and electricity, it is used extensively in wire and cables. It is also used in boilers, kettles, vacuum pans, etc. Copper is used extensively in scientific instruments. One of the most important uses of copper is in photoengraving; if it were not for zinc and copper, the advertisements you see in magazines with their elaborate pictures, and the pictures in newspapers, books, display cards, etc., would not be possible.

The most important compound of copper is copper sulphate ($CuSO_4$), a blue substance (blue vitriol) which is used in electric batteries and in electroplating, and in Bordeaux mixture—a common fungicide made of copper sulphate, lime, and water.

SILVER (Ag)

Silver, gold, and platinum are the precious metals—precious because they are rare and useful. Silver, with its salts, is by far the most useful. However, the rarity of gold and platinum makes them much more valuable. The Latin name for silver is *argentum*, and its symbol is Ag. Silver is grayish white, and is the best conductor of heat and electricity known. It is capable of receiving and retaining a very high polish, and consequently is the best reflector of light known. The better-grade mirrors are glass with silvered backs.

Silver does not combine readily with air, but in the presence of sulphur it blackens. This explains why silver spoons become discolored when used continually for eating eggs, for the eggs contain a compound of sulphur.

Pure solid silver is not hard, and consequently cannot be used commercially. It is only when silver is alloyed with copper that it is hard enough to stand the wear and tear of constant use. The half dollar contains 90% silver and about 10% copper. The British coins are a little higher in silver content (92½% silver); this is the best possible combination and is known as sterling silver.

Silver is used in making mirrors and in silver-plating. A mirror is made by pouring silver nitrate on polished plate glass. Over this solution are poured some ammonia and a reducing agent, and the whole is warmed. Ammonia, together with the reducing agent, reacts with the nitrate in the silver nitrate, leaving a deposit of pure silver on the glass in a very thin film. This is then washed, dried, and varnished to protect it.

Silver-plating is done in an electric bath. This bath consists of a solution of potassium cyanide and silver cyanide, two intensely poisonous chemicals. A bar of sheet silver is used at the positive end of the bath, and the article to be plated is placed at the negative end. When the current is turned on, it flows through the solution from the silver to the object to be plated, carrying with it atoms of silver and depositing them on the object to be plated.

The most important salt of silver is the bromide. Silver bromide is extremely sensitive to light, a fact which is made use of in photography. A photographic plate is of plain glass coated with gelatine and silver bromide. When the plate is put in a camera and an image is thrown upon it (through a lens), the light spots affect the silver bromide, and the dark spots leave it unaffected. The change in the plate cannot be noticed until a developer is used, and then we can detect what has happened. A developer is really a weak reducing agent which affects the silver bromide only where the light has struck it. In the parts where the light has struck silver bromide, chemical action has already started, and when the developer touches these spots the silver bromide is immediately reduced and an extremely thin deposit of silver remains on the plate. Silver is an excellent reflector of light; this is because it is most opaque. These silver deposits are black, and wherever the light has struck the silver bromide plate there will be black deposits of silver, the blackness varying according to the intensity of the light. When the plate is developed and these black deposits are brought out, the unaffected bromide (in parts which were not struck by light) is washed away in a solution of sodium hyposulphite known as "hypo."

When the plate comes out of the hypo, it is a negative—that is, it is just the reverse of the original picture: all the whites are black, and all the blacks are white. By reversing this principle—that is, putting the negative over a highly sensitized paper—the true picture is obtained, because no light can come through the black parts of the negative and light does enter the light parts of the negative (often just clear glass). The paper used is treated in much the same way as the original plate.

The making of line cuts and halftones for reproduction in books, newspapers, and magazines is more complicated. The principle is this: A pen-and-ink drawing is photographed on a regular photographic plate. This negative is printed on another photographic plate to make a positive. The positive is stripped onto a sheet of zinc, and where the dark parts are there will be a deposit of gelatine and silver bromide, and where the light spots are there will be nothing. When the zinc is treated with acid, the plate is eaten into or etched. All exposed parts of the plate—the parts which the light struck in the original picture—will be eaten away, because they are not covered with the protective coating of gelatine; but all the unexposed parts will be unaffected, because they are covered with the protective gelatine. The result is that all the blacks will be raised and all the whites eaten away, and when ink is run over this plate, the raised surface, or the lines in the line drawing, will reproduce black just as they did in the original drawing.

GOLD (Au)

Gold occurs free as fine particles in stone or sand. In the amalgamation process, often used in refining gold, the solid ore is crushed, pounded into a fine powder, and placed in iron troughs. Water is allowed to circulate through it. In doing this, it carries the muddy substance over a bed of mercury. As we have mentioned, mercury immediately amalgamates with any gold present and leaves the rest of the ore alone, to be drawn out by the running water. This amalgam is distilled, and the mercury goes off in vapor, leaving pure gold.

Impure gold is frequently refined by electrolysis, in which a current of electricity is passed through a hot gold-chloride solution in a porcelain cell. Pure gold is thus deposited from the solution onto the cathode plates (bars of pure gold) suspended alternately between the anode plates (impure gold bars) above the cell.

Gold is a soft, heavy metal which is extremely valuable. (Only osmium and platinum exceed it in density.) It can be hammered out to about 1/200,000 inch in thickness. This thin foil is known as gold leaf and is used for gold letters on signs, windows, etc. The chief use of gold is in jewelry and coins.

Pure gold is too soft for commercial use, except as gold leaf. To harden it, various alloys are employed. The fineness of gold, which is to say the proportionate amount of pure gold a coin or other object contains, is expressed in "carats." A carat is a twenty-fourth part—in 14-carat gold there are 14 parts of pure gold and 10 parts of other metals. Gold does not react with any dilute acid. A mixture of concentrated hydrochloric and nitric acids known as aqua regia does act upon gold to produce gold chloride.

PLATINUM (Pt)

Platinum is one of the most valuable metals known. It is extremely scarce and is used chiefly in electrical instruments and jewelry. Because of its tremendously high boiling point and its resistance to acids, it is used in the preparation of sulphuric acid. Huge platinum pans costing about $25,000 each are used in the process of manufacture to hold the hot, boiling sulphuric acid. Platinum is the most indestructible metal known, and one of the heaviest.

ALUMINIUM (Al)

Aluminium—commonly called aluminum—is used because of its extreme lightness, extensively for kitchenware, and in the construction of airplanes and in various other places where a strong but extremely light metal is needed.

Aluminum is also used in a process for repairing heavy iron machinery, for welding rails, beams, crankshafts, etc. In the Second World War, the process called thermit reaction was used extensively in the repair of breaks in large steel casings. Aluminium powder is mixed with Fe_3O_4 and ignited with magnesium ribbon. The reaction is as follows:

$$8Al+3Fe_3O_4 \rightarrow 4Al_2O_3+9Fe \ (+heat)$$

The molten iron becomes white hot and flows between cracks, thus joining broken ends together.

The compounds of aluminum are very useful, particularly aluminum hydroxide. This is used in the purification of water and in dyeing. Aluminum silicates form the basis of all porcelain, pottery, and chinaware.

LEAD (Pb)

Because of its softness and its ability to be molded, lead is used in lead pipes, lead molds, and in the making of type. Type metal contains mostly lead, with a little tin and antimony in it to harden it. Lead is used also in solder, which is especially valuable in plumbing. Of course a great quantity of lead is used in shot. Its most important uses, however, are in the manufacture of pipes and of type metal.

Contrary to what one may think, lead is not used in "lead" pencils. The material here is carbon or graphite (popularly called "black lead," or plumbago), an entirely different element.

Lead carbonate is the most useful salt of lead, being the basis of most paints.

TIN (Sn)

Tin is a lustrous white metal which will not rust. Pure tin is a comparatively expensive metal. The most important use of tin is to cover other metals. Tinware is sheet iron which is thoroughly cleaned and dipped in molten tin. What many call a tin can is not a tin can at all. It is a can of sheet iron dipped in molten tin to prevent rust. The coating of the tin can is very thin, and after a while the can rusts because the coating of tin wears off.

Tin foil is used in wrapping candy and confections. This is pure tin, hammered and rolled into thin sheets. Soda-water fountains use tin pipes, since the carbonic acid would react with lead pipes. Tin is also used to make bronze, solder, and other alloys.

NICKEL (Ni)

Nickel is a hard metal resembling silver in color. Air does not attack it, and consequently it is used for plating metals that air does attack. Being a rather expensive metal, it is not used so much as tin. Nickel-plating is more expensive than tin-plating, but it is more permanent.

ORGANIC CHEMISTRY

CARBON (C) AND ITS COMPOUNDS

Of all the elements, carbon is the most basic in living matter. The human body must have carbon. Everything that lives needs carbon to maintain life. Carbon combines with hydrogen and oxygen in thousands of different ways. Plants contain carbon in various forms. Coal deposits consist mainly of carbon from the bodies of plants which existed millions of years ago.

Carbon is the basic element in that branch of chemistry known as *organic chemistry,* the chemistry of carbon compounds. Through organic chemistry we have been able to produce synthetically or artificially many things which were previously found only in nature. The first instance of this occurred in 1828, when a German chemist, Friedrich Woehler, synthesized urea, a compound formed in the bodies of animals. Since then many important compounds have been synthesized. In addition, our knowledge of organic chemistry has enabled us to make entirely new materials which never existed before. Among these are synthetic textiles such as rayon and nylon, and the plastics which are used in making fountain pens, telephones, airplane noses, and many other things. The most common forms of carbon are coal and graphite, two very plentiful and cheap substances. We have also a form of carbon which goes to the other extreme, and which, instead of being soft, black, and cheap, like graphite, is the hardest substance known, sparkling, brilliant, and very expensive. This crystallized form of carbon, produced by great heat and pressure, is diamond, the hardest substance in existence and one of the most precious.

Almost a million compounds of carbon are known. This is more than the total number of compounds made by all the other elements together. The number of carbon compounds seems to be almost unlimited. This is due to the ability of carbon atoms to join other carbon atoms in numerous combinations, forming chains of various lengths. The only other element which can form chains in the way that carbon does, but to a lesser degree, is silicon, present in many minerals.

The same laws of chemistry apply to organic and inorganic chemistry. However, the behavior of organic compounds shows some general differences. Most organic compounds do not dissolve in water but will usually dissolve in organic liquids such as alcohol, ether, carbon tetrachloride, etc. Organic compounds decompose more readily in heat than do inorganic compounds. If sugar is heated, for instance, it breaks down into water and a black charred mass of carbon.

Hydrocarbons are, as the name implies, compounds of hydrogen and carbon. The simplest hydrocarbon is methane (CH_4). Since carbon atoms link readily to other carbon atoms, each of which in turn may be linked to hydrogen atoms, the formulae of the heavier hydrocarbons contain over 100 atoms.

If the four hydrogen atoms in methane (CH_4) are replaced with chlorine atoms, we have carbon tetrachloride (CCl_4). If only three are substituted, we have chloroform ($CHCl_3$). It is possible to form numerous substitution products from hydrocarbons and thus produce a wide variety of substances.

Alcohols are produced by substituting one or more hydroxide (OH) groups for the hydrogen atoms. If one of the hydrogen atoms in methane (CH_4) is replaced by an OH group, we have methyl alcohol (CH_3OH) (wood alcohol, a poison). Similar substitutions in other hydrocarbons produce a wide variety of alcohols, including ethyl alcohol (C_2H_5OH) (which is the alcohol of alcoholic beverages), propyl alcohol, and glycerin.

Just as the alcohols are a counterpart of the *inorganic bases* in that they contain the OH group, so we have the counterpart of *inorganic acids* in *organic acids,* which are characterized by the presence of carboxyl (COOH). Formic acid, the material found in the sting of bees and ants, has the formula HCOOH. Other important organic acids are acetic acid, tartaric acid, and salicylic acid (which is the base from which acetyl salicylic acid, or aspirin, is made).

FUELS

Crude petroleum as it flows from oil wells is a mixture of many hydrocarbons. Petroleum is believed to be a material resulting from the partial decomposition of marine animal and vegetable organisms.

The various hydrocarbons in petroleum are separated out by a process known as fractional distillation. This process is based on the fact that different hydrocarbons have different boiling points. As the petroleum is heated, the first vapor to appear and be distilled is that of a mixture of light hydrocarbons called gasoline. Gasoline is mostly a mixture of hexane (C_6H_{14}), heptane (C_7H_{16}), and octane (C_8H_{18}). As the temperature of the petroleum is raised, kerosene begins to boil out. This is followed by fuel oil, then lubricating oil, and finally by greases, paraffin, and petroleum coke.

The United States produces more than 25 billion gallons of gasoline each year, and to increase the yield several processes have been developed. Cracking is the process by which the heavier hydrocarbons are broken down under great heat to form the simpler gasolines. Polymerization is the opposite of cracking. In this process the simple molecules, such as methane CH_4 and ethane C_2H_6, are forced to join together to make heavier molecules which constitute gasoline.

RUBBER AND PLASTICS

Rubber is a plastic hydrocarbon that is obtained from the sap or latex of rubber trees. Rubber molecules consist of long chains of isoprene (C_5H_8) molecules bound together—such chains being called polymers. This concatenation is what accounts for the elasticity of rubber.

With the advent of World War II and the loss of our sources of latex, the chemist applied his knowledge of natural rubber to produce several varieties of synthetic rubber. The principle was essentially that of polymerizing (joining together) molecules of the monomer (single particle) of isoprene (C_5H_8). By starting with chloroprene, the rubber called neoprene was produced. Buna is made by polymerizing butadiene.

The techniques applied in making synthetic rubber soon began to be used in producing other organic materials. A class of materials to which we give the name plastics was created. The raw materials for synthetic plastics include phenal, formaldehyde, urea, etc. Plastics may be divided into two groups, thermoplastic and thermosetting. The thermoplastic materials may be softened and changed in shape by gentle heating. Those which permanently harden under heat are thermosetting.

The plastic which came as a direct result of the researches on synthetic rubber is polystyrene. Styrene (C_8H_8) is polymerized to form polystyrene. This plastic is chemically inert and is capable of resisting the action of water, acids, etc. It is used greatly in the manufacture of containers.

The methacrylate plastics are made with acetylene (C_2H_2) as their base. This plastic can be rolled into large, very transparent sheets and is strong and shatterproof. Methyl methacrylate is thermoplastic.

TEXTILES AND PAPER

Textile fabrics are produced by weaving threads of the material in a variety of ways. The threads are derived from plant, animal, mineral, or synthetic sources. Our most important natural fiber is cotton, derived from the cotton plant. This fiber consists of molecules of cellulose ($C_6H_{10}O_5$) hooked together in long chains. The yarn is made by combing the fibers parallel to one another and then twisting them together to form a long strand. Cotton absorbs moisture readily and is a poor conductor of heat. It burns readily and is affected by acids. Linen, also a vegetable product, is processed from the fibers in the plant stem of the flax plant. Linen can absorb large quantities of water and the thread is extremely strong.

Wool is an animal product, made from the fur of sheep, goats, llamas, etc. Wool is a protein which contains carbon, hydrogen, oxygen, nitrogen, and sulphur. Therefore it burns, but not readily, and it is affected by alkalies. It is an excellent heat insulator.

Silk comes from the cocoons of the silkworm. It is a remarkably strong fiber considering its thinness; it is essentially protein in its constitution. Silk is used largely for its beauty as a lustrous, smooth fabric, but it does not have the heat-insulating qualities of cotton or wool, nor is it as durable as they.

There are several fibers obtained from minerals, the two most important of which are asbestos and glass. Asbestos is obtained by shredding magnesium silicate rock and twisting the long, thin crystals together to form a strand. It is fireproof and resistant to chemical attack. It is also used for heat insulation. Glass wool, a fluffy mass of very fine glass fibers, has many of the characteristics of asbestos but can more readily be spun into yarn and woven into cloth.

In recent years synthetic fibers have been developed which rival the natural ones in beauty and durability. Most of the synthetic fibers are produced by squirting a solution through a fine hole in a metal plate and passing the fine stream through another solution in which it hardens. Rayon is made by dissolving cellulose or wood to form a solution and then squirting this into dilute sulphuric acid, which hardens it into a fiber.

Of all the synthetic fibers, nylon is the most versatile. Nylon is made by a series of complex reactions between coal, air, and water, which produce a powdery mass called nylon salt. The molecules of nylon salt are polymerized to form giant spirally elongated molecules. The polymerized salt is then melted and forced through a spinneret (a metal plate with tiny holes). This lines up the molecules parallel to each other and produces a strong, elastic fiber. Nylon is relatively unshrinkable, relatively unaffected by chemicals, and wears well.

Paper is a fibrous material made from cellulose. Wood, cotton, and linen are the chief sources of cellulose. In making paper, individual fibers are separated by shredding and are bleached. The fibers are then suspended in water, and the mixture is forced through a slit onto a moving wire screen. As the water drains off, the fibers remain tangled together; after being squeezed to remove the water, they are tested to give the surface a smooth finish. The best papers are made from cotton and linen rags. Rag paper is strong and durable. Other types of paper are made by varying the wood-pulp concentration.

FOODS AND MEDICINES

In any proper diet there are five essential groups of nutrients which must be present. They are carbohydrates, fats, proteins, minerals, and vitamins. Each performs a specific and necessary function.

Carbohydrates are compounds of hydrogen, carbon, and oxygen, usually with the hydrogen and oxygen present in the same proportion as in water, namely two to one. Cane sugar ($C_{12}H_{22}O_{11}$), for example, exhibits the typical formula of a carbohydrate. Starch and the various sugars are the two classes of foods that make up carbohydrates. Carbohydrates make up the bulk of our diet and are used in the body chiefly as a source of readily available energy. When burned in the body, carbohydrates yield carbon dioxide (CO_2) and water (H_2O).

Fats are related to the organic acids and are likewise energy-producers. Weight for weight, fat yields twice as much energy as carbohydrates.

Proteins are complex compounds of carbon, nitrogen, hydrogen, oxygen, and sulphur. Protein molecules are relatively huge and their structure is not yet clearly understood. Their primary work in the body is to build tissue and repair cells that have been broken down in the normal functioning of the organism. No other nutrients can take the place of proteins for this purpose.

Minerals, derived from the salts in food, supply the calcium and the phosphorus essential in the building of bones, the iron for forming blood, and the iodine needed by the thyroid. In addition they supply the minute quantities of other elements, such as chlorine, copper, zinc, sodium, magnesium, etc., which are necessary to keep the body functioning normally.

Vitamins must be present in the diet for normal health. These are organic substances which seem to be necessary for the proper assimilation of food. There are more than a dozen substances which have been recognized as having the properties of vitamins. Some of them have been analyzed to the point where they may be prepared synthetically.

RADIOCHEMISTRY

Chemistry and Physics have both developed in new directions as a result of the recent work in the field of nuclear energy and its use. In addition to generating power, a nuclear reactor has provided the means for converting such common elements as hydrogen, iodine, phosphorus, and carbon into radioactive elements. (For a fuller discussion of radioactivity and nuclear energy see the section on Nuclear Physics on page 1145.) These radioactive isotopes are chemically identical with their non-radioactive counterparts. There is, however, one significant difference. They are emitting particles and rays and can thus be followed or traced by a Geiger counter. Such "tagged atoms" can be used to form part of any compound.

When these compounds are fed to plants and animals the movement of the radioactive isotope can be followed with great accuracy. Studies using the "tracers" reveal a great deal about the complex process taking place in living things. Radioactive carbon, for example, has been traced in photosynthesis from the carbon dioxide taken in by the plant to the final production of starch and sugar. Some day in the very near future we shall learn, through our use of the radio-isotope, the secret of the plant, and be able to undertake photosynthesis outside the plant. It may even be possible for us to get more information concerning cancer by the same technique.

Tracer atoms have also been of great importance in agriculture and industry. They are used to study the effectiveness of fertilizers and to determine the nutritive value of cattle feed. Radioactive isotopes are used to trace leaks in pipes, to observe the results of friction and wear, and to give us an insight into increasing the efficiency of complex industrial chemical processes.

These new applications in radiochemistry are additional indications of the constantly increasing ways in which chemistry influences and assists us in our daily lives.

EXAMINATION QUESTIONS

1. What chemical changes take place daily in iron, in fruit, in wood?
2. What two elements combined produce water?
3. What is an element?
4. What are formed through the combination of oxygen with most metals?
5. To what is the luminous quality of a flame due?
6. What usually governs the kindling temperature of a substance?
7. What gas is necessary for burning or combustion?
8. Of what is the earth's atmosphere composed?
9. What is the most common way of preparing oxygen in the laboratory?
10. What substance is almost pure carbon in a crystal form?
11. What part of water, by weight, does hydrogen form?
12. What color does an acid turn blue litmus paper?
13. When is a salt produced?
14. Of what is hydrochloric acid composed?
15. What is a saturated solution?
16. Of what are molecules composed?
17. What does the chemical formula for starch ($C_6H_{10}O_5$) signify?
18. What elements are represented by the following symbols: Au, Ni, P, K, Ra, Na, Sn, and W?

19. Of what gas has the United States the principal source of the world's supply?
20. Are there more metal elements than nonmetal?
21. Into what basic particles do atoms break down?
22. How many electrons could an atom with five protons have?
23. What does the chemical property of an atom depend upon?
24. When is a chemical equation balanced?
25. What gas, used in small quantities as a disinfectant, is highly poisonous in large quantities?
26. What happens when a small piece of sodium or potassium is put into water?
27. What are some uses of sulphur?
28. What does a sulphate contain that a sulphide never does?
29. In what way is nitric acid unique?
30. How is ammonia prepared?
31. What are the five halogens?
32. Where is iodine obtained?
33. Why is hydrofluoric acid kept in wax bottles?
34. What is the lightest gas known?
35. What compound do we get when calcium oxide is mixed with water?
36. What is the only liquid metal?
37. What is steel?
38. Why do silver spoons become discolored when used for eating eggs?
39. With what is a photographic plate coated?
40. How pure is 14-carat gold?
41. What is the most indestructible metal known?
42. What is the chief component part of type metal?
43. Is a tin can made of tin?
44. What element is the most basic in living matter?
45. Why is the number of carbon compounds almost unlimited?
46. What is the simplest hydrocarbon?
47. What is the process known as "cracking"?
48. What two important fibers are obtained from minerals?
49. What is paper?
50. What is the chief source of ready available energy in the human body?

FOR FURTHER STUDY

MAN AND THE CHEMICAL ELEMENTS, by J. Friend. (Charles Scribner's Sons, New York.)

NEW PRACTICAL CHEMISTRY, by N. H. Black and J. B. Conant. (The Macmillan Co., New York.)

THE SCIENCE OF CHEMISTRY, by George W. Watt and Lewis F. Hatch. (McGraw-Hill Book Co., New York.)

USING CHEMISTRY, by Oscar E. Lanford. (McGraw-Hill Book Co., New York.)

THE WORLD OF ATOMS, by J. J. G. McCue. (The Ronald Press, New York.)

XXVI

Biology for Beginners

WHAT IS BIOLOGY?

BIOLOGY IS the science of life, or the science of organisms. A single living thing—animal or plant—is called an *organism*. Living substances are described as *organic*, in contrast to nonliving or *inorganic* substances.

Biology consists of two main divisions: botany (the science of plant life) and zoology (the science of animal life). It also includes the study of microorganisms (living things so small that they can be observed only under the microscope, and which are in a realm where plant and animal often are much alike). Physiology (the science of the functions and functioning of tissues and organs) and anatomy (the science of the structure of organisms) are other phases of biology. Organic evolution, or the gradual development of higher forms of life from pre-existing lower forms, is an accepted principle of biology.

PROTOPLASM, BASIS OF LIFE

Whatever the phenomenon of life may ultimately be scientifically proven to be, it is definitely known that all living things—animal and plant—owe their characteristics to the substance called *protoplasm*. Protoplasm is contained in units of structure which are called *cells*.

A *cell* is usually microscopic in size, the average being not more than 1/100 millimeter in diameter, which may be long, cubic, oval, or spherical in shape. It is enclosed by a *cell membrane* which will permit certain substances to pass into and out of the cell. Within the cell is the *nucleus,* a spherical body which serves as the control center for the activities of the cell. The nucleus contains granules of material; and under certain conditions these form thread-like bodies called *chromosomes*. Chromosomes are important agents during cell reproduction. One or more

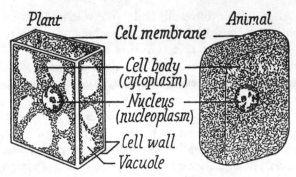

FIG. 1. Plant and animal cells.

smaller spherical structures known as *nucleoli* are sometimes present in the nucleus.

All of the protoplasm outside the nucleus but within the cell membrane is called the *cytoplasm*. Under the microscope, the cytoplasm appears to be granular. Some of the granular material is food embedded in the cell. Other rod-shaped granules are specialized structures which play an important role in the metabolism of the cell. Also within the cytoplasm are usually one or more cavities, called *vacuoles,* which are filled with cell sap (organic and inorganic substances in solution).

Plant cells differ from animal cells in that they are commonly covered by a wall of cellulose or other materials. The cytoplasm of all green plants contains large bodies called *chloroplasts,* which are colored green by a pigment known as *chlorophyll.* Chloroplasts are the sites where *photosynthesis* takes place. (This process will be explained later.)

The chemical composition of protoplasm is known. It is not a compound in the sense that water is a compound of hydrogen and oxygen atoms. Protoplasm can best be described as an *association* of chemical substances.

Protoplasm consists principally of oxygen, hydrogen, carbon, and nitrogen—these four elements in various organic combinations and also including water make up approximately 99 per cent of its composition; the remainder consists of minute quantities of phosphorus, sulphur, chlorine, sodium, magnesium, calcium, iron, potassium, iodine, and occasionally (though rarely) other elements, all in the form of salts. The chemical composition and physical structure of protoplasm is extremely complex.

The organic compounds found in protoplasm fall mainly into four classes: proteins, carbohydrates, fats, and nucleic acids. The general nature of carbohydrates, fats, and proteins is discussed under "Foods and Medicine" near the end of our section on Chemistry. We are familiar with such fats as butter, olive oil, and various animal fats and tallows. The carbohydrates consist of the simple and complex sugars, starches, and glycogens. The nucleic acids are very complex organic acids, composed of at least four types of units, combined in a great variety of proportions and sequences. These nucleic acids are very important in cell reproduction.

Proteins seem to be the typical substances of life, therefore their constitution is of great interest to biologists. They are characterized by infinite variety and great specificity. The units of protein structure are the *amino acids,* of which there are nearly thirty. These amino acids are strung together in chains of hundreds of thousands of units, in all types of sequences and with a great variety of folding and branching. The most typical shape found in the structure of proteins is a spiral or helix, or a rope-like bundle of these.

Despite its enormous complexity of composition, protoplasm exhibits consistent and dependable behavior. In it are inherent all the basic characteristics of living matter, which may be summarized as follows. Protoplasm has irritability—it responds to light, gravity, heat, contact, electricity, chemicals, and other stimuli. Cells have the power of motion; they create energy within themselves. Cells have the ability to assimilate substances, and thus secure fuel for their own activities and raw material to increase their mass. Cells can reproduce their own kind.

ONE-CELLED ORGANISMS

The number of cells in an organism may vary from only one cell up to millions of highly differentiated cells. Organisms which consist of only one cell are called *unicellular;* many-celled organisms are called *multicellular.* Man is a multicellular animal.

AMOEBA

The *amoeba* is the simplest unicellular animal. It exhibits all the characteristics that we have outlined in our discussion of protoplasm and cells. Amoeba's single-celled body contains a *nucleus* and *cytoplasm* and a whitish space called, because it alternately contracts and expands, a *contractile vacuole,* and a *gastric vacuole* in which digestion occurs. A common species of amoeba is 1/100 of a millimeter in diameter.

Among many curious things about the amoeba is its method of locomotion, which can be observed under a microscope. It appears to stretch out one side of its cell, whereupon the cytoplasm flows into it, and a further projection is drawn in "from behind," and thus the animal seems to stretch out front "feet" and withdraw back "feet," and move along fairly steadily. These "feet" are called *pseudopodia* ("false feet"). As the amoeba moves through the water (in which it lives), it meets and surrounds (ingests) food particles, which become imbedded in its cytoplasm, until their nourishment is absorbed, when the indigestible matter is cast off from the surface of the amoeba as it moves and flows about.

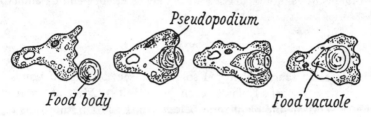

Fig. 2. The feeding process of an amoeba.

The amoeba absorbs (by respiration) oxygen from its surroundings, and this oxygen combines with the protoplasm to liberate energy. The oxidation of living substance to liberate the energy with which the organism performs its activities is a phenomenon common to all living things. In the human being, respiration is a highly complex process, requiring the muscular co-ordination of the epiglottis, trachea, and chest, and the apparatus of nose and mouth, throat, windpipe (trachea), and lungs, with the elaborate system of lung capillaries containing the blood, sent there by pulmonary arteries and carried away by pulmonary veins, pumped by the beating of the heart. In human respiration, millions of cells take part, each group specially differentiated to perform its particular work, and dependent on the rest of the organism for other functions, as nourishment. In the amoeba, respiration is simplicity itself—it takes place directly between the cytoplasm and the surrounding medium (water).

The amoeba assimilates food: thus it grows. At a limit of size, it divides into two amoebae, by *fission*. Fission (reproduction) consists of the splitting of the full-grown single cell into two cells; the nucleus divides at the same time, one part going to each of the two new cells. The parent amoeba thus ceases to exist when its offspring are produced. If there is no moisture, the amoeba can dry up (become encysted) and live for an indefinite period without performing its usual functions. But as soon as it is in water again, it will go on as before.

Other one-celled animals move by means of *cilia,* which are tiny
threads of protoplasm branching out from the cell wall, or by the lashing
action of a long whip-like process, called the *flagellum.* Unicellular animals are collectively known as *protozoa* or *protozoans.* More than
10,000 different species are known and named. They are of varying complexity, though each organism contains only one cell, like the amoeba.
The so-called flagellates exhibit both plant and animal characteristics.
Indeed, in this microscopic realm many unicellular and even more complex organisms cannot be classed absolutely as either plant or animal.

ALGAE AND YEAST

The greenish scum which you sometimes see floating on ponds is a
mass of tiny one-celled plants, each being but 1/2500 of an inch in
diameter. This minute plant form belongs to the group known as *algae.*
Most algae, however, consist of more than one cell. All algae contain a
green coloring matter, by means of which they are able to make their
own food.

This green coloring matter is the pigment *chlorophyll.* It is present
not only in algae but in almost all higher plants. Chlorophyll takes part
in a chemical process known as *photosynthesis,* by which, in the presence
of carbon dioxide and under the action of sunlight, sugar is made by a
chemical union of water with carbon dioxide. This unicellular plant,
since it has chlorophyll in its single cell, can make its own food from the
carbon dioxide in the air and the water present in its protoplasm or
absorbed from its surroundings. All green plant cells, whether separate
organisms or units of higher organisms, have this power to make their
own food, provided that they have water, carbon dioxide, and sunlight.

A single-celled plant performs all the functions of a multicellular organism, including assimilation, respiration (breathing), and photosynthesis. It also reproduces itself by growing in size, then splitting into
two new organisms. This is the method of reproduction known as *fission,*
which we have already described. Cellular reproduction always takes
place by fission or some modification of it.

Yeast is a familiar unicellular plant, but since it has no chlorophyll it
is colorless. Nor can yeast make its own food. It is an example of a
saprophyte, which must get its food outside itself, from non-living organic matter such as sugar. The sugar absorbed by yeast which it does
not use is broken down, in the familiar process of fermentation, into
alcohol, carbon dioxide, and small quantities of other substances.

Bacteria

The tiniest and simplest plants are *bacteria*. They are found everywhere, some beneficial and some dangerous to man. Bacteria are unicellular plants, without chlorophyll, and are either saprophytes or parasites. *Parasites* live on other living organisms, from which they get nourishment.

A spherical bacterium is called a *coccus;* a rod-shaped bacterium is called a *bacillus;* a curved or spiral bacterium is called a *spirillum.* Some do not move; others move about by means of *cilia,* which are tiny threads, composed of protoplasm, branching out from the cell wall. The average length of bacilli is so small that it would take 800 of them, placed end to end, to reach across the head of a common pin; and it would take some 4,000 cocci (spherical bacteria), side by side, to reach the same

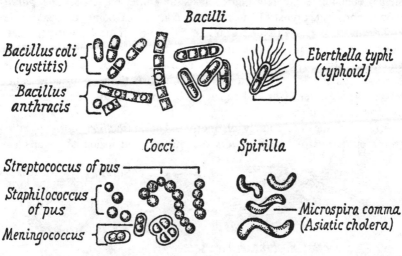

Fig. 3. Types of bacteria.

distance. Bacteria contain no clear nucleus; their structure is simple indeed. They reproduce very rapidly by fission; sometimes the divided cells remain together to form colonies or chains.

Many bacteria are present in the human body, especially in the alimentary tract, from the mouth down through the intestines. Most of these are harmless.

MANY-CELLED ORGANISMS

Some unicellular organisms remain together in colonies after multiplying by fission. These colonies sometimes approach the appearance and characteristics of the simplest many-celled organisms. For, somewhere in the process of evolution, such colonies of unicellular organisms began to develop special functions for groups of cells and to differentiate into multicellular organisms.

A multicellular organism consists of more than one cell, and these cells are of more than one kind. Division of labor results—some cells, all alike within a group, perform certain functions to the exclusion of others, and become dependent on the other cells for the functions which they do not themselves perform, and vice versa. A group of cells differentiated to perform a particular function is known as a tissue. The more complex the organism, the more kinds of tissue it has.

Plants have several characteristic tissues (see Fig. 5). The *epidermis* is the layer of cells which protects the surface of leaves, parts of flowers, stems, etc. There are few chloroplasts in epidermal cells. The *parenchyma* constitutes most of the plant; it comes just below or next to the epidermis. The *xylem* tissue forms the woody portion of plants; the cells are alive and contain protoplasm, but the cell walls are not alive and are chiefly cellulose. The xylem develops as a kind of passageway for fluids; it occurs chiefly in roots and stems. The *cork* tissue is usually called bark; it is an outer layer and replaces the epidermis on roots and stems as growth advances.

Animal tissues are equally distinctive. The *epithelium*, corresponding to the epidermis of plants, covers the outside and inside of organs (an

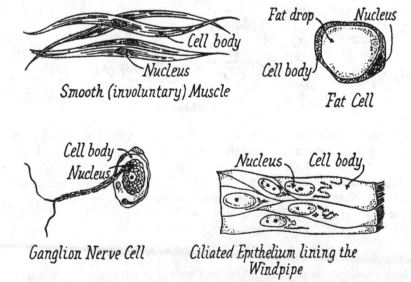

Smooth (involuntary) Muscle

Fat Cell

Ganglion Nerve Cell

Ciliated Epithelium lining the Windpipe

Fig. 4. Kinds of cells found in the human being.

organ is a specialized part, made up of several tissues). The outer skin of man is composed of epithelial tissue. *Muscle* tissue is specially adapted to contract; muscle cells, when stimulated, can shorten their length. There are three kinds of muscle tissue, usually called smooth, cardiac, and striped or *striated;* the voluntary muscles (under the control of the will) of man are striped; and among the smooth muscles (they act automatically or involuntarily) are those in the walls of the intestine. Cardiac muscle is a special type found only in the heart. *Nerve* tissue is very complex and highly specialized, being adapted to transmit impulses. A nerve is a bundle of nerve fibers, composed of protoplasm, extending from nerve cells, often for long distances. Various other tissues serve to connect parts of the body and support them; these include *bone, cartilage, tendon, ligament, blood,* and *fat.* The hardness of bone is due to accumulated mineral matter.

The tissues make up organs, which in plants are the roots, stem, leaf, flower, pistils, and stamens. In animals the organs vary, depending on the degree of development of the particular organism. In the higher animals the organs include the eyes, ears, brain, heart, lungs, kidneys, liver, ovaries, and stomach. Organs appear only in the higher plants and animals. Unicellular organisms have no organs, and many of the simpler multicellular organisms have no organs. Farther up the scale, organs are grouped into systems, as the nervous system, vascular system, and digestive system.

Let us summarize points which differentiate plants from animals, especially among the higher forms: (1) the cells of plants are enclosed in walls of cellulose, but animal cells usually are enclosed only in membranes; (2) plants usually possess a green-colored substance, chlorophyll; (3) plants usually either make their own food by photosynthesis or suck it up in liquid form, but animals take in solid food and have organs to digest it; (4) plants are usually fixed or stationary, but animals can usually move about from place to place.

THE PLANT KINGDOM

The plant kingdom includes a group of some 250,000 different species, subdivided into the following four great groups. The number of species given for each group is that now known and named.

The *thallophytes* (80,000 species) include all the algae, fungi, and lichens. The simpler forms are unicellular (as yeast), but multicellular forms are many. There are no distinct vegetative organs, such as root, stem, and leaf, although higher forms appear to have such organs (as some marine algae, commonly called seaweed). The scum on ponds is made up of tiny algae. Molds, bacteria, mildew, blight, and plant rust are fungi—they live on dead organic matter or on other organisms. Mushrooms are also fungi. Thallophytes have no seeds.

The *bryophytes* (16,000 species) include all the mosses and liverworts. They are not aquatic, but they seem to prefer moist places. There is some development of stem and leaf, but no root. They do not reproduce by seeds, but have a system of reproduction intermediary between the thallophytes and higher plants, called "alternation of generations."

The *pteridophytes* (5,000 species) include the ferns and allied forms. They are the highest type of flowerless plants, showing complete development of leaf, stem, and root. In reproduction, they exhibit very conspicuously the phenomenon of "alternation of generations," having no seeds. Horsetails and club mosses belong in this group.

The *spermatophytes* (135,000 species), the largest and most advanced group, are the seed-bearing plants. They have complex leaves, stems, and roots, and reproduce by flowering and developing seeds. Most familiar flowers, vegetables, and trees belong in this group. Spermatophytes are subdivided into *angiosperms* (the more numerous), those bearing seeds enclosed in a capsule (fruit); and *gymnosperms,* those bearing naked seeds (such as the evergreens, which bear naked seeds in cones).

THE PARTS OF HIGHER PLANTS

THE ROOT

The root of a seed plant serves two purposes: it absorbs water and needed minerals (dissolved) and gases (also dissolved) from the soil, and it also anchors or fixes the plant to one spot, where it can grow. Roots are of various forms. One kind is a central taproot with branches; others are a cluster of many main shoots and branches. Root tips are ever growing and penetrating more deeply into the soil.

The growing part of a root is just back of the protecting cap which extends over its tip, protecting it as it pushes through the soil. The cells in the growing part divide and constantly increase in size. Farther back along the root is a region in which "root hairs" develop; these hairs are outgrowths from the root epidermis, and each is a single cell. Root hairs increase the absorbing surface of the root.

The fully developed (mature) root, if cut across and examined under the microscope, shows an outer layer, or *cortex,* and a central cylinder of cells, called the *vascular cylinder.* This part of the root is stiff and tough, the cortex having supporting parenchyma cells and a kind of cork tissue on the outside. The vascular cylinder is composed of a conducting system of specialized cells, differentiated into xylem and phloem tissues. Water passes upward through the xylem and dissolved food passes downward through the phloem.

Plants are popularly differentiated as annuals, biennials, and perennials. The annual plant lives for a year only; the biennial for two years; the perennial, year after year. In the autumn, the roots of all annuals die. But the roots of biennials accumulate food during the ensuing winter, so that the plant has a second season; in the second autumn, however, the roots of biennials die. The roots of perennials last through winter after winter, storing up food so that, though the part of the plant above ground may die, the root lives and sends up new stems and leaves year after year.

THE STEM

The stem of the plant supports the leaves. It also has a conducting system, an extension of that in the root, acting as a go-between from leaves to root. Leaves are joined to the stem at nodes (points of attachment), according to a regular system or pattern which varies with the species of plant, and so arranged that one leaf does not come directly over another.

In the angle above the leaf, at the point where it joins the stem, there is usually a bud, which may, as the plant develops, shoot out to form a leaf-bearing branch of the main stem. Some buds, as those on most trees, last through the winter, even after the leaves have fallen off. The main stem extends itself or grows by means of a terminal bud at its upper end.

Most stems grow upright from the ground. Some, however, are specially differentiated for climbing or creeping. A few plants have stems running under the ground (not to be confused with true roots) which store up food. If the stem dies at the end of the growing season, the plant is classed as *herbaceous,* but if the stem survives (as in many perennials), the plant is *woody* (as are most trees). Some perennials are herbaceous.

The internal structure of the stem in most plants consists of an outer cortex, a hollow vascular cylinder, and a central core of pith. The vascular cylinder is mostly xylem, which helps to stiffen the stem. Between the phloem and xylem is a group of cells known as the *cambium;* it is this layer which grows and multiplies to form new xylem and new phloem. The successive layers of xylem (the rings in a cross section of tree trunk) indicate the number of years of growth. When the stem re-

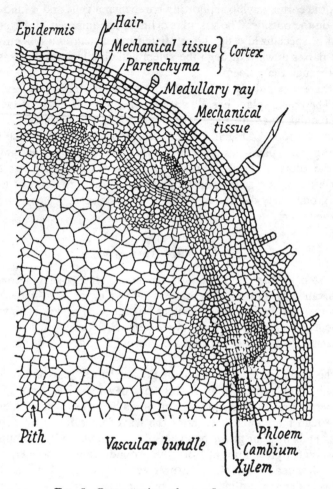

FIG. 5. Cross section of a sunflower stem.

mains above ground through the winter season, cork tissue develops year after year into the dead layer of cells forming the protective bark of trees. The living cells of a large tree are confined to a thin layer of inner bark.

THE LEAF

Most plants are conspicuous by their leaves. If deprived of their leaves in the growing season, they cannot live. For it is in the cells of the leaf, with their chloroplasts of green pigment (chlorophyll), that the photosynthesis of the plant takes place. The arrangement and development of the leaves provide for the greatest possible amount of sunlight over

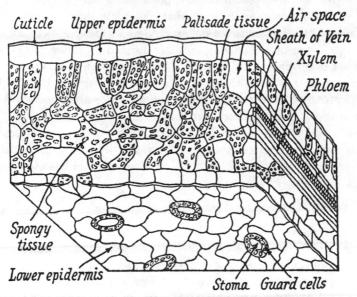

FIG. 6. Cross section of the blade of a leaf.

the largest possible surface. Inside the leaf, usually visible, are veins which extend from the vascular cylinder or bundles of the stem, carrying water to the leaf and taking away the nourishment produced by photosynthesis.

Leaves vary greatly in form and size. A pine needle is an extremely narrow leaf in contrast with the large and frond-like leaf of the banana tree. The edge of the leaf is sometimes smooth, sometimes serrate (saw-toothed), or otherwise modified. The pattern of the leaf is utilized by botanists as an aid to classification and identification. Leaves have a protective cuticle, which is waterproof and prevents evaporation of the fluids in the inner tissues. Gases pass in and out of the interior of the leaf through tiny openings called *stomata*.

PLANT PROCESSES

GROWTH

Plants require ten chemical elements for their growth; chief among these are carbon, hydrogen, and oxygen; the other seven are nitrogen, sulphur, phosphorus, potassium, calcium, magnesium, and iron. The process of securing these substances and utilizing them is *metabolism*.

If it were not for green plants, no other forms of life could exist, for they are the ultimate source of all food. Food is a substance that can be assimilated by an organism to maintain life and foster growth; all foods are organic substances—that is, they are formed by living things. They include carbohydrates, fats, and proteins, which supply energy to protoplasm, which is itself made up mostly of protein material. In addition to these foods, both plants and animals need water and minerals (which are inorganic) for complete nourishment.

Plants which are not green (not having chlorophyll), such as saprophytes and parasites, take their food from non-living organic matter, or from other living organisms, so they are dependent ultimately on green plants.

A green plant gets the necessary substances from the air and from the soil. Oxygen and carbon dioxide enter, for the most part, through the stomata of the leaves. Water is taken up through the roots from the soil. Along with the water are taken dissolved mineral salts, which contain the other substances the plant requires in order to make its own food.

Substances enter the plant body by *diffusion,* which is a physical process. If a soluble substance is placed in water, it will gradually disintegrate into molecules which pass evenly throughout the water, forming a solution. The molecules move steadily from higher to lower areas of concentration, until they are evenly distributed. This is diffusion, which explains *osmosis,* another physical process. If a solution is separated from pure water by a membrane, through which only water molecules can freely pass, *osmosis* takes place. That is, either the particles of dissolved substance diffuse into the pure water as though no membrane were present, or, if the membrane is not permeable to the dissolved substance, the water passes through the membrane into the solution, tending to reduce its concentration. Therefore, if a plant cell contains a fluid that is more concentrated than pure water and that cell is bathed by pure water, the water will pass through the membrane of the cytoplasm into the cytoplasm itself, that is, into the cell sap. (But the sugar inside the plant cell will not pass out into the water in the soil.) It is by this process of osmosis that the root cells of the plant absorb water from the soil, together with such dissolved mineral salts as may be needed (if the cell sap is low in them). In fact, all substances enter and leave living cells, in solution, by osmosis.

Soil water enters the root cells (in the root hairs) by osmosis, passes from cell to cell of the cortex, also by osmosis, finally reaching and passing up the xylem tissue through the vascular bundles to the stem and leaves.

In the leaves, water is being constantly evaporated during the process of photosynthesis. This evaporation cannot be avoided and must be compensated for by water sucked up from the root cells. Plant leaves constantly give off water vapor to the air during such evaporation. During drought, therefore, the plant is likely to wither and perhaps die.

In the green parts of the plant, in the stem and leaves, but especially in the latter, *photosynthesis* takes place. This profoundly important process has only recently begun to be understood in any detail. It is now considered to consist of two major stages, a *light reaction* and a *dark reaction*. Photosynthesis is possible because of the presence in green plants of *chlorophyll,* the green pigment in the small bodies called *chloroplasts*. It has now been shown that chlorophyll is a complex of several substances. One of these is especially involved in the first stage, the light reaction.

A simple equation is often used to express photosynthesis:

$$\text{carbon dioxide} + \text{water} \xrightarrow[\text{chlorophyll}]{\text{sunlight}} \text{sugar} + \text{oxygen}$$

This long accepted equation, though essentially correct, oversimplifies the process in stating that the water and carbon dioxide are combined in the plant cell by the action of light to form sugar.

The process of photosynthesis begins when several *quanta* (atoms or units of light energy) absorbed by chlorophyll split one molecule of water to release a hydrogen ion and one electron. This is the so-called *light reaction.* The energy of light is absolutely essential for the splitting of the water molecule in this stage. The second stage, the *dark reaction* (in which light is not necessary), consists of many individual chemical reactions which break up carbon dioxide molecules, rearrange carbon atoms, and add hydrogen atoms to carbons and oxygens to build up sugar molecules. The final product is the six-carbon sugar called *glucose.* During the process, energy is stored in the sugar.

An important by-product of photosynthesis is *oxygen,* which is released as the free gas and so passes into the atmosphere. Oxygen is important in the oxidation of nutrients by plants as well as by animals.

Although the direct product of photosynthesis is the sugar known as glucose, the plant cells, through their enzyme systems, proceed further, making more complex sugars and starches, converting some carbohydrate molecules to fats and amino acids, then using these amino acids to form proteins, vitamins, and hormones. Thus the converting of solar energy into chemical energy through photosynthesis is the beginning of all subsequent plant activities. And since plants are a primary source of essential animal and human nutrition, photosynthesis is seen as one of the most fundamental processes which make life and growth possible.

In the structure of a plant, roots and underground stems are storage areas. Seeds also store up reserve food for the use of plant offspring. Digestion, which is the chemical change of food into products the organism can use, occurs throughout the plant body—not in any special system of organs, as in most animals.

The irritability of protoplasm enables the plant to adapt itself to its immediate environment. Plant protoplasm is stimulated by gravity, so the root always grows downward into the soil; and the protoplasm is also stimulated by moisture, and the stem grows upward through the soil, breaking through into the sunlight. Plant protoplasm is also stimulated by light; a house plant will "lean toward" a window.

REPRODUCTION

In green plants, the root, stem, and leaves, when such a system is present, are concerned with plant nutrition. In seed plants, the flower, fruit, and seed are concerned with carrying on the species—with reproduction.

Reproduction by fission (splitting in two) of the single cell occurs in unicellular algae. In a more complex plant, made up of many cells, the cells still reproduce by fission, but this contributes to the growth of the organism and not to the *reproduction of the organism*. A special group of tissues develops into organs which are concerned exclusively with reproducing the parent species.

One of the simplest forms of plant reproduction occurs by means of so-called spores. In the less complex algae the individual cells give off *spores,* which are cells without cell walls (and are therefore naked), having cilia, which enable them to swim through the water. These spores can develop directly into a new plant organism, exactly like the parent (the source of the spores). The spore develops into the new organism by cell fission; the process is called *germination.*

Some algae and most of the fungi have a specially adapted organ called the *sporangium,* in which spores are produced and set free. This is the beginning of the highly developed reproductive system in the higher plants. Also, in most fungi and in most higher plants, the spores are not the swimming type, but are given off into the air. Not naked, they are protected by a cell wall.

Yeast cells reproduce by a process called *budding*. In this process, instead of the parent cell dividing into two exactly equal cells, it divides unequally. At first the baby cell or bud remains attached to the parent cell until it reaches a size equal to that of the parent, after which the cells separate.

Every gardener knows that plants can be multiplied in other ways than by planting seeds. Strawberry plants send out runners, which take root at intervals, forming new plants. The tubers of the potato plant, which are specializations of the underground stem, also grow into new plants. Gardeners frequently plant "slips" (also called "cuttings") from growing plants, to increase the number of that species. Roots form on the lower end of the stem of a slip, and the new plant develops. These various methods of reproduction may be termed *vegetative propagation*.

Sexual reproduction, which occurs in many types of plants, requires sex cells, called *gametes;* two gametes (usually male and female, though in some organisms the gametes which fuse are alike) must unite, becoming one cell; the single cell resulting from the union of two gametes is called a *zygote*. In the lower algae, gametes are sometimes formed very much like the swimming spores. But the gametes cannot develop directly into a new plant—two unite, forming a zygote, which may have a rest period, later giving off spores which germinate, or itself developing into a new plant. Organisms reproducing sexually in one generation and reproducing asexually (without fertilization) in the next generation exhibit the phenomenon of *alternation of generations*.

In most plants above the lower algae, the gametes are differentiated into male and female; the male or sperm is small and active, and the female or egg is comparatively large and passive, waiting to be "fertilized" by union with the male gamete. Usually the zygote resulting from the union develops directly, soon after fertilization, into a new plant which grows and becomes like the parents which produced the gametes. In the higher algae, and on up the scale of plant life, gametes are produced in special sex organs, developed for that purpose exclusively—with the exception of the seed plants.

Plant reproduction in the spermatophytes (seed plants) requires the reproduction of seeds, enclosed in fruit (in the angiosperms) or naked (in the gymnosperms).

The process of reproduction in seed-bearing plants is familiar. First, a characteristic flower appears; the flower may be separated into a *calyx* (composed of sepals, or green leaf-like parts which cover the flower while it is a bud), a *corolla* (composed of the petals, white or colored), *stamens* (inside the corolla, producing a yellow powder called *pollen*), and *pistil* (one or more in the center of the corolla, each with an enlarged base called the *ovary*). The slender stalk of the pistil, projecting upward from the ovary, is the *style*. The tip of the style is developed into a *stigma*, specially adapted to receive pollen. The pollen grains are tiny cells, constituting the male element. In the ovary are larger cells, called *ovules* ("little eggs"), which may develop into seeds.

The ovules in the plant ovary must be fertilized. In the first step the pollen must pass from stamen to pistil. This is called *pollination*. The

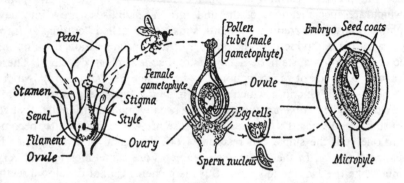

FIG. 7. The life cycle of a flowering plant.

pollen grains germinate *on the stigma,* each grain sending a tube-like extension down the inside of the style, called the pollen tube. After this happens, the petals and sepals of the flower usually wither and drop off, the pistil enlarges, and the style grows shorter as the ovary swells. The pollen tube, growing down inside the style, penetrates one of the ovules, forming a zygote (the pollen tube is not itself a gamete, but contains two nuclei, which correspond to the sperms or male gametes). The zygote germinates in the ovule, growing into a tiny plant called the *embryo*.

The embryo can be readily examined by splitting open a sunflower seed or a good-sized bean. It consists of a short stem (the *hypocotyl*), a kind of tiny bud (the *plumule*), and one or two leaf-like parts (the *cotyledons*). Beans, peas, and the like, in their seeds, consist of embryos only. But in many seeds, such as corn and wheat, there is a secondary development, a storage of nourishment, called the *endosperm,* which surrounds or is adjacent to the embryo. The embryo stops growing when it has reached the proper size of the seed, water is withdrawn from it, and it becomes comparatively dry and hard. Its development is stopped until it is deposited in a suitable spot, where it may germinate. Seeds can remain dormant for rather long periods of time (varying in different plants) and still germinate.

When the seed sprouts, if there is plenty of moisture, oxygen, and a suitable warm temperature, the embryo starts to grow. It develops into a mature plant, exactly like its parent, and goes through the same processes of making food, assimilating it, and blossoming into flowers which ultimately produce new seeds. The new plant is called a seedling as long as it derives nourishment from the endosperm (stored-up food).

The fruit is the enlarged ovary—a ripened ovary, containing ovules which are developing into seeds. The edible fruits are usually fleshy and juicy, such as plums, apples, and oranges. Nuts are dry fruits. The fruit contains the seeds by means of which the plant reproduces.

THE ANIMAL KINGDOM

There are something like 600,000 species, already named and catalogued, in the animal kingdom; most of these are insects. There are ten major groups or divisions of the animal kingdom, as follows:

The *protozoans* include 10,000 species of simple animals of one cell each, usually microscopic in size. All animals above the protozoans, which is to say all multicellular animals, are called *metazoans*.

The *sponges* (Porifera) are the simplest metazoans, numbering about 2,500 species. They live in water (usually salt water). They have simple tissues, but no organs; each cell receives and digests its own food. Sponges are fixed to objects in the water; they are radially symmetrical.

The *coelenterates* (animals with "hollow intestines"), 4,500 species, include corals, sea anemones, jellyfishes, and hydroids. They are mostly marine animals, and are found attached, free, or in colonies. The special characteristic of the coelenterates is the *coelenteron,* a kind of cavity into which there is only one opening—the mouth, often surrounded by tentacles. The body wall consists of only two cell layers (as in the sponges). There are organs, but the bodily processes are simple; the animals are radially symmetrical.

The *flatworms* (Platyhelminthes), about 5,000 species, include the tapeworms and other "flat" worms. They have soft bodies, are bilaterally (instead of radially) symmetrical, noticeably flat, and may or may not be segmented. There is no true body cavity, but there are various organs, with one opening to the outside. The flatworms exhibit increasing complexity, though still very simple as compared with higher animals.

The *roundworms* (Nemathelminthes), about 1,500 species, are cylindrical and unsegmented. The hookworm is perhaps the best-known example; the trichina also belongs to this group. They exhibit the characteristics of all higher animals in having both an alimentary tract (*enteron*) and a body cavity (*coelom*); the enteron has two openings, mouth and anus. Most of the roundworms are thread-like.

The *echinoderms,* about 4,000 species, are all marine animals, including the starfish, sea urchins, sea cucumbers, and brittle stars. They usually have both radial and bilateral symmetry; most of them are spiny on the surface, and many have star-like shapes of five prongs each. Somewhat more developed than the next nearest group below them, they are the surviving descendants of a very ancient type of animal.

The *annelids,* about 4,000 species, are the segmented worms, including earthworms, leeches, and sandworms. They are bilaterally symmetrical, having both coelom and enteron; they are increasingly complex, with a nervous system fairly well developed and a vascular system with red blood.

The *mollusks* number some 60,000 species, popularly called shellfish. They include oysters, clams, snails, mussels, and such "shell-less" forms as squids, cuttlefish, octopi, and slugs. All these animals have an organ which they use for locomotion, called the foot. Most of them have protecting shells covering their soft, bilaterally symmetrical bodies.

The *arthropods* (animals with "jointed feet"), some 500,000 species, are the largest single group of the animal kingdom. The body has appendages, such as *antennae* (feelers), legs, and mandibles. The segments of the body are grouped into distinct regions, as the head and the rest of the body. They have a hard outer shell or covering. Major divisions are the following: *crustaceans,* 16,000 species, including the crabs, lobsters, crayfish, shrimps, and barnacles, mostly marine; *myriapods* (many-footed), 1,000 species, including the centipedes and millipedes; *insects* (Hexapoda, "six-footed"), over 450,000 species, including butterflies, beetles, flies, mosquitoes, wasps, bees, ants, grasshoppers, moths, dragonflies, and locusts (the body has a distinct *head, thorax,* and *abdomen,* with six legs and two pairs of wings or rudimentary wings attached to the thorax); *arachnids,* 20,000 species, including the spiders, scorpions, mites, and ticks (the head and thorax are fused into the cephalothorax, and all have eight legs and no wings).

The nine preceding groups are referred to together as *invertebrates,* because they have no vertebral column (or backbone).

The *chordates* are the highest group of animals in development. They have a vertebral column, and are classed together as *vertebrates.* It is to this great group, some 38,000 species, that man belongs. They are bilaterally symmetrical animals, all having at some stage of life the distinctive feature of a rod of supporting tissue, called a *notochord,* developing into the *spinal cord* in higher forms, though the spinal cord does not correspond exactly to the notochord, being encased in the vertebral column which supplants the notochord in the adult. All chordates exhibit gill slits (for breathing in water) at some stage of life, even man showing them in the embryonic stage. The nerve cord is hollow.

The major groups or subdivisions of the chordates are the following:

Fishes (15,000 species) are aquatic and cold-blooded vertebrates (that is, their temperature changes with their environment); they breathe through gills, lack limbs, move through water by means of fins, are scaled, and have a two-chambered heart.

Amphibians (15,000 species) are cold-blooded vertebrates, breathing with gills in early stages, and usually later breathing with lungs; amphibians live both in water and on land; most of them have four limbs,

Protozoa   Porifera   Coelenterates

Flatworms   Roundworms   Segmented Worms

Mollusks   Echinoderms   Arthropods

Chordates

FIG. 8. Animal Kingdom.

with clawless toes, and a three-chambered heart; they include frogs, toads, salamanders, and newts.

Reptiles (3,500 species) are cold-blooded vertebrates, never breathing with gills but always with lungs; most of them have four limbs (snakes being exceptions), with clawed toes, plate- or scale-covered skin, and a three-chambered heart (four-chambered in crocodiles and alligators); they include lizards, snakes, turtles, tortoises, crocodiles, and alligators.

Birds (13,000 species) are warm-blooded, feathered vertebrates, never breathing with gills but always with lungs; they have four limbs (two feet and two wings); a four-chambered heart; scaled skin on the feet, with claws.

Mammals (about 3,500 species) are the highest class of vertebrates, including all warm-blooded animals that suckle their young, such as man, apes, monkeys, mice, rats, squirrels, dogs, cats, lions, tigers, moles, bats, whales, wolves, bears, deer, cows, sheep, horses, pigs, camels, elephants, hippopotami, giraffes, and kangaroos. Mammals never breathe with gills, but always with lungs. They have a four-chambered heart. The nervous system is highly developed, especially in man, where intelligence appears. There are nearly always four limbs, differentiated into two arms and two legs in man. The skin is nearly always covered with hair, and even shows some hair in man.

ANIMAL PROCESSES

METABOLISM

The chemical changes that go on in the organs of animals are very much the same as those which take place in the metabolism of plants, except that the metabolism of animals is much more complex, particularly in the higher animals. Animals, having the power of locomotion in all higher forms and in many lower forms, consume a great deal of energy, and consequently require a great amount of food. Food is necessary for energy and growth. That food, as in plants, consists of proteins, carbohydrates, and fats. Some animals live entirely on vegetable matter, and are therefore called *herbivorous;* others live entirely on animal matter, preying on other animals, and are called *carnivorous;* man is remarkable for the fact that his diet is all-inclusive—he eats a variety of different foods, animal and vegetable, and is therefore said to be *omnivorous.*

Only foods of the simplest chemical composition, such as simple sugars, can be directly used by the body as fuel. Other foods must be digested or "broken down" into simpler chemical composition. The processes of digestion are chemically complex, taking place only in the presence of substances called *enzymes,* which are secreted into the digestive cavity from adjacent body cells. Only in the very lowest animals (in protozoans and in sponges) is digestion distributed among the individual cells of the whole animal; in higher forms, digestion takes place in a special part of the body, usually in a hollow cavity or digestive tract, such as the human stomach and small intestine.

In the human body (which is a typical animal body) the first digestive juice is secreted in the mouth, during chewing; it is saliva (spit), which contains the enzyme *ptyalin,* which changes some of the starch in chewed food to sugar. Most of the digestion takes place in the stomach and small intestine. The gastric juice contains the various stomach secretions; gastric juice has in it the enzyme *pepsin* and some hydrochloric acid, which provides the acid medium needed for pepsin to act. Pepsin changes some proteins to peptones. The gastric juice also contains the enzyme *rennin,* which digests milk. In the small intestine, into which the food passes in a semi-liquid condition from the stomach, further foods are digested, especially the fats. The pancreatic juice is secreted by the pancreas (sweetbread) with three important enzymes: *amylopsin* (changes starch to sugar), *trypsin* (changes proteins to peptones), and *steapsin* (changes fats to glycerine and fatty acids). The pancreatic juice acts in the presence of bile from the gall bladder; the bile itself does not digest food, but its presence is chemically necessary for fat digestion. The small intestine secretes an intestinal juice containing the enzyme *erepsin,* which further aids the digestion of a protein called *casein.*

No digestion goes on in the large intestine, where the indigestible parts of the food, particularly the cellulose from vegetable food, is stored for a time until it can be evacuated from the body. Here colonies of beneficent bacteria partially decompose this waste matter before it leaves the body.

Dissolved foods, rendered soluble during digestion, pass through the walls of the small intestine by diffusion, reaching the blood, in which the food (fuel) is carried to all parts of the body, where it is assimilated by the cells. The blood also takes away from the body cells waste products, which are ultimately evaporated from the body through skin pores (as perspiration), in the lungs (in respiration), or are secreted from the kidneys (as urine). If there is an excess of food, it is stored in the body as adipose tissue (commonly called fat).

What happens in animal respiration is similar to the respiratory process in plants. For the transportation of nourishment through the body, animals (in higher groups) have a marvelous circulatory or vascular system (the blood stream and its vessels), with a pumping organ (the heart). This vascular system also takes part in animal respiration, sending venous blood (blood in the veins) to the lung capillaries (tiny blood vessels in the lungs) to be oxygenated (aërated). This process of oxidation is chemically much like burning—the oxygen of the air, breathed into the lungs, combines chemically with hemoglobin (the red coloring matter of the blood), and is taken to all parts of the body by the blood, where the oxygen is liberated, as needed, to oxidize the protoplasm in the cells during bodily activity. The liberation of oxygen is necessary to supply the energy required for the body to do its work, in which it acts like a great chemical machine.

In lower animals the system of lungs is not so well developed, or is lacking. Fish breathe through gills, utilizing the oxygen dissolved in the water. Some lower animals "breathe" through the outer cells of their skin; that is, the skin cells absorb oxygen directly. Insects have a complex system of tubes (tracheae), which open out of the body through many spiracles here and there about the surface; this system brings air directly to all parts of the body, instead of to specialized organs like the lungs in higher animals.

The most distinctive feature of higher animals, especially mammals, is a highly developed nervous system. The nerves, or, more exactly, the nerve cells, are specially developed to receive and transmit sensations and impulses. All protoplasm is irritable, but nerve cells have specialized protoplasm which is irritated only by specific stimuli. This elaborate nervous system enables animals to respond to their environment much more quickly than plants. An animal can hear a loud noise and flee from it, or see food and hurry toward it, with great rapidity, due to skillful coordination of muscles and other organs. The lowly earthworm has a relatively simple nervous system. In the frog the nervous system is quite well developed, and in mammals it is very complex. In man it reaches the apex of complexity in *intelligence*.

To summarize: animals secure food, take it into the body, usually through an opening (mouth) adapted to that purpose, digest it in a suitable tract (digestive tract), evacuate waste matter derived from the assimilation of digested food, breathe by taking oxygen into the body (usually in special organs, such as lungs), and, in general, go through the continuous round of replacing used-up protoplasm (utilized in bodily work) with new food (fuel). Animals have the power of locomotion, the better to get food of the right kind and in sufficient quantity for their needs. Bodily functions are performed by systems of highly specialized organs, especially in the higher animals, which also adapt themselves to their environment and escape danger because of a highly complex nervous system.

REPRODUCTION

In the protozoans, and in a few lower animals above the protozoans, reproduction takes place by simple fission; the one-celled animal divides into two. Occasionally fission is modified into a kind of budding, the

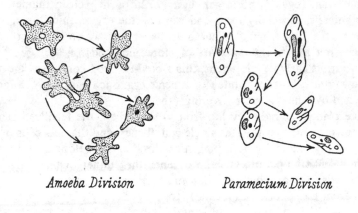

Amoeba Division　　　　　*Paramecium Division*

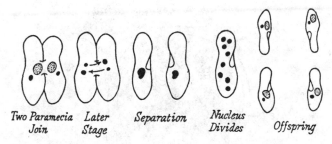

Two Paramecia *Later*　　*Separation*　*Nucleus*
Join　　　*Stage*　　　　　　　*Divides*　*Offspring*

FIG. 9. Fission, Conjugation, and Offspring of each original adjoining adult.

bud growing into a new animal. In most animals reproduction is sexual, requiring the union of male and female to produce offspring.

Usually, in the animal kingdom, each species of animals has two kinds, male and female, differentiated from each other by special characteristics which may or may not contribute directly to the process of reproduction. The union (conjugation) of male and female is necessary, or at least the male gametes must meet and unite with the female gametes, in order that new animals may grow and carry on the species. The special cells, known as *sperm cells,* devoted to reproduction are distinct from the other cells of the body, which are concerned with metabolism. The latter are usually called *somatic.*

In general, the male gametes are called *sperms,* and are produced in male sex glands, called *testes;* the female gametes are called *ova* (eggs), and are produced in female sex glands, called *ovaries.* The sperms, or sperm cells, are active, often swimming; the ova are passive, awaiting the arrival of sperms. Both sperms and ova are very small; even the human ovum (egg) is no larger than 1/125 of an inch in diameter. In some animals, especially birds and reptiles, the egg is quite large; here, however, the "egg" includes not only the ovum, which the sperm will fertilize, but a surrounding mass of stored-up food for the use of the embryo in its early development; this stored-up food comprises the yolk (yellow) and albumen (white) of a hen's egg. Such eggs are commonly protected by a heavy outer covering (shell).

Like plants, animals develop from a single cell—the fertilized female gamete (egg), or zygote. This single cell divides, and the new cells divide and multiply, gradually becoming specialized and developing into a new individual like its parents. Of the parents, the "father" (male) gives off sperm cells, one of which reaches and penetrates (fertilizes) an egg or ovum from the "mother" (female), forming thereby a zygote which develops into the embryo and ultimately into the young animal. In some

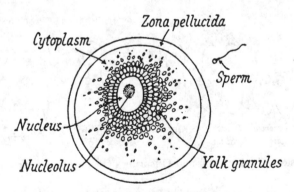

FIG. 10. Human egg cell and a sperm.

aquatic animals the female simply lays her eggs in the water, and the male ejects his sperms into the water; these are laid or ejected in great numbers, so that some of the sperms are almost sure to find and fertilize some of the eggs. This is external fertilization. But in most animals internal fertilization must take place. The male meets the female, conjugates with her, and, by means of a specially developed male organ, ejects the sperms into a specially developed cavity of the female, where they can swim to the eggs and fertilize one or more.

In a few animals (usually invertebrates) an egg may develop into a new individual without being fertilized. This process is called *parthenogenesis*. Bees exhibit this phenomenon to some degree. The female (queen) lays both fertilized and unfertilized eggs. The fertilized eggs develop into queens (females who can lay eggs) and workers (females who cannot lay eggs). Unfertilized eggs develop into drones (males), who do no work. The drones are born by parthenogenesis. Parthenogenesis occurs almost exclusively in certain insects, crustaceans, and worms. In the aphids or plant lice a number of generations produced by parthenogenesis, being females only, occur after the generation which is sexually produced. Finally males are produced, also by parthenogenesis, and sexual reproduction again occurs. Parthenogenesis is a modification of sexual reproduction which must not be confused with asexual (non-sexual) reproduction. In parthenogenesis the young develop from true eggs (unfertilized), not from buds or parts of the body as in asexual reproduction.

As the embryo develops from the zygote (fertilized egg), it goes through a series of changes which are outwardly similar in all metazoans. This phenomenon has greatly helped to demonstrate organic evolution.

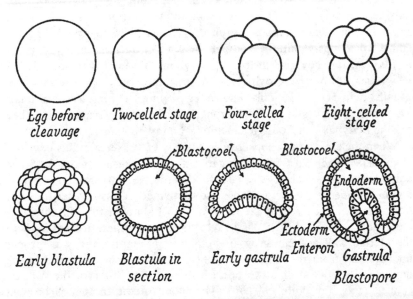

Egg before cleavage Two-celled stage Four-celled stage Eight-celled stage

Early blastula Blastula in section Early gastrula Gastrula Blastopore

Fig. 11. Early stages in the development of a starfish.

For at a very early stage there is very little difference between the embryos of a fish, a salamander, a tortoise, a chick, a hog, a calf, a rabbit, and a man; they look nearly alike.

The embryo develops by cell fission. In general, starting from a single cell (zygote), it becomes a hollow ball or *blastula*. This ball then seems to have one side pushed in, which grows inward until it joins the outer side, forming a ball-shaped body with a hollow inside and an opening at one side (at this stage called the *gastrula*). A sponge is not developed beyond this stage; in general, the two lowest groups of metazoans remain in this stage.

In higher metazoans the embryo develops further, the cells dividing into millions, and the various organs and parts of the body forming slowly but surely into an image of the parents. There are three primary cell layers. From one of these (the *ectoderm*) develop the outer skin and scales, hair, nails, feathers (if present), and the nervous system. From another layer (the *endoderm*) develop the linings of digestive and respiratory cavities. From the third layer (the *mesoderm*) develop muscles, blood vessels, the blood, connecting and supporting tissues.

"Birth" takes place in two forms among animals where fertilization is internal. Animals which lay eggs are called *oviparous;* the egg, usually in a protective shell, is laid after fertilization, and the embryo develops outside the body of the female (though often protected, as when a hen sets). But in higher animals, fertilization takes place internally and the embryo develops within the body of the female. Such animals are called *viviparous,* for they give birth to their young alive. Most mammals are viviparous; all birds are oviparous; fishes, amphibians, and reptiles are usually oviparous. The only known egg-laying (oviparous) mammals are found in Australia, the last stronghold of ancient forms of life; they are the platypus (duckbill) and echidna (spiny anteater).

When the embryo develops inside the body of the female, this development takes place in a special organ called the uterus (womb). Some animals have two such organs, or a divided uterus. Only in human beings and in the apes is the uterus single and undivided in form. After fertilization, which takes place in the oviduct (the Fallopian tube in woman), the zygote (fertilized egg) passes into the uterus, where it fixes itself to the uterine wall and can grow in suitable temperature and with proper nourishment from the female (mother). The placenta is formed in the uterus as the special organ to nourish the growing embryo; the two are connected by the umbilical cord. The blood of the mother is brought into osmotic contact with the blood of the embryo; there is, however, neither direct blood nor direct nervous association between mother and embryo. Nourishment passes to the embryo, and waste products are taken away, entirely by osmosis. Mental or nervous excitement of the mother, contrary to popular notions, does not affect or "mark" her offspring.

In the process called birth, in viviparous animals, the fully developed embryo—often more than one among animals below the primates (man and the apes), but usually only one in human beings—is "born," which

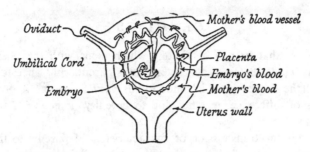

FIG. 12. Embryo of mammal in uterus.

is to say, it is passed out of the body of the mother during labor (parturition). The placenta follows as the "afterbirth." The newborn offspring is still attached to the mother by the umbilical cord, which is chewed apart by most animals, or severed by the attending physician in man. After birth, among mammals, the offspring is suckled at the female's mammary glands, which supply milk.

Insects exhibit a quite different process of development. With some exceptions, insects go through a series of changes called *metamorphosis.* The egg hatches into the *larva:* the caterpillar of butterflies and moths, the grub of beetles, and the maggot of flies, bees, wasps, and ants. The larva feeds and grows, and then passes into a semi-dormant state, called the *pupa.* The pupa does not usually feed, but it undergoes a series of changes, finally emerging as the *imago* or adult, like the parent. The butterfly pupa is sometimes called a *chrysalis.* The pupa of the mosquito, contrary to the general rule, is active, and is one of those "wrigglers" commonly present in stagnant pools, the other wrigglers being mosquito larvae.

As in the mosquito, the early stages of some other animals are aquatic. Amphibians, such as frogs and toads, also have larval stages. The eggs are laid and fertilized in water, and the young larvae, called tadpoles, grow and develop in water. There is no pupal stage among amphibians.

Some animals lay their eggs and promptly forget them. The parents give no attention to their young, which quite ably manage to shift for themselves. Among other animals, particularly among birds and mammals, the parents watch over their young in what seems to be paternal and maternal loving care, though it is wholly instinctive. With man's aid, even young chicks can do without their fussing mother hens, being hatched in an incubator and raised under mechanical "wings."

GENETICS

Genetics is that branch of biology which deals with the phenomena of heredity (inheritance of characters from parents and ancestors) and variation (the degree in which individuals vary from one another, and the points of difference, whether due to heredity or acquired from environment).

Heredity is the transmission of characteristics of parents to their offspring. Animals and plants strikingly resemble their "parents"; indeed, the resemblance is complete in all essential particulars. Heredity results from the actual connection existing between parents and offspring: the offspring grows from a single cell which has resulted from the union of two cells of the parents, one from the male and one from the female parent; or, in lower forms of life, from the simple division of one cell into two just like the original. Heredity is never altogether complete, for variation exists which makes the differences between individuals and which may give rise to new species.

The laws of heredity apply in general to all living things, whether plant or animal. When the organism multiplies by simple cell fission, the two resulting organisms are naturally like the one cell which gave rise to them. Some organisms are self-fertilized and exhibit a similar uniformity in offspring.

But in sexual reproduction, as we have seen, two parents give rise to the offspring, through the union of gametes (male and female). Since the offspring obviously resembles the parents, not only in belonging to the same species but in minor variations between individuals, these characters must be passed on to the offspring from the parents through the germ cells, since these cells are the only organic connection between parents and offspring. Also it appears that male and female are of equal influence in heredity.

Inherited characters must be distinguished from *acquired* characters. The latter are fostered by the individual's environment or surroundings. Inherited characters represent potential factors in development, such as musical inclination in human beings; or inherited characters are matters of physical appearance, as blue eyes. But the *ability to play* the piano is distinctly acquired (learned) and cannot be inherited.

Modern conceptions of the hereditary process in living things rest upon certain assumptions that are being increasingly borne out by experimentation. One assumption is that hereditary instructions are in some way passed along from parent to offspring so that the two generations closely resemble each other. It is believed that each offspring— be it a single cell or a multicelled organism—receives a set of chemical instructions from its parent. These instructions control development.

Another assumption is that these chemical instructions are contained mainly in the nucleus of reproductive or reproducing cells. The instructions are believed to be contained in hypothetical units called *genes*. The modern study of heredity is called *genetics*. The gene theory assumes that inherited traits are controlled by pairs of genes which are located on the *chromosomes* which are formed in the nuclei of cells. Much experimental evidence supports the validity of the chromosome theory of inheritance and the presence of genes on or within chromosomes. Chemical studies of chromosomes and several microorganisms, such as bacteria and molds, seem to indicate that the gene is composed of a certain kind of nucleic acid, known as DNA or deoxyribonucleic acid.

It is further assumed that genes do two things: first, they control the process of reproduction of cells, and secondly, in some fashion, they control each and every step in the development and life of cells. These ideas are supported by evidence which suggests that genes do affect the activity of enzymes, for when a gene appears to be impaired in some manner, the activity of a certain enzyme system is also impaired. Genes also seem to affect the structure of protein molecules synthesized in cells.

Since genes are located within the nucleus of a cell, and most of the cell activities occur outside the nucleus in the cytoplasm, it is assumed that the genes exert their influence upon cytoplasmic cell activity in an indirect manner. Results of experiments support the belief that this extranuclear influence is exerted through the medium of a special kind of nucleic acid that is found in the cytoplasm.

MENDELISM

Gregor Mendel (1822–1884), an Austrian abbot, made an exhaustive study of variations in sweet peas grown by him, and discovered a law of heredity (Mendel's law of inheritance) which has since been found true of all organisms. If a red four-o'clock flower is crossed with a white flower of the same species (by taking pollen from one and placing it on the pistils of the other), the offspring will be a pink flower. The pink flower is called a *hybrid*. If two pink flowers (two hybrids) are crossfertilized, the resulting offspring will include red, white, and pink flowers, and the offspring will vary approximately in the proportion of one red and one white flower to every two pink flowers. Further, if the red flowers born of pink parents are interbred, their offspring will all be red. The same is true of white flowers. But, in general, half the offspring of hybrids will always be hybrids. Suppose that a white flower is crossed with a pink flower—a pure flower with a hybrid. The offspring will occur in the ratio of half pink and half white; of a hundred, fifty will be white, fifty pink.

The variation is simple up to this point, but becomes more complicated, for there are what are known as *dominant* and *recessive* characters. In guinea pigs short hair is dominant over long hair; that is, if one of two parents is short-haired and the other is purebred long-haired, the offspring will be short-haired.

Tallness is a dominant character in a pea plant. If a purebred tall and a dwarf plant of the same species are crossed and the hybrid tall offspring crossed or interbred, according to the principle just formulated, the offspring should include one tall, one dwarf, and two intermediate. But tallness is dominant over dwarfness, and a somewhat different result follows. If the hybrid tall plants are interbred, they will produce offspring in the ratio of three tall plants to every dwarf. The dwarf plant (one in four) appears in the second generation, because a dwarf factor is taken from a hybrid tall parent and also from a dwarf. If organisms (of the same species) with various dominant and recessive characters are crossed, the resulting offspring will necessarily exhibit many variations.

Every flower possesses a pair of factors (genes) for each characteristic. The genes are located on corresponding *chromosomes* in the nucleus of

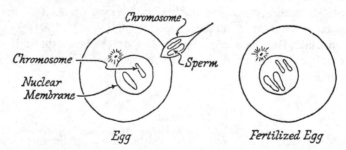

FIG. 13. Organism which has four chromosomes in each body cell.

each cell. As mentioned in the very beginning of our discussion of biology, on page 1196, the chromosomes are rod-shaped bodies located in the nucleus of each cell; these chromosomes are basic in the transmitting of hereditary traits from parents to offspring. Thus if we represent the tall factor by *T* (the dominant trait) and the dwarf factor by *t* (the recessive trait), then the genetic make-up of a purebred tall plant is *TT,* that of a dwarf plant is *tt.* When a *TT* plant is crossed with a *tt* plant, the result is a *Tt* or hybrid. When two *Tt* plants are crossed, the offspring are always in a ratio of 1*TT:* 2*Tt:* 1*tt.* This is due to the phenomenon of segregation, in which the members of each pair of factors separate before going into the sex cells and recombining. Thus:

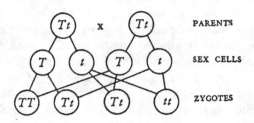

This explanation has been successfully applied to heredity in many other organisms, including man. Scientific plant and animal breeding depend upon correct understanding of the laws of heredity.

Color-blindness is a human recessive character that occurs mostly in males, but is inherited through the mother; thus, if a color-blind man mates with a woman who has normal vision, all his children will have normal vision and his son's children will have normal vision. But his daughters are carriers; though not color-blind themselves, they may transmit color-blindness to some of their children (males). A color-blind woman's sons will all be color-blind. But a color-blind woman must be the daughter of a color-blind father and a mother who is either color-blind or a descendant of a color-blind man or woman; the fact that this seldom happens explains the rarity of color-blindness in women.

BREEDING

Gardeners and animal breeders know the value of careful breeding. Luther Burbank won fame with his experiments on flowers and fruits. Seedless oranges and grapefruit, white blackberries, large and juicy strawberries, hardy apple trees, all have been scientifically developed by watching and observing the laws of heredity.

A hit-or-miss process of breeding consists in taking seed from only the tall plants and sowing it for a new crop. From the new crop seed is again taken only from the tall plants, and so on. Gradually a seed may be developed which will grow mostly into tall plants. But some of the tall plants are hybrids, and the hybrid tall plants, in succeeding generations, will produce a few dwarfs.

The more scientific system of breeding is according to pedigree, considering "relatives" in order to determine the purity of the parent stock. The pedigree system was used with animals long before it was applied to plant breeding, but it can also be used with plants. The system is especially successful with plants which naturally pollinate themselves with their own pollen, for this enables the breeder to keep the strain pure.

Hybridization, that is, crossing breeds, increases the hardiness or virility of the offspring. Continuous inbreeding is likely to result in a weakening of the native strength of the organism, especially its ability to resist disease or other adverse conditions. Cross-breeding in plants tends to restore vigor—many hybrids are hardier than either parent. Interbreeding among human beings is sometimes thought to result in a similar increase of vigor, and inbreeding to result in deterioration. However, human inbreeding (as the marriage of first cousins) is not likely to result in abnormal offspring unless undesirable recessive characters are in the family strain.

EUGENICS

Eugenics is scientific human breeding—the application of scientific principles to the birth of human offspring. Birth control and deliberate childbearing enter into the question.

Before eugenics can be applied, definite data must be collected as to what human beings inherit and what they acquire from their environment and training. Experiments have been conducted to determine the relative effects of environment and heredity in determining human characteristics. Identical twins (presumably originating from a single fertilized egg which accidentally became divided into two parts at an early stage of development), when reared apart, show fewer differences in intelligence than in characteristics such as emotion, social qualities, and personality. Some experiments, however, do indicate marked differences in intelligence when identical twins are reared in different environments. It is difficult to draw any conclusions.

THE FITNESS OF NATURE

Every organism, plant or animal, lives in a definite relation to its environment, and it appears to be able so to live because of its inherited characters. A fish is adapted to life in sea water; it has gills for breathing in water, fins for swimming through water, and the like. The biological study of organisms in relation to their environment and to other organisms is called *ecology*.

Adaptation to Environment

So happily adapted do many organisms appear that it is a great temptation to speak of them as having developed in that way because they desired or definitely tried to do so. To say that a polar bear has white fur to blend with his snowy surroundings in arctic wastes in order to protect himself is not scientific. The polar bear's white color is undoubtedly protective, but all that the scientist can ask is how it came about that the polar bear is so colored. Probably white bears survived in snowy regions, and their offspring tended to survive also, because of their greater protection from enemies, and the white color therefore became characteristic of the species. But the polar bear has no consciousness of his color, and does not choose to be white—nor could his ancestors have chosen to be white. A polar bear in a zoo in the temperate zone remains white; he would probably change his character, and become more adapted to zoo conditions, if he could, or if he had any consciousness that could control such adaptation. But in the zoo the polar bear is protected by man's aid, and even in thousands of years he would not change.

Instances of adaptation in nature are so remarkable that we are inclined to marvel at them. Cacti and other desert plants are particularly fitted to the dry sand and great heat of arid wastes. Many seeds are tufted to be borne by the wind, or barbed to be carried in the furry coats of animals or even on human trouser legs, thereby effecting wide dispersal of the offspring. We watch a bee invading a flower, to secure nectar or pollen, and wonder at the structure of the blossom which so effectively provides that the hairy bee shall brush off the pollen and carry it to other flowers, to bring about cross-pollination of the species. Some flowers attract bees, others attract butterflies and moths. The butterfly has a long tongue-like "mouth," called a proboscis, with which it can probe the sacs of certain flowers which contain a deposit of nectar, on which the insect feeds. Grasshoppers that live in grass are green; there is an insect called the walking stick, which looks almost exactly like a twig of the tree or bush on which it lives; there are moths which rest on the bark of trees in the daytime and are mottled to look exactly like that bark. The chameleon changes his hue, to match more nearly the surface on which he rests. The striped tiger blends with the foliage of his tropical jungle, and is not so much protected from enemies (chiefly man) as hidden from his prey.

Examples are plentiful. Walking and scratching birds have feet and claws developed seemingly for that purpose. Flying birds do not walk so well, and seldom, if ever, scratch. Hawks and eagles have claws for clutching and carrying prey. Ducks and other swimming birds are web-footed, their feet serving as paddles. Even among higher mammals there is great adaptation, particularly in the teeth. Incisors, canines, and molars are variously developed to suit the eating of grass or other green vegetables, or to rend and chew meat. The giraffe's long neck enables him to eat leaves from comparatively tall trees. The bat has his forelimbs adapted to flying (it is the only mammal capable of true flight), and catches insects on the wing or feeds on luscious fruits.

Such adaptations are always inherited; they are characteristic of genus and species, and have so existed for hundreds of centuries. But most organisms are capable of showing particular and incidental adaptation to environment, in slight degrees. Plants develop differently if conditions of light, moisture, and temperature are changed. Even human beings take on a coat of tan under prolonged exposure to the sunlight. Such temporary adaptations in the individual are not inherited. They must be distinguished from the more permanent variations due to heredity.

THE CHEMICAL CYCLE OF LIFE

Specially adapted plants take their part in the great chemical cycle of life: the compounding of inorganic elements into organic protoplasm, and the later breaking down of that protoplasm once more into inorganic substances. Green plants make protoplasmic material out of carbon dioxide and water, under the action of sunlight and chlorophyll, by the process called photosynthesis. The living plant gives off some waste products; and when the plant dies it wilts and "decays." What we call decay is really the outward manifestation of the result of a living process—the action of plants which live on dead organic matter.

When a stale piece of bread becomes "moldy," we regard it as spoiled. It has become the food of a saprophyte, a kind of tiny plant, which grows on the bread and will consume some of it. Dead organic matter is fed upon by a succession of organisms, mostly bacteria, which reduce it ultimately to inorganic compounds or elements, bringing about decomposition or decay. These inorganic substances are returned to the air or the soil, where they may again be utilized by green plants or by animals as oxygen, carbon dioxide, ammonia, or nitrates, phosphates, and the like. Meanwhile, living plant and animal organisms are eaten or consumed as food by other organisms, which eliminate waste materials, or are decomposed when they in turn die and decay. So it is an endless cycle, from inorganic to organic, and from organic to inorganic matter.

PARASITES AND SYMBIOSIS

Organisms which live on other organisms, taking their nourishment from those organisms (called "hosts"), are called *parasites,* as we mentioned earlier. They are to be distinguished from animals which prey on other organisms—that is, herbivorous animals which eat living plants, or carnivorous animals which eat living animals or kill them and feed on the carcass. A parasite takes up its abode on the body of its host, and feeds on it without killing it, or without killing it immediately.

What we call disease is often the manifestation of the activities of parasites (usually bacteria or protozoans). Potato blight, a disease of potato plants, is caused by a parasitic fungus which feeds on the potato. Smuts, rusts, blights, mildews, and rots are caused by fungi, or sometimes by bacteria. Human diseases caused by bacteria include pneumonia, tetanus (lockjaw), tuberculosis, diphtheria, cholera, and typhoid fever. What we regard as the disease of typhoid is a sum of the symptoms of bacterial invasion of the human body by a particular microorganism.

Mistletoe is a familiar parasitic plant of a higher order of development. It takes as its host various kinds of trees, often the oak. Some mistletoe has chlorophyll (green leaves), and thus supplies some of its own food by photosynthesis, but it penetrates the stem of its host to get water and dissolved mineral substances, for the mistletoe has no roots in the soil.

Parasitic animals are particularly obnoxious to man, especially such insects as fleas, mites, ticks, and "cooties." They often live on furred animals; everyone knows how likely a dog is to have fleas. Some diseases are caused by animal organisms (protozoans) which invade the human body. Notable among them is malaria, caused by the malarial parasite, which requires both man and a particular kind of mosquito (Anopheles) for its development or life cycle. The female mosquito bites a person infected with malaria (or someone who has had malaria and is not completely cured), and takes some of the malarial organisms into its body. There the malarial parasite undergoes the sexual phase of its existence, and forms slender, pointed cells which are later injected into some other human being by the mosquito, shortly giving rise to "chills and fever" which characterize the disease. Malaria can be transmitted only by the female Anopheles mosquito. Other examples of human parasites are the trichina worm (which is obtained by eating infected uncooked or insufficiently cooked pork, and inhabits human muscle) and the tapeworm, which lodges inside the intestine.

A parasite is usually harmful to its host, if only in a small degree. The phenomenon of two organisms living together for mutual advantage is termed *symbiosis*. A lichen, which looks like a single plant, is an example of symbiosis—of an alga and a fungus living together, closely associated, seemingly one plant; the alga performs photosynthesis and provides extra food for the fungus, and the fungus secures moisture for the alga. Ants which tend aphids (plant lice) like "cattle" are another instance of symbiosis. The aphids are protected by the ants, and the ants take the sweet secretion or "milk" of the aphids.

Some bacteria are particularly adapted to utilizing free nitrogen of the air, forming nitrates, which they leave in the soil. Such bacteria live in a kind of union with legumes (beans, peas, clover, alfalfa, etc.). If a crop of some legume is planted, it will have the effect, because of these bacteria, of restoring nitrates to the soil. This is one of the reasons for the "rotation of crops" in farming.

EVOLUTION

The evidence of the obvious relationships between different animals and plants, their similarities as well as their differences, their adaptation to their environment and to other organisms, their anatomical structure and their physiology, the essential unity of all living things, all point to the fact of evolution. The *theory of evolution,* given its most noted exposition by Charles Darwin (1807–1882), accounts for the development over long periods of time of higher, more complex organisms from lower, or simpler ones—a process of extremely slight modifications throughout many generations. Embryology offers supporting evidence, for every multicellular organism begins as a single cell—just as originally multicellular organisms evolved from unicellular ones.

Evolution does not mean that "man is descended from a monkey." It may mean that man and monkey are different branches (apes and monkeys forming lower branches) of the same main stem of the tree of life. No one can deny that man and the anthropoid (man-like) apes show remarkable similarities in anatomy: they are classed together in the animal kingdom as *primates.* The "missing link," so called, often mentioned in popular discussions of evolution, will not, if ever found and so designated, link man directly with any ape, but it may link man and the apes to a common, though very remote, ancestor.

EVIDENCE FROM ANATOMY

A student of anatomy is impressed with the evolutionary evidence of vestigial structures; they occur more commonly in animals than in plants, and are still inherited, generation after generation. The vermiform appendix of the human body, which may be inflamed in the condition called appendicitis, is probably such a vestigial structure—that is, may have served some vital capacity in a remote human ancestor, although it is dormant and useless in man today. It is actually used by certain lower animals for digestive purposes. Another vestigial structure is the remnant of the nictitating membrane in the eye. In the inner corner of the human eye is the so-called semilunar fold (readily to be seen in a mirror); this fold is the vestige of the nictitating membrane which, in birds, comes down over the eyeball in place of an eyelid.

The human animal has a vestigial tail. The coccyx, or the peculiarly shaped lower end of the vertebral column, is reminiscent of a movable tail. Indeed, it is strikingly similar to the vestigial tail bones of the gorilla or of any other tailless ape. Snakes have vestigial limbs in their skeletons. Horses, and other ungulates (hoofed animals), actually walk upon one

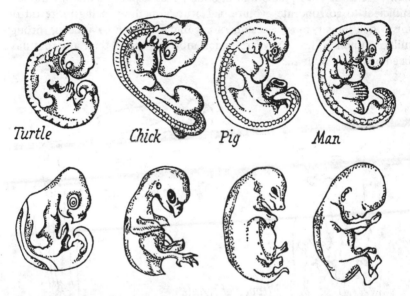

Turtle   *Chick*   *Pig*   *Man*

FIG. 14. Early and later embryonic stages of various animals compared.

extended toe; the other digits are present higher up the leg as vestigial structures. All mammals exhibit signs of having descended from five-toed ancestors. Even the external human ear may be regarded as vestigial, for it serves no vital purpose in modern man, although in such animals as dogs and horses the outer ear may be slightly moved to catch sounds.

EVIDENCE FROM EMBRYOLOGY

The embryo, in its development, recapitulates the evolution of the race. In the first stages of development from the zygote (fertilized egg), animal embryos are remarkably alike. The very early stage of the embryo of a pig appears outwardly almost identical with the embryo of a human being at a comparable stage. As development proceeds, they become less and less alike, each embryo developing the peculiar characters of its parents.

All animal embryos exhibit, at some stage in their development, rudimentary gills or "gill slits." This indicates that all animals went through, in a more or less remote period of evolution, an aquatic existence. Land animals, therefore, are evolved from aquatic ancestors. Lungs, with which to breathe air, came comparatively late.

Breeding and the familiar practices of the cultivation of plants and the domestication of animals have resulted in the formation of practically new species of both plants and animals. This aspect of biology alone is sufficient to corroborate evolution. Nature's method, being more hit-or-miss, took longer, but the results of organic evolution have been, through millions upon millions of years, much more profound than any that have been achieved by man.

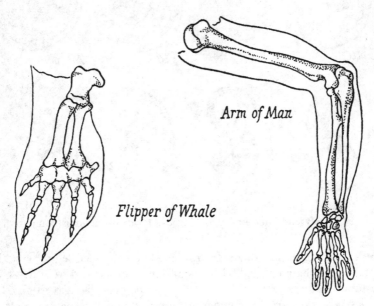

Arm of Man

Flipper of Whale

FIG. 15. Flipper of whale and arm of man compared.

The scientific classification of animals and plants points up the evidence for organic evolution, for organisms are classified strictly according to their similarities. All the animals of one species closely resemble one another; two domestic cats are noticeably alike. But the domestic cat differs markedly from a lion, though there are points of similarity—cats, lions, tigers, and leopards all belong to the cat family. Cats are like horses and cows and bears in that they suckle their young—a point of common likeness in all mammals.

Zoological (and usually also botanical) classification proceeds from higher to lower groups, from phylum to class, then, in descending (less inclusive) groups, through order, family, genus, species, and subspecies. Every organism is given a scientific name, usually Latin (so that it may be understood by all scientists, no matter what their native tongue), of two parts—first, the name of the genus to which the animal belongs, and, second, the name of the species. The giant kangaroo, the largest and best-known species, has the scientific name *Macropus giganteus*—species *giganteus* of the genus *Macropus*. Kangaroos, or most of the pouched mammals commonly known by that name, belong to the genus *Macropus*. Kangaroos of all genera belong to the family Macropodidae. This family belongs to the order Marsupialia, which includes not only the kangaroos, but also wombats and opossums. The Marsupialia is an order of the class Mammalia, which is the highest class of the vertebrates, including all animals which suckle their young and have mammary glands for that purpose. The vertebrates, scientifically designated as the Vertebrata, are a division of the phylum Chordata (chordates), which includes all organisms having a notochord at some stage of development.

THE EARTH'S BIOLOGICAL PAST

The study of the earth's crust or rocky envelope (called the lithosphere) reveals that in remote ages of the past there were other forms of plant and animal life, ancestors of the living organisms of today. Some of those former inhabitants of the earth's surface died and fell into water or sand in such a way that their bones became preserved or have left a clear impression in hardened rock. These remains of organisms are called *fossils*. The study of fossils is called *paleontology*. Fossils are prime exhibits as evidence of organic evolution.

The land surface of the earth is constantly being altered under weather conditions and as a result of erosion (wearing away) by rivers, ocean waves, rain, and the like, and by sediments laid down by standing bodies of water or by running streams. Geologists, who have studied the earth's rocks, know that the layers were put down, in past ages, in a definite order, the lowest layers (unless displaced by earthquakes) being the oldest. Physical and chemical changes in those layers (or strata) of rocks give a fair indication of their age, or of their age relative to other strata. The stratum in which a fossil is found is the key to the age of the fossil and to the time in which the animal or plant lived.

Fossils are of three kinds. The rarest, and the most desirable for study, are actual organic remains, marvelously preserved by some accident of nature. Most fossils, however, are really rocks; they are petrified forms of bones or hard parts of plants, in which mineral matter has supplanted the original organic matter. Many fossils are molds or casts, such as footprints in mud that later hardened into rock, or shapes of skeletons that decayed but left their form as a kind of mold for deposited sediment. Specimens of the various kinds of fossils can be seen in a museum of natural history.

The earliest forms of life on the earth were certainly unicellular, and probably were bacteria. Just how life began is still a mystery. Exceptionally favorable conditions probably existed at some time in the remote past, for the earth was warmer and more moist millions of years ago, and warmth and moisture are especially conducive to life, as is clear from the profuse life in the tropics today.

From these primitive unicellular organisms, higher organisms developed, becoming multicellular and specialized. Higher invertebrates appeared—giant "insects," huge scorpions, and the like, and many fishes that seem odd and strangely monstrous to us today. Ferns as large as trees grew in those remote warm and marshy ages. Amphibians appeared, and primitive reptiles. During the late Paleozoic Era the great plants died, became buried under layers of soil, and gradually solidified into the coal deposits, also forming adjacent petroleum and gas deposits so important to the machinery of our modern civilization.

In the Mesozoic Era, the Age of Reptiles, giant "monsters" stalked the earth. This was the time of the dinosaurs, pterosaurs, ichthyosaurs, plesiosaurs, and others. Reptiles swam in the sea, flew through the air, and roamed over the land. Brontosaurus was a herbivorous dinosaur 66 feet long and probably weighing something like 37 tons! Birds and mammals began to appear in the late Mesozoic Era. Birds are directly descended from reptiles; feathers are modified scales. The giant reptiles became extinct at the end of the Mesozoic Era, and made way for further development of birds, and for the Age of Mammals, which brings evolution down to our own time. We are living in the Psychozoic Age of Recent or Cenozoic time—in the age of human beings, so to speak. Meanwhile, plants had further developed, the seed-bearing plants taking the place of the early pteridophytes (ferns and such), and the angiosperms becoming the dominant type as they are today.

The trend of evolution has ever been from general types to more highly specialized and more specifically adapted forms of life. The highly adapted organism does not revert to the more general type, and cannot give rise to a new general type, but can evolve further in the direction of greater specialization.

Evolution has proceeded by descent, with the inheritance, in some way, of modifications. The process has been extremely gradual, operating

FIG. 16. Life in various stages of the history of the earth. Reading from bottom to top, we see the successive geological eras and the principal forms of life which are believed to have originated in each era.

through many millions of years and through countless millions of generations. Natural selection and the inheritance of acquired characters have both been advanced as theories to account for the fact of evolution. There is no scientific evidence to support the idea of inheritance of acquired characteristics. Much evidence supports a modified theory of natural selection, which is widely accepted by scientists today.

THE STORY OF MAN

That man is an animal cannot be disputed, in the light of anatomical, physiological, and psychological evidence. Further, evolutionary evidence, particularly fossils, indicates that man has descended from a remote animal ancestor. Man is classified as belonging to the primates, the highest order of the class Mammalia. The primates are divided into six main families: Lemuridae (lemurs), Hapalidae (marmosets), Cebidae (monkeys of South America), Cercopithecidae (monkeys of the eastern hemisphere), Simiidae (anthropoid or man-like apes), and Hominidae (human beings). Man is of the species *Homo sapiens,* of which there are several racial varieties or subspecies.

The anthropoid (man-like) apes include the chimpanzee, gibbon, orangutan, and gorilla. They are alike in having no tails, in having manlike teeth, in walking somewhat erect like man, in having short thumbs, and in having more brain development than the lower primates.

Man is unlike the anthropoid apes and other primates in that he has a truly highly developed brain and especially a large cerebrum; in having a vertically long face; in having a distinct chin; in having smaller teeth; in walking definitely erect, with an upright vertebral column or backbone; in having arms shorter than the legs; in having a highly opposable thumb (which can be brought against the forefinger), but without an opposable great toe; and in being able to speak. Man has reached his remarkable development as a civilized being because of two important characteristics: the opposable thumb, making him a tool-using animal, and high brain power, giving him the intelligence which has enabled him to dominate the earth.

The evolutionary family tree of man shows the following known ancestors in this order: primitive primates in the Eocene and Oligocene periods, a primitive anthropoid in the Miocene, the famous Ape Man (*Pithecanthropus erectus*) of Java in the Pliocene, the Heidelberg Man (*Homoheidelbergensis*) a little later in the Pleistocene, Neanderthal Man (*Homoneanderthalensis*) still later in the Pleistocene, and, about the same time, Cro-Magnon Man, the immediate ancestor of *Homo sapiens*. The modern races of man all developed from the Pleistocene ancestors just named. The bushmen of Australia are thought to be the most primitive living examples of the human race. Meanwhile, another link in the chain has been unearthed in China, the Peking Man.

How old is man? It is a difficult question, but probably man's ancestors have roamed the earth for a million years and perhaps longer. The Java Ape Man is sometimes placed at about 500,000 years ago, and the Cro-Magnon race at less than 100,000 years ago.

Paleontology and geology are still young sciences. Every year furthers our knowledge of the story of man, and a final word cannot yet be said about man's remote and fascinating past. The possibilities of finding further fossil human remains are by no means exhausted. "Diggers" are searching assiduously, and carefully correlating their findings.

BIOLOGY IN RELATION TO DAILY LIFE

Biology, and the science of life, includes within its scope the structure and functioning of the human body; and at various points in this section we have indicated how basic biological principles express themselves in the human body's activities. The subject of human anatomy and physiology is of such major concern to all of us that it is customary to devote a separate course to this very personal aspect of biology. The term Physiology is used to describe this division of biology, and we present it here as the next section of this book.

EXAMINATION QUESTIONS

1. What is biology?
2. What is the word used to describe living substances in contrast to non-living substances?
3. Name five sciences that biology embraces.
4. What is the basis of all life?
5. In what shape does protoplasm appear under the microscope?
6. What are the cavities within the cytoplasm called?
7. Describe the method of reproduction known as fission.
8. What is the amoeba?
9. What one-celled animals display both plant and animal characteristics?
10. What are the tiniest and simplest plants called?
11. What are the tiny threads by means of which some bacteria move called?
12. What forms the woody portion of plants?
13. What are the voluntary muscles?
14. How many different species are included in the plant kingdom?
15. What group of plants comprise those bearing seeds?
16. Tell the difference between annual, biennial, and perennial plants.
17. What ten chemical elements do plants require for their growth?
18. By what process does soil water enter the root cells of plants?
19. What is the sugar formed in plants called?

20. Why will a house plant "lean" toward a window?
21. Explain how yeast cells reproduce by budding.
22. What part of the flower of a seed-bearing plant produces the pollen?
23. What is pollination?
24. What contains the seeds that reproduce the plant?
25. How many species are there named and catalogued in the animal kingdom?
26. What constitutes the largest single group of the animal kingdom?
27. Do amphibians live in water or on land?
28. How are the highest class of vertebrates classified?
29. What is the classification of animals that live entirely on vegetable matter?
30. What enzyme does saliva contain?
31. How do fish breathe?
32. How do most animals reproduce?
33. What are the female gametes called?
34. How large is the human ovum?
35. What animals are called oviparous?
36. In what animals is the uterus single and undivided in form?
37. How is the offspring attached to the mother in viviparous animals?
38. What glands of the female supply the young with milk?
39. What is genetics?
40. What color will be the offspring if a red flower is crossed with a white flower of the same species?
41. How have seedless oranges and grapefruit been developed?
42. What increases the virility of animals and plants?
43. With what is the science of eugenics concerned?
44. What is the name of the biological study of organisms in relation to their environment and to other organisms?
45. What is the butterfly's long tongue-like mouth called?
46. What brings about decay in organic matter?
47. What are parasites?
48. In what one way can malaria be transmitted?
49. What is evolution?
50. What evidence shows that man is an animal?

For Further Study

The Biotic World and Man, by Milne & Milne. (Prentice-Hall, New York.)

Cells and Societies, by John Tyler Bonner. (Princeton University Press, Princeton, N.J.)

The Chemicals of Life, by Isaac Asimov. (Abelard-Schuman Limited, New York.)

Foundations of Biology, by Lorande Loss Woodruff. (The Macmillan Co., New York.)

General Biology, by James Watt Mavor. (The Macmillan Co., New York.)

Microbe Hunters, by Paul de Kruif. (Harcourt, Brace & World, Inc., New York.)

XXVII

Physiology Simplified

GENERAL DESCRIPTION OF THE BODY

THE HUMAN BODY IS made up of many parts, all working together in a unified whole. The study of the structure of the human body and of its parts is called *anatomy*. The study of the functions of the organs and parts of the body and how they work is called *physiology*. The study of the conditions favorable to normal growth and activity of the body, and of circumstances conducive to good health, is called *hygiene*. The study of the tissues and the microscopic inspection of the materials which make up both external and internal organs is called *histology*.

To understand descriptions of the parts of the body, a few fundamental terms must be defined. The end of the body toward the head is referred to as *anterior* (or *cephalic*); the end toward the "tail" as *posterior* (or *caudal*). The side of the body corresponding to the belly is called *ventral*; the opposite side corresponding to the back is called *dorsal*. These terms apply regardless of the position of the body—whether it is erect, reclining, or otherwise.

In the trunk of the human body, as in all vertebrates, there are two great cavities, one on the dorsal side (the spinal cord, culminating at the anterior end of the brain, protected by the vertebral column or spine), and one on the ventral side (the alimentary canal, stomach, and intestines, running from the mouth to the anus, together with the related organs, such as the liver, heart, lungs, and kidneys). In the dorsal cavity are the organs of control and feeling: the central nervous system. In the ventral cavity are the organs of digestion, respiration (breathing), and circulation of the blood.

The ventral cavity of the human body, as in all mammals, is again divided into two parts by a membrane called the diaphragm. Above this diaphragm (*i.e.*, toward the head) is the chest (or *thoracic*) cavity; below it is the abdominal cavity. In the chest cavity are the heart and lungs, and, behind them (dorsally), the anterior part of the alimentary canal (Fig. 1).

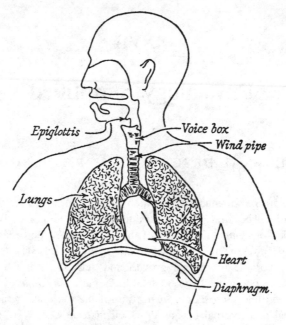

FIG. 1. Position of heart, lungs, etc.

In the abdominal cavity are the stomach (into which the alimentary canal empties), the small and large intestines, the liver, pancreas, spleen, kidneys, etc. What is usually called the stomach from the exterior appearance of the abdomen is the bulge of the massed coils of the intestines. The stomach itself is higher, under the lower ribs. The digestive system terminates in the anus and the genito-urinary organs. The latter are the organs for the elimination of waste liquids (urine) and the organs of reproduction.

Lining the walls of the ventral and dorsal cavities are membranes, moist and smooth, called the *serous* membranes. They have distinguishing names: the *arachnoid,* lining the dorsal cavity; the *pleura* (whence *pleurisy,* inflammation of this membrane), lining the chest; and the *peritoneum* (whence *peritonitis,* inflammation of the peritoneum), lining the abdominal cavity. The skin covers these cavities, on the outside, just as it does the rest of the body. The skin has two layers: the *epidermis,* or outer layer, and the *dermis,* which contains blood (you have perhaps noticed that a very light cut in the skin does not bleed, because the dermis has not been penetrated).

Beneath the skin, and sometimes between the skin and the serous membranes of the body cavities, are the bones (which give rigidity to the body) and the muscles, which move the parts of the body. The muscles of animals form the lean portion of meat, as in beef or pork. The chest cavity opens into the mouth, which is lined with mucous membranes (soft and moist, being kept wet by gland secretions); and it also opens into the nose, which is similarly lined. The *mucous membrane* is an extension of the skin, and has two layers also: corresponding to the epidermis is the *epithelium,* and corresponding to the dermis is the *corium.* The genito-urinary openings are also lined with mucous membranes (so called because their secretions contain *mucus,* the name given to the slippery fluid which moistens them). At the lips and nostrils, and at other points where the mucous membranes meet it, they are continuous with the outer skin.

The arms and legs are made up principally of bones, muscles, and protecting skin, with the necessary blood vessels and nerves. The brain controls the mechanisms of the body and is the center of intelligence. The posterior tapering of the brain leads into the spinal cord, which is a kind of switchboard controlling the telegraph system of nerves that reach to all parts of the body. Along the back, protecting the spinal cord, is the backbone or spine. Surrounding the brain is the heavy cranial bone or skull, which is further protected by an overgrowth of hair.

In animals that go on all fours, the vital parts of the body are protected. The ventral cavity, with its organs of respiration, digestion, and blood circulation, is fairly well hidden since it is toward the ground and between the legs. The back is protected by hair, and the spinal cord is protected by the backbone. The head is protected by the skull and hair. When man began to walk upright, he inevitably exposed the ventral and vital side of his body, and found it necessary to devise artificial protection in the form of clothing, or armor, or a shield to be held in front of him when fighting.

If any piece of the human body is carefully dissected and examined under the microscope, it will be found to be composed of cells. The *cell* is the smallest unit of composition of a living thing. A cell is made up of protoplasm (the basic substance of living organisms), with a nucleus (or center). The cells are massed into parts which make up the body as a whole. Any mass of similar cells is called a *tissue,* as a muscle or a gland.

Many scientists regard the human body as a kind of chemical machine. Many chemical elements enter into its composition; namely, carbon, hydrogen, oxygen, nitrogen, sulphur, phosphorus, chlorine, fluorine, iodine, silicon, sodium, lithium, calcium, potassium, magnesium, manganese, iron, zinc, and copper. Although these numerous elements are present, the body is more than two-thirds water. If you weigh 150 pounds, of that weight at least 100 pounds is water.

The elements named above do not exist in the body in an uncombined state (with a few exceptions), but in compounds, of which there are a large number. The body is known to contain such substances as sodium chloride (common salt), potassium chloride, calcium phosphate, hydrochloric acid (in the stomach), and such organic compounds as proteins, pigments (the coloring matter of hair, skin, blood, etc.), enzymes, fats, carbohydrates, acids, etc. The proteins include albumins, globulins, hemoglobins, proteoses, peptones. In general, the greater part of the material of protoplasm is *colloid,* which means that when evaporated the resultant mass will not form crystals but will be shapeless and gummy. A substance which becomes crystallized when the water has been evaporated from it is called *crystalloid.* Human body cells are made up of a small number of crystalloids and a large number of colloids.

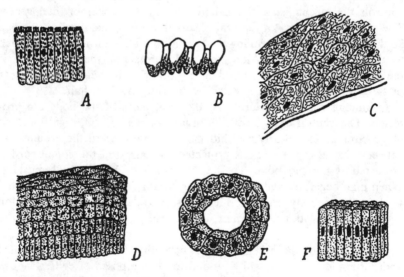

Fig. 2. Surface tissues. *A,* ciliated columnar cells; *B,* single-celled glands (the clear spaces are where the secretions are stored until discharged); *C,* squamous; *D,* stratified epithelium; *E,* cuboidal; *F,* columnar.

Each cell is enclosed in a cell membrane, which keeps it distinct and whole. Between the cells, which lie close together but not necessarily quite touching one another, are spaces filled with a watery fluid called *lymph.* Each cell must be fed, and food reaches it by way of the lymph in which it is bathed. As the cell feeds, it gives off waste products, which are passed into the lymph. The lymphatic fluid, therefore, is the medium in direct contact with the cells, which are the units of which the body is built. The lymph, in its turn, secures nourishment for the cells, from the circulating blood, and gives off its waste products to the blood. The blood is a great transportation system for bringing nourishment to all parts of the body and for carrying waste products from all parts to a central department for the elimination of that waste. The exchange of chemicals between blood and lymph, and lymph and cells, takes place *through* the intervening membranes. These processes of exchange are known as filtration, osmosis, and dialysis.

From the union of male and female cells in conception, through the stages of embryonic development, and from birth onward to adulthood, the cells of the body—of which there are many hundreds of different kinds, each with its special functions to perform—grow and multiply and divide, die and are replaced, in a marvelous and intricate process known as *mitosis*. Groups of cells form tissues and organs, which are teamed and grouped into systems, each with highly important functions. These systems are then co-ordinated into the whole body, which lives and acts as a unit made up of many separate and interacting parts.

Living organisms, of which the human being is the most highly specialized example, have the capacity to develop by growth, to assimilate nourishment or energy for that growth, to eliminate the waste products resulting from the use of that energy, and to reproduce themselves so that descendants may repeat the life cycle through countless generations. In order to maintain life in the face of various kinds of opposition, the living organism has senses which enable it to find food and secure it, or to perceive danger and escape it. Reduced to essentials, by far the majority of the activities of most living organisms are devoted to the finding and eating of food (as a source of energy), and the recovery (in sleep) from the fatigue engendered in the search for food. In man, between times, surplus energy is devoted to other pursuits which make up the great complexity of interrelated human lives in what we call civilization. For man has faculties which lower animals do not possess: intelligence, consciousness, and what they imply—the ability to understand his own activities, and, to some extent, to control them as he may wish.

THE SKELETON

The human body is soft to the touch: the skin is warm and resilient. Were it not for the supporting skeleton, made up of comparatively hard bones, the body would be an almost shapeless mass. The skeleton keeps the various parts in place and facilitates motion and increases the power of action. The skeleton, the framework on which the softer parts of the body are hung, is held together and jointed by the softer muscles, cartilages (supporting tissues), and tendons (the "wires" with which the muscles yank the movable parts about, in response to the impulses from the brain, sent along the nerves), and ligaments (tough elastic and fibrous tissues which connect the bones together at the joints).

THE BONES

The bones of the body are not exposed (except by injury or in a surgical operation), but are imbedded inside the skin, and, for the most part, are rather deeply hidden under muscles and the complex tissues of veins, arteries, etc. Some of the bones, nearer the surface, can be felt, as those beneath the scalp, in the face, at the elbows, knuckles, shins, ankles, and heels. These bones, and the others more deeply embedded, can be studied in a skeleton from which all the soft parts have been removed.

If the adult human skeleton is taken apart, bone from bone, more than 200 separate bones are found. In the growing child there are more, but as he reaches the adult state some multiple bones grow together into one. The *axial skeleton* is the main system of bones to which the limbs, and shoulder and pelvic arches, are attached. It consists of the skull, or head, the spine (vertebral column) or backbone, the breastbone (sternum), and the ribs.

The *skull* consists of 22 bones, eight of which form the upper part or cranium, which is a box holding the brain. The other 14 skull bones form the face. In the vertebral column, from which the whole skeleton may be said to hang, are 33 bones, called *vertebrae;* you can feel them with your finger as you bend your neck or back. They are so jointed that the neck can be turned, and the back can be bent backward and forward. The seven neck bones are called *cervical* vertebrae; the 12 *thoracic* bones come next below, and in the lower back are five *lumbar* bones (in the region where you may have lumbago), five *sacral* bones (united in the adult in the sacrum), and the four tail bones of the *coccyx*. The ribs are arranged in 12 pairs, which are linked to the 12 thoracic vertebrae. The *sternum* (breastbone) connects the upper ribs in front (ventrally). All are united and somewhat cushioned by gristles (cartilages) to prevent their scraping against each other. The cartilage pads of the spine are so flexible that in the morning, after a night's sleep, a man may be almost an inch taller than at night.

The *cranium* is formed of the forehead (*frontal*) bone, the crown (*parietal* bones, two), the base of the skull (*occipital* bone), two bones of the ear regions (*temporal*), and, just in front of the temporal bones,

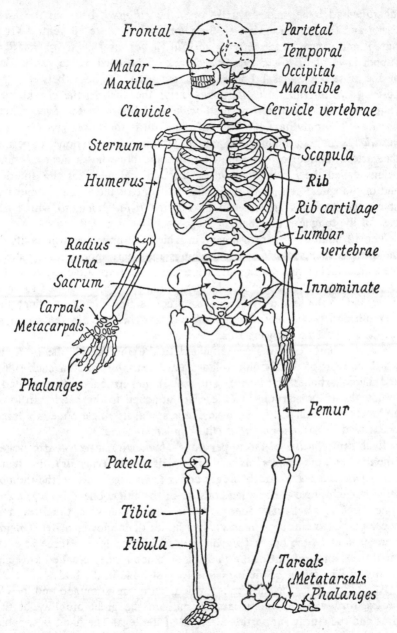

Frontal — Parietal
— Temporal
Malar — Occipital
Maxilla — Mandible
Clavicle — Cervicle vertebrae
Sternum — Scapula
Humerus — Rib
— Rib cartilage
Radius — Lumbar vertebrae
Ulna
Sacrum — Innominate
Carpals
Metacarpals
Phalanges
— Femur
Patella
Tibia
Fibula
Tarsals
Metatarsals
Phalanges

Fig. 3. The human skeleton.

the *sphenoid* bone, and a small bone, the *ethmoid*, between the nose cavity and the cranial cavity. In the face the bones are all ventral (forward), and consist of the *inferior maxilla* (lower jaw), *superior maxillae* (upper jaw), the two *palatine* bones back of the hard palate, the bridge of the nose (two nasal bones), the partition (*vomer*) between the nostrils, two *inferior turbinate* bones inside the nostrils, the cheekbones (*malars,* two), and the two small *lachrymal* bones in the eye sockets (*orbits*). The only movable bone of the skull is the lower jaw (*inferior maxilla*), which is articulated or jointed with the temporal bones to permit the various motions of chewing. The occipital bone has a large opening below, called the *foramen magnum,* through which passes the anterior end of the spinal cord, into the brain. In front of the throat, somewhat above the "Adam's apple," can be felt the *hyoid* bone, to which the base of the tongue is attached.

The 12 pairs of *ribs* form a cage in which the upper ventral cavity of the trunk is enclosed, protecting the lungs and heart and, to some extent, the stomach. The first seven pairs (anterior seven) are attached ventrally to the sternum or breastbone. The next three pairs are attached to each other and to the seventh pair above by connecting cartilages. Since the eleventh and twelfth pairs of ribs are not attached on the ventral ends, they are called the "floating ribs."

The forelimbs or arms are attached to the shoulder girdle or arch, which consists of the shoulder blades (two *scapulas,* one on each side) and the collarbones (*clavicles*). The collarbones articulate (are jointed) in notches of the sternum. The legs are attached to the *pelvic* girdle or arch, which is attached to the base of the spine; its single bone is a large one, called the *os innominatum* (the "unnamed bone").

Each arm consists of the upper bone (*humerus*), two forearm bones (the *ulna* and the smaller *radius*), eight wrist bones (*carpals*), five hand bones (*metacarpals*), and 14 finger bones (*phalanges:* two in the thumb, three in each finger). Each leg consists of the thighbone (*femur*), shinbone (*tibia*), small calf bone (*fibula*), seven bones of the heel and upper part of the instep (*tarsals*), five bones of the lower instep (*metatarsals*), and 14 toe bones (*phalanges:* two in the big toe, three in each small toe); and in front of the joint of the knee is the so-called kneecap (*patella*). The femur of the leg is the longest bone in the body.

Notable features of the limbs, which, with the shoulder and pelvic girdles, form the *appendicular* skeleton, are the great mobility of the arms and the sturdy supporting strength of the legs. The hand is capable of a wide variety of movements, largely because of the thumb, which is so articulated that it can be brought against any or all of the fingers. The foot, with its arch, is admirably adapted to walking and running, and is built to relieve as much as possible the consequent jar to the spinal column. If the arches of the feet are "fallen," the condition known as "flat feet" results, which increases the difficulty of walking and liability to fatigue.

The joinings of the bones are called articulations; there may or may not be the possibility of movement at the point where bones are united with one another. Where movement is possible, the articulation is called a joint; the most movable joints act according to the familiar mechanical principle of the ball-and-socket. Ligaments keep the bones united, and limit the possible movements. The joints permitting the least movement do not have the ball-and-socket arrangement of the upper arm and thigh bones, but are divided into hinge joints (as between the bones of the fingers), pivot joints (in the cervical or neck vertebrae), and gliding joints (which permit very slight movement, as in some of the bones of the feet). A dislocated bone is one that has been torn from its joint.

THE MUSCLES

The muscles are the chief organs of movement in the human body. The muscles, superimposed on the bony skeleton, give the body its characteristic shape, producing bulges and the roundness of limbs. The usual curves of the muscles may be increased or modified by layers of fat (adipose tissue). Some muscle tissue is differentiated to operate the contractions of the stomach, intestines, and other inner organs of the body. The muscles on the bony skeleton are distinguished by calling them *skeletal* muscles (also called, because of their microscopic structure, *striped* muscles); the muscles of the internal organs (*viscera*) are called *visceral* muscles (microscopically, they are unstriped or *smooth*). The skeletal muscles are controlled by voluntary impulses from the brain; the visceral muscles operate automatically, and are therefore described as *involuntary*. However, even the so-called *voluntary* muscles, which we regard as controlled by our wills, may be called into action involuntarily, as in the "start" of surprise or fear and in the blinking of the eye. Cardiac muscle is a special variety of involuntary, striped tissue which exists only in the heart.

A muscle consists of a bulging central portion or belly, tapering at the ends, which are attached by cords or tendons to the skeleton. A muscle easy to feel beneath the skin is the biceps muscle of the upper arm (humerus), which is connected to one end of the scapula and an adjacent muscle, and, at the other end, to the radius of the lower arm. The schoolboy who asks you to "feel" his "muscle," refers only to the biceps, and he bends his arm upward to flex the muscle, or contract it and "make it hard," so that you will be properly impressed.

The motive power of a muscle depends on its ability to contract under a nervous impulse. Thus, if you regard your bent arm as being like the capital letter L, the biceps is in the upright stroke and is attached to the lower stroke (corresponding to the radius of the lower arm) a little beyond the angle (elbow). If the L is straightened into an obtuse angle,

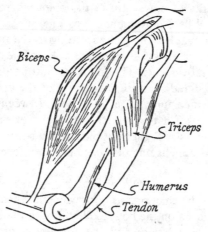

FIG. 4. Muscles of the upper arm.

the muscle is correspondingly extended or relaxed; the lower stroke of the L may now be brought upward into a right angle, or further into an acute angle, by the contraction of the muscle. In a similar way, all the skeletal muscles are suspended by tendons between two different bones or groups of bones. In general, skeletal muscles are described in terms of what they do. Those that cause hinge joints to fold up (such as the biceps) are called *flexors*. Those muscles that open a hinge joint, like the calf muscle of the lower leg, are called *tensors*.

Between and within the muscles are nerves or nerve fibers, which carry impulses from the spinal cord, some of them having been sent down

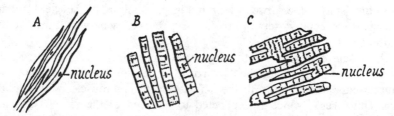

FIG. 5. Contractile tissue. *A*, smooth muscle fibers; *B*, skeletal muscle fibers; *C*, cardiac muscle.

it from the brain, to the muscles, causing them to expand or contract. Also around and within the muscles is the network of blood capillaries, connecting the system of veins and arteries, carrying energy (food) to the muscle cells and taking away the waste products of muscular activity.

The smooth or involuntary muscles enclose various viscera in muscular sacs which expand or contract to churn the food in digestion, or to pass the food or waste products along the great tubes of the intestines. These smooth muscles have no tendons. The heart or cardiac muscle is very similar; from before birth until death this muscle tissue (unless it is diseased) tirelessly keeps up its incessant work without our having to think about it. The heart muscle rests only between beats.

The activity of a muscle depends on complex chemical reactions. When the muscle does work (which means that it expands and contracts), it forms waste products within its cells, which are given off into the lymph and the blood stream. These waste products are chiefly carbon dioxide, water, and nitrogen compounds. Normally, the swiftly coursing blood keeps the waste products eliminated, so that there is no muscular fatigue. If, as in extreme athletic activity, the waste products are formed more rapidly than the blood can carry them away, muscular fatigue ensues. Smooth or involuntary muscles contract rhythmically, as in the intestines, or remain contracted for long periods at a time, as the sphincter muscles or openings into the stomach and bladder, without fatigue.

The skeletal muscles and their many duties may be classified as follows: (1) an arrangement of muscles to maintain the erect posture of man (or other "still" positions of the body), distributed chiefly in the front and back of the neck, down the back and over the abdomen, and in front of and behind the lower limbs; (2) an elaborate system of muscles of locomotion, used in walking, running, jumping, etc.; (3) a series of grasping or prehensile muscles, highly developed in the human hand, but almost atrophied in the human foot, and also present to some extent in the lips; (4) the muscles of the jaw (inferior maxilla), used in chewing (mastication), and the muscles of the throat, used in swallowing; (5) the tiny muscles which move the eyeballs and eyelids, enabling us to see all about us; (6) the muscles which enable us to speak and breathe. The muscles of breathing are kept in motion by an involuntary relationship to the autonomic or sympathetic nervous system. It is impossible to stop the motions of breathing voluntarily for more than a few minutes at a time.

The erect posture which characterizes the human body in its activities is maintained unconsciously, but is nevertheless controlled by the nervous system. Certain activities, such as standing upright, are learned with difficulty at first (in early childhood), and then become seemingly automatic, being taken over by a division of the brain called the cerebellum. That standing upright is controlled by nerves of consciousness which keep in proper position a large number of muscles, though we are not aware of it, is proved by the familiar fact that if a person is struck on the head into unconsciousness, or if he faints, the body immediately drops to the ground, even though no bone or muscle is injured.

Exercise keeps the muscles in good condition, and, moderately indulged in, keeps the body "feeling good." Muscles may be made to grow in size and strength by use, as is shown by the large biceps of men who engage in heavy manual work.

THE NERVOUS SYSTEM

The control of the many functions of the several parts of the human body depends on an intricate nervous system, which may be likened to a carefully co-ordinated telegraph organization, sometimes controlled by the brain and sometimes activated by automatic or semi-automatic "control boards." The impulses are usually due to some sensory reaction of sight, hearing, taste, smell, or touch. If someone says to you, "Look there!" your sense of hearing transmits the sound of the words to your brain, and in response, your brain sends the necessary (and highly complicated) messages along the proper nerves to the proper muscles to move your head and eyes as may be required in order to look as directed. The impulse may be involuntary, as when you jump for safety if an automobile horn sounds loudly almost in your ear.

THE CENTRAL NERVOUS SYSTEM

You do not stop to think about *what* messages to send along your nerves. The brain takes care of that for you. If you wish to wiggle your big toe, you merely *think the action* and your big toe wiggles! This process seems simple only because the body has become accustomed to it. The nerve channels along which the various impulses are sent, for various movements, were established, for the most part, in early childhood. The baby's experimental movements are the beginning of this process. The relations between things seen and heard and the objects themselves, and the following reactions, are soon learned, never to be forgotten.

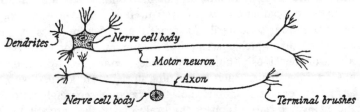

FIG. 6. Sensory neuron.

The brain and the spinal cord form the central nervous system of the body. They occupy the dorsal cavity of the trunk; the brain is enclosed in the skull and the spinal cord is protected by the vertebrae of the spine. Twelve pairs of nerve trunks (lines of nerves which branch farther at their extremities and into side lines along the way) lead out from the brain itself (the cranial nerves), and 31 pairs lead out from the spinal cord (spinal nerves). These 43 pairs of nerve trunks make up the peripheral nervous system. Part of this peripheral nervous system is specialized, forming the autonomic (sometimes called the *sympathetic*) system.

The spinal cord is almost cylindrical in shape, is about three-quarters of an inch in diameter (average), and is about 17 inches long. Its total weight is only an ounce and a half. At its anterior end the spinal cord passes almost imperceptibly into the brain; the division is made, for convenience in anatomy, at the outer margin of the opening (*foramen magnum*) in the occipital bone.

The brain normally weighs a trifle over three pounds in the male, and a trifle under three pounds in the female. The masses of the brain are commonly divided into forebrain, midbrain, and hindbrain, three in all.

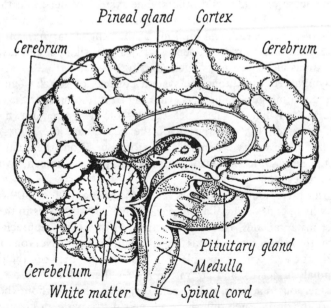

FIG. 7. Cross section of the human brain.

Of these three parts, the forebrain is by far the largest; it consists of two large convoluted masses, called the *cerebral hemispheres*. The midbrain connects the fore- to the hindbrain. The latter includes the *medulla oblongata,* which is continuous with the spinal cord, being a kind of expanded portion of it; the brain itself rests upon the spinal cord somewhat as though the cord were a stem. The deep folds or convolutions are characteristic of the human brain; it is believed that in these folds lie the cells in which are centered human intelligence. The so-called gray matter of the brain is the gray-colored material which characterizes all nerve-cell bodies in the brain; the surface of the convolutions, which is much increased in area by the deep folds, is gray on the surface and white on the inside of the lobes.

The spinal nerves branch variously to different parts of the body, some branches going to organs of sense, some to motor muscles, and so on. Wherever nerves branch into a neighboring trunk line, without making communication through the spinal cord, the network is called a *plexus.* The muscles and skin of the neck, the outer ears, and rear of the scalp are supplied by the *cervical* plexus; the upper limbs are reached from the *brachial* plexus; the *lumbar* plexus, in the lower back, supplies the lower trunks, buttocks, front of the thigh, and inner side of the leg.

The 12 pairs of cranial nerves include the *olfactory* (sense of smell), the *optic* (sense of sight), and others. The system of nerves in the head is extremely complex, controlling motions of the eyeballs and eyelids, wrinkling of the forehead, and motions of the tongue, larynx, soft palate, lips, etc., besides the important senses of hearing, sight, smell, taste, and the local areas of the sense of touch (feeling).

The sympathetic or autonomic system consists of *ganglia* (masses of nerve tissue forming nerve centers) running from the base of the skull to the *coccyx* (tail bone). The chief centers of these are known as the *cardiac plexus* on the dorsal side of the heart, and the *solar plexus,* in the abdominal cavity, "behind" the stomach. From the solar plexus branch the nerves which control, automatically, the stomach, liver, kidneys, intestines, etc.

Impulses travel along human nerves at the rate of 200 or 300 feet per second, which, considering the comparatively short distances in the body, is almost instantaneous. Nerve fibers apparently are not appreciably fatigued by the passage of nervous impulses along them. Nervous fatigue, so called, when it occurs, takes place in the "spaces" between the branching terminals of nerves, and not in the nerves themselves.

Some nervous reactions, called reflexes, take place without the intervention of the brain. Such reflexes, and their nerve paths or channels, are already present in the newborn infant—they do not have to be learned from experience or improved by training. Sneezing is a familiar reflex which is very hard to resist; sneezing cannot be duplicated voluntarily, although it can be imitated. Simple reflex actions are much more common in lower animals than in man.

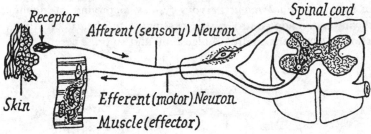

FIG. 8. The path of a simple reflex action.

More complicated reflexes take place in the *cerebellum,* part of the hindbrain. These are not born in us—we must learn them. Such highly complicated locomotor reflexes as walking, running, leaping, swimming, and riding a bicycle, once well learned, are taken over by the cerebellum, which co-ordinates the various stimuli coming from sensory nerves into the stimuli that cause the proper muscles to move the body as desired. For this reason it is only necessary for us to think of walking, and we walk; the cerebellum notes such visible sensory stimuli as the condition of the ground and the direction we are taking, and adjusts the co-ordination accordingly. The cerebellum, by taking over these complicated actions and making them almost automatic, releases the upper part of the brain, or forebrain, for the higher activities of thought which we term intellectual.

The forebrain is the center of human intelligence. The *cerebrum,* part of the forebrain, must acquire all its knowledge, for it is born with none. To acquire knowledge, the cerebrum has effective communication with the central nervous system. The spinal cord, in addition to its branches of nerve trunks, contains also the paths along which "information" is sent to the cerebrum of the brain.

The superficial gray matter of the cerebrum, a thin layer of its convoluted surface, is called the *cortex.* In this cortex are cells which take care of the complex activities we collectively call "thinking," memory, "will power," consciousness, and the like. Various areas of the cerebral cortex are confined to various sense impressions—as the body sense area, the visual area, the auditory (hearing) area, the olfactory (smelling) area, the gustatory (taste) area, and the motor area; in the last named are located the controlling centers of locomotion, when the movements are voluntarily directed from the cortex of the cerebrum instead of from the cerebellum. The consciousness, emotions, memory, and the like, which are believed to originate in the cerebrum, are studied in *psychology*.

The sympathetic nervous system was originally so called because it was believed to bring various organs into sympathy with one another. The better name is the *autonomic nervous system*, signifying an involuntary, practically automatic control of the beating of the heart, breathing, the secretion of sweat, the control of digestion, and so on. There is, however,

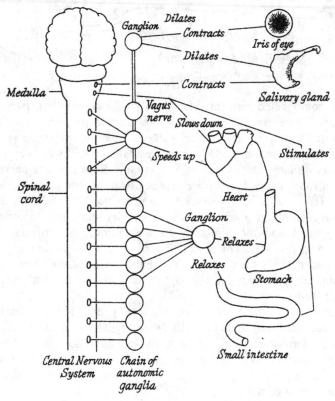

FIG. 9. The autonomic nervous system.

a connection with the sensory stimuli passing through the brainstem to the areas of consciousness, so that the autonomic nervous system is equipped to modify the activity of the "automatic" organs to accord with the immediate needs of the body. In an emergency, as when one is severely scared, the autonomic system can put the body in condition to meet danger: if sensory stimuli suggest impending peril, the autonomic system can dilate the eye pupils, inhibit the secretion of saliva in the mouth, make the hair seem to stand on end (a throwback to primeval times), reduce the blood in the skin's blood vessels (causing paleness), increase the speed of the heart, and hold up the digestive processes temporarily. All these actions, which are involuntary in the sense that they are not consciously controlled, tend to put the body in a state of resistance: the eyes can see more clearly, the stopping of secretions of saliva and digestive activity preserves energy for combat, taking the blood away from the skin reduces the chances of bleeding and also sends it to other parts of the body (as to the brain and muscles) where it may be needed more.

HORMONES

Hormones are the chemical messengers of the body. A *hormone* is a substance which is secreted by one organ (as a gland) and carried in the circulation of the blood to some other organ or organs, which it stimulates. Thus the adrenal bodies, each weighing about half an ounce, located on the kidneys, secrete a hormone called *adrenaline*. This substance keeps the body toned up, so to speak; in an emergency, it is released into the blood stream and causes the same reactions, during fear, as just described. When the symptoms of fear continue long after the cause of fear has been removed, adrenaline is still circulating in the blood.

Adrenaline also relieves fatigue, particularly during great exertion. Getting one's "second wind" and fighting with "the strength of despair" are familiar phenomena. What is regarded as reserve strength is brought to the body by the stimulation of adrenaline released under excitement or exertion. Adrenaline does not add strength to the body; it merely makes available, to the greatest possible extent, the strength already present, by causing the liver to release stored sugar into the blood stream.

The *thyroid,* a gland in the neck (its diseased enlargement is called *goiter*), also secretes a hormone. The thyroid controls the vital processes, collectively called *metabolism,* and is particularly influential in mental development. Lack of thyroid secretion in childhood produces cretinism or a bodily degeneration accompanied by mental deficiency. The condition can be remedied by feeding a medical preparation of animal thyroid. Indeed, the hormones are becoming important medical aids, being prepared from the corresponding glands of lower animals for the greater health and comfort of human beings.

The *pituitary* gland, located at the base of the brain, is known as the master gland, because it secretes hormones which regulate the flow of hormones from all other glands. It secretes a hormone which regulates growth of the long bones. Excess of this hormone produces giantism. Lack of it results in dwarfism. Another pituitary hormone regulates production of milk in mothers. Still another, known as ACTH (adreno-

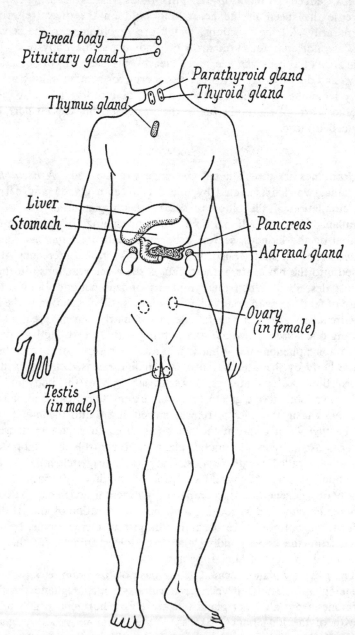

Fig. 10. Location of the endocrine glands in the human body and some which may be endocrine.

corticotropic hormone), stimulates the production of *cortisone,* a hormone of the adrenal glands essential to mobilizing the defenses of the body when under stress.

The *pancreas* contains the *Islands of Langerhans,* which produce *insulin,* a hormone essential to metabolism of sugar. People suffering from diabetes lack insulin, and consequently their blood and urine contain much sugar which cannot be utilized by the body. Such individuals lack energy and by receiving daily injections of insulin may recover the ability to metabolize sugar and live normal lives.

The *thymus* gland secretes a hormone essential to development during adolescence. The *parathyroid,* four tiny glands located in the thyroids, regulate calcium metabolism. Proper formation of bones, teeth, and muscle action depend upon normal functioning of these glands.

The *sex* glands secrete hormones which determine secondary sex characteristics. The *androgenic* hormone, *testosterone,* produced by the testes, determines the hair, voice, and body characteristics of the male. The *estrogenic* hormones, produced by the ovaries, determine female body traits. Healthy men and women have some of both of these hormones, though males have a preponderance of androgens and females more of the estrogens.

Interaction occurs among the various glands and the nervous system through the stimulation of hormones, which go through the blood stream to all parts of the body.

THE SENSES

The average person thinks of himself as possessing five senses: touch, sight, taste, smell, and hearing. There are at least six other physiological senses: temperature (heat and cold), pain, hunger, thirst, balance or equilibrium, and the muscle sense. The stimuli causing these sensations are received and carried by the nervous system of the body.

The temperature sense is distributed over the whole skin of the body, and also in the mucous membranes of the mouth and the passage to the pharynx, in the pharynx itself, in the upper part of the alimentary canal, and in the openings of the nostrils. The centers which receive sensations of cold are different from those which receive sensations of heat. Such sensations of heat and cold are perceptible only when they represent sudden changes in the temperature stimuli of the body. This may be deceptive, as, when we touch a piece of iron, we have a sensation of cold, not because the iron is any colder than other objects with which we are then in contact, but because iron conducts heat rapidly away from the skin which touches it. Internal changes in the body may also cause heat or cold sensations—as when we have a chill or a fever—and sometimes we cannot tell whether the stimulus is from within or from without.

The brain associates the sensations it receives, not with the *areas of the brain* which are stimulated, but with the *ends of the nerves* which bring the stimuli to the brain. Every sensation is thus referred to the region of the body in which it arises, with the exception of the "external" senses of sight and sound, when the sensation is referred to the *object* which causes it, no matter how far away it may be from the body. If a nerve is stimulated midway of its length, the stimulus is still referred to its *ends;* it is for this reason that a man with an artificial leg appears to have sensations in the limb which has been amputated, for the stump of his leg contains the stumps of the nerve trunks which led to the leg, and if they are stimulated his brain refers to the stimuli to the ends of the nerves—even though they are not there.

The senses, wonderful as they are, are imperfect. We cannot always believe our senses (as we sometimes exclaim), for they are stimulated in ways which we cannot always judge accurately. A sensation of light may be caused by pressure on the eyes; that is why you see "stars" after a hard blow on the head. Optical illusions are familiar to everyone. Since there are corresponding illusions of the other senses, we can never be sure that what our senses tell us about the *sensations of our bodies* is completely indicative of conditions in the world outside of us.

The Ear

You naturally think of the ear as that appendage on the side of your head. The ear, however, includes much more than that. The outside visible portion is a very small part of the complicated mechanism with which we hear an amazing variety of sounds.

If you could see one of your ears in cross section (that is, sliced through the middle of the parts, rendering visible the "insides"), you would notice that the opening of the external ear leads into a passage which goes to the tympanum, or eardrum. This drum membrane is so constructed that it will respond to a range of sound vibrations varying from 60 to 4,000 vibrations per second (and to an even wider range in people with exceptionally good hearing). These vibrations are transmitted to a series of interarticulated small bones, called (from their shape) by the quaint names of the hammer (*malleus*), the anvil (*incus*), and the stirrup (*stapes*). These bones are so arranged that, in turn, they transmit the sound vibrations (with diminished amplitude but increased power) to the internal ear, in which vibrations are set up in a fluid which affects the ends of auditory nerve fibers and causes in the brain the sensation we know as sound.

The human ear can detect not only noises, but musical sounds or notes, the quality of which depends on the regularity of their vibrations.

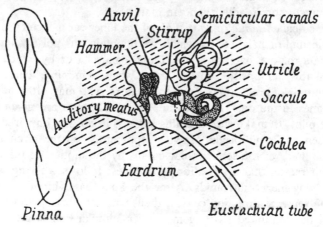

FIG. 11. The parts of the human ear.

The ear can also distinguish loudness (intensity of sound) in various degrees, pitch, and tone quality (the timbre, as, for example, the difference which exists between the note of a cornet and the note of a violin). Indeed, the range of the ear is truly marvelous, for it has been variously estimated that the normal ear can distinguish from 6,000 to 11,000 different tones. The art of music depends on the nice distinctions of which the human ear is capable.

The air pressure on both sides, inner as well as outer, of the eardrum (tympanum) is equalized by means of the *Eustachian tubes,* one from each ear, leading into the pharynx (back of the mouth). When a person swallows, he opens these tubes, and if the barometric pressure (of the atmosphere) has changed, the swallowing permits equalization on the inner side of the tympanum, in the cavity of the middle ear. The pain in the ears which sometimes accompanies ascending high mountains or going down into deep mines may be relieved by frequent swallowing.

Defects of hearing, in the normal ear, include the limitations of its range—some people cannot hear a cricket chirp, its pitch is so high—and the rather marked difficulty of judging the direction from which sounds come. Of course we naturally project sounds to their apparent source; that apparent source, however, is often wrong. It is extremely difficult to tell whether a sound comes from the front or from behind. We recognize best the direction and distance of the human voice, with which we are most familiar; yet we are easily fooled by the ventriloquist.

If the sound is prolonged, we can, by turning the head about, get a fairly accurate notion of its direction and distance. Animals whose outer ears are movable—as dogs and horses—can probably judge the direction of sounds much more readily than can man.

In the so-called *semicircular canals* of the inner ear is located the sense of equilibrium or balance, by which we maintain our poise when standing upright, or our balance when riding a bicycle, or by which we are able to know our position in the water when swimming. This sense of equilibrium is of great importance to aviators, who may often be driving their planes in the dark or in clouds; elaborate tests are given to prospective pilots to make sure that this sense is in no way impaired.

The sense of equilibrium depends, apparently, on the circulation set up in the fluids of the semicircular canals by the motion of the body. It is for this reason that a sensation of dizziness follows whirling or riding on revolving merry-go-rounds. After the body has whirled for a short time, the sense of direction ceases; then, when the body suddenly stops moving, the continued swirling in the semicircular canals gives the impression of movement even though the eyes inform the person that he has stopped. Objects continue to appear to revolve, so the person feels dizzy and totters drunkenly if he tries to walk.

THE EYE

The eye includes the eyeball and its appendages. The eyeball is very nearly the same size in all persons; apparent difference in the size of the eyes is due to a difference in the distance between the angles of the eyelids from end to end of the visible portion of the eyeball.

The eye socket (orbit) is a cavity filled with the muscles which move the eyeball, blood vessels to supply nourishment, nerves, and cushions of fat. The eyeball rotates or moves in the socket, pulled about by suitable muscles. It is protected in front by the eyelids, of which the upper lid is the more movable, being able to cover the entire eyeball in front. The eyes are said to be closed (as in sleep, to protect the eye and also to prevent distraction by visible phenomena) when the upper eyelid is shut down over the eyeball. The inner sides of the eyelids are covered with mucous membrane (the *conjunctiva*), which also covers the front of the eyeball. The edges of the eyelids are lined with hairs (eyelashes) which help to keep out flying particles of dust. Since wherever there are hairs there are sebaceous glands, which secrete a fatty substance to soften and lubricate the hair and skin, the edges of the eyelids are equipped with such glands. When their secretion is excessive the yellowish matter (hard and dried) occurs along the eyelids after a night's sleep, sometimes even being abundant enough to stick the lids together momentarily.

The *lachrymal* or tear-producing apparatus is in the eye. The lachrymal or tear glands supply the moisture which keeps the eyeball wet. Under

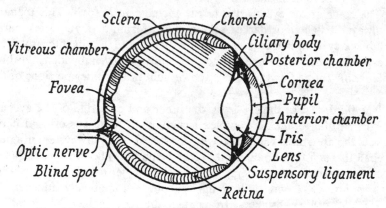

FIG. 12. The parts of the human eye, seen in cross section.

emotional stress, as when one cries, the tears are produced in abnormal quantity and sometimes overflow down the cheeks. Usually, however, the tears are carried off by the lachrymal canals, which open by a pore into the inner corner of each eye (this pore can be seen in a mirror, in either of your eyes, if you pull down the inner corner of the lower lid slightly). Tears carried off into the nose in this way run into the pharynx and are swallowed. This causes the gulping that accompanies prolonged weeping. The act of blinking keeps the moisture from the lachrymal glands evenly distributed over the eyeball, wiping off accumulated dust, washing it clean several times a minute.

The muscles of the eye, attached to the back of the eyeball in the orbit, are so arranged that they can move the eyes from side to side, or up and down, or obliquely, or rotate them, at will. These movements increase the range of vision, which is further amplified by turnings of the head. The two eyes are kept in alignment, moving simultaneously by a nice adjustment of muscles and nerves. If this adjustment is impaired, conditions known as squinting and "cross-eyes" ensue.

The eye itself is the shape of a globe, and is nearly spherical in its main part, being one inch from side to side and nine-tenths of an inch from front to back. The eyeball is protected by three coats of tissue: the outer is the *sclerotic,* of which the transparent part in front of the pupil and iris is the *cornea;* the sclerotic, where visible, is white, forming the "white" of the eye. The second coat includes the *iris,* which is the visible colored portion of the eye; in its center is the aperture through which we see, called the *pupil,* which looks black. A ring of muscle in the iris permits the contracting or narrowing of the pupil; the pupil is smaller in bright light than in diffused light.

The color of the eyes is due to the pigment in the iris. This pigment is always of lighter or darker yellow color, forming what we ordinarily call black eyes, brown eyes, or gray eyes, depending on its intensity. Blue eyes occur when this same pigment is more deeply imbedded, the blue color being formed by the absorption of light in the outer portions of the iris.

The third coat of the eye is on the inner and rear side of the eyeball; it is called the *retina.* Its complex structure of blood vessels and nerve cells is the apparatus which receives the stimuli of light rays entering the eyeball through the cornea and the lens behind it. The eye is constructed somewhat like a small camera, with the shutter perpetually open (during waking hours), having a lens that can be automatically adjusted for nearer and farther distances. In front of the lens (called the *crystalline lens*) is a space filled with transparent *aqueous humor* (water fluid); behind it is the great inner globe of the eye, which is filled with *vitreous* (jelly-like) *humor,* which is also transparent. The lens acts somewhat like an artificial glass lens (although not so perfectly as the finest lenses made by man) to focus on the sensitive retina the rays of light passing through the cornea and pupil.

The "blind spot," one of the defects of the eye, is at the point in the retina where the optic nerve enters the back of the eyeball—this spot is not sensitive to light stimuli. You can prove the existence of your own blind spot as follows: make a cross on a piece of paper and draw a circle about two inches to the right of it. Hold the paper in front of your eyes; close the left eye; with the right eye concentrated on the cross, move the paper away from your face. About ten inches away from the eye, the circle should disappear from your sight. It will reappear a little farther away.

The eye can detect only relative changes in the intensity of light. For example, stars cannot be seen in bright daylight; but from the bottom of a deep shaft, where the daylight does not enter to affect the vision, the stars can be seen at the upper opening of the shaft even though the sun is brightly shining elsewhere in the heavens. A cat's eyes seem to shine in the dark, although they are relatively less bright than in the light, because a cat's eyes reflect proportionately more light (what little light there may be) than other surrounding objects.

Very faint stimuli do not affect the center of vision, but may affect the fringes of the eye. Thus a very faint star may be seen out of the "tail" of the eye, and seem to disappear when one gazes directly at it. Faint impressions received by the fringes of the retina are sometimes not consciously noticed, but the eye acts upon them nevertheless, as when it blinks at a flying dust particle.

Light stimuli affect the retina for a short time after they have ceased; that is, the eye seems to see light for a brief moment after the light has vanished. Rockets and shooting stars thus appear to have luminous tails: the "memory" of the flash in the retina suggests a continuous streak. The stage magician's catchword that "the hand is quicker than the eye" is very true, for there is a limit to the quickness with which the eye can follow a movement.

Images on the retina are upside down, just as they are upside down on the plate of a camera. But we are not aware of this, and cannot possibly become aware of it, because from early childhood our other senses —touch, particularly—tell us how objects are arranged in the world. We quickly learn that an image in the lower retina is really, in the outside world, relatively *above* our eyes. The position of the image on the retina therefore helps us to locate its position in the picture before us at any given moment. The difference, slight though it is, in the images of our two eyes, enables us to judge the distance the object is away from us. However, optical judgments of distance are notoriously unreliable, and optical illusions of various kinds are extremely common. It is not always possible to believe what we see; the expression, "I could not believe my eyes," may sometimes be quite truthful.

Color vision is determined by special cells known as rods and cones, located in the retina. Normal eyes have a very good color sense. Some "color-blind" people do not distinguish between reds and greens. Difficulty with other colors is more rare. Distinguishing the finer tints and shades of color seems to depend somewhat on practice; women, being more familiar with colors, are usually more expert in picking them out than are men.

THE CIRCULATORY SYSTEM

THE BLOOD

The functions of the blood include not only carrying food and oxygen to the cells and carrying the waste products away, but also uniformly distributing heat over the body, properly dissipating excess heat, carrying the various hormones from organ to organ, and defending the body against dangerous organisms such as germs and bacteria, which, if unopposed, may cause death.

The blood—the familiar red fluid which oozes out when you cut yourself—reaches nearly all parts of the body, pumped through tubes (*veins* and *arteries,* with their tiny *capillaries*) by a pumping machine (the *heart*). The epidermis of the skin, the hard parts of the teeth, the hair, the nails, the cartilages, the lens and similar parts of the eye, do not have blood circulating through them. With these few exceptions, the blood travels swiftly to every part of the body, to feed and serve all the many thousands of cells.

Blood does not come directly into contact with the cells, except for the cells within itself and in the walls of the blood vessels. The veins, arteries, and tiny branchings of the hair-like tubes called capillaries form throughout a closed system of tubes. In the capillaries, where the blood is thinned out so that its cells can nearly all touch the intervening membrane, the lymph passes from the blood to bathe the tissue cells (the supply of lymph is replenished from the blood stream). The cells are constantly bathed in this watery fluid called lymph. Briefly, the process is this: if the capillaries containing blood are bathed by lymph, which is low in food content, the lymph takes food (energy or nourishment) from the blood, *through* the membranes (by diffusion); if the adjacent lymph is low in the waste products which the blood has picked up from lymph in other regions, it absorbs those from the blood; and so the process continues. The lymph near the muscles will need food and give off waste; the lymph of the kidneys (excretory organs), being kept free from waste by its adjacent cells, will be low in waste and take it from the blood as it flows through neighboring capillaries. The process of exchange, between blood and lymph, of food and waste, is aided by an additional system of lymphatic vessels.

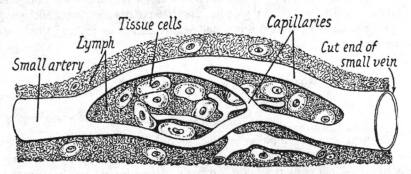

FIG. 13. Body cells surrounded by lymph.

The blood is made up of plasma or fluid (two-thirds) and corpuscles (one-third). The chief corpuscles are the red, which give the blood its characteristic color; when seen singly, or in diluted blood, these corpuscles are yellow. There are also present, in much smaller numbers, the white corpuscles, which are true cells; some of the white corpuscles, called *phagocytes,* literally eat dangerous microscopic organisms, broken-down tissue cells, etc., thereby removing them from the blood stream. The coloring matter of the red corpuscles is hemoglobin, a substance which readily and loosely unites with oxygen in the lung capillaries and carries it to the lymph, which bathes the tissue cells in other parts of the body, where it rapidly gives up the oxygen as needed. The average male has in his blood 75,000,000,000 red corpuscles to the cubic inch; the average female has somewhat fewer. All the hemoglobin in all the red corpuscles of a man weighing 140 pounds weighs only about 1½ pounds. Yet this hemoglobin, distributed in the circular red corpuscles as the blood stream passes through the lung capillaries, presents an effective area of more than 3,000 square yards (about ¾ of an acre of surface) exposed to the oxygen of breathed-in air every thirty seconds.

The red blood corpuscles are replaced from the red marrow of some of the bones of the body, where they are manufactured. Broken-down or worn-out corpuscles are picked out of the blood (so far as is known) by the spleen, one of the abdominal organs; the hemoglobin from these "old" corpuscles is passed on to the liver, where it is disintegrated.

When foreign organisms (microscopic in size, being bacteria or germs, also called microbes) enter the body, they do so through abrasions of the skin, cuts, wounds, etc., and through the mucous membranes or the walls of the alimentary tract. Some infections are poisonous because of the substances they give off; others act upon the tissues, tending to destroy them. Various protective mechanisms known as *antibodies* are set up by the body, usually in the blood—first, to prevent the entry of such organisms into the body, and, second, to resist infection once it has set in. Many sicknesses are manifestations of the body's fight to resist infection. The physician aids the resistance of the body with medicines which do one or more of several things—aid the body's natural strength, counteract fatigue, help to kill the invading organisms, or help to offset the poisons or toxins produced by them. On the tendency of the blood to immunize itself against infection by foreign organisms is based the use of vaccinations, antitoxins, and serums as preventives of disease.

Another protective mechanism of the blood—or chemical reaction, as it should be called—is coagulation, or clotting. Clotting is made possible by tiny bodies in the blood called *platelets,* which work with other materials in the blood plasma. You have noticed that when you bleed, the blood flows smoothly only at first. Almost at once—unless the cut is very large, or an artery has been severed (when a doctor should be summoned immediately)—the blood begins to harden and darken. A clot is formed which effectually stops the bleeding.

THE HEART

The heart is a kind of pump which keeps the blood in motion throughout the body during life. When the heart stops beating for any length of time, death occurs. Connected with the heart are the arteries and veins, which immediately branch into a complicated network of tubes, known collectively as the blood vessels. The arteries carry blood *from* the heart; in their narrowest branches the arteries become the tiny hair-like tubes called capillaries—it is these capillaries which are present in the dermis of the skin, and all the other parts of the body, tissues, muscles, membranes, walls, and so on. The capillaries branch finer and finer, until they connect with and expand into the smaller branches of the veins, which carry the blood—full of waste products, and having lost its oxygen—back *to* the heart. The heart pumps the blood into the arteries again, and they then carry it to the lungs, where it is refreshed with the oxygen of the air. This cycle of circulation is kept up endlessly while life lasts. The steady beat of the heart can be felt in arteries near the skin, particularly in the wrist, where the "pulse" may be counted to determine the rate of the heart beat. The normal beat of the heart is about 70 times each minute, though it varies with age, sex, and activity.

Although the heart is commonly thought of as being on the left side of the chest (because its beat can be more strongly felt to the left), it is actually situated almost in the center, just above the diaphragm. The "heart shape" used in Valentine symbols is a good approximation of the shape of the human heart, though the heart itself is less definitely outlined—it does not have the deep indention at the top nor the sharp point. The membrane surrounding the 'heart is called the *pericardium*. The internal membrane is the *endocardium*. The heart wall itself is mostly muscular tissue, mingled with blood vessels, nerve cells, etc.

The heart is divided into two chambers, and each chamber is divided into the *auricle,* into which the veins lead, and the *ventricle,* into which the arteries lead. Running into the heart at its "top" are a mass of arteries and veins, which lead, in various directions, to the greater branchings in the farther parts of the body, and to the lungs (pulmonary veins and arteries). The main artery is the *aorta,* at the back of the chest, which further branches to the head and brain, the arms, and other important parts. Various valves in the heart control the inflowing and outflowing blood.

A close study of the blood vessels shows us that a capillary blood vessel is about 1/1500 of an inch in diameter—so small that only two, or at most three, red blood corpuscles can race through it side by side. The work of the blood—its dispensation of nourishment and oxygen and its picking up of waste—is done in the capillaries.

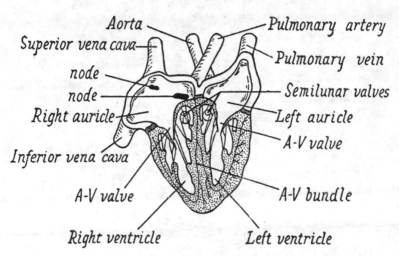

FIG. 14. The internal structure of the human heart. *A-V* stands for *auriculoventricular.*

As we have mentioned, the capillaries, at their "ends," branch into the veins, which lead back to the heart. Various valves throughout the system of blood vessels prevent the blood from flowing backward, as it might do between heart beats from the attraction of gravity or other causes if it were not prevented. The arteries are more deeply imbedded in the body and limbs than the veins, for they carry the fresh blood, full of oxygen from the lungs, and are more vital. The veins are frequently near the surface, and appear blue (or bluish red), because the blood they carry is loaded with carbon dioxide (formed when the tissue cells utilize oxygen); venous blood does not appear blue when a vein is cut, because the moment it touches the air it is immediately oxygenated.

The dark bluish-red blood which the arteries carry from the heart *to* the lungs has been brought back to the heart from other parts of the body. This impure blood is forced through the capillaries of the lungs, where it gives up its carbon dioxide (which is breathed out in exhalation) and takes up oxygen (by means of its hemoglobin), becoming bright scarlet in color. This oxygenated blood returns *from* the lungs to the heart by way of the pulmonary veins. Elsewhere in the body the veins always contain "stale" blood and the arteries always carry "fresh" blood.

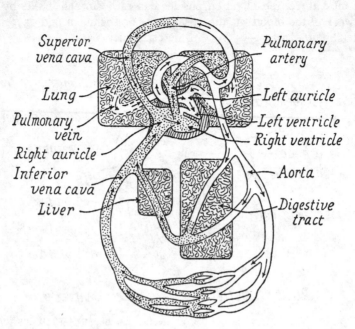

FIG. 15. The course of circulation of the blood in the human body. The stippled vessels contain blood that is poor in oxygen; the clear vessels contain blood that is rich in oxygen.

The beat of the heart is an alternate contraction and relaxation that pumps out one lot of blood and admits another. The contraction is called the *systole;* the relaxation is the *diastole.* As the heart beats, it makes a characteristic sound which a physician recognizes when he listens through the stethoscope, the instrument he places against the chest to check the heart and lungs. The beating of the heart produces small movements of the body which can be detected by sensitive scales. The heartbeat's rate is controlled by a nerve center called the *pacemaker.*

The blood pressure is the force exerted by the blood in the blood vessels, usually measured by physicians in the arteries; it depends on the condition of the body. The blood flows through the body with astonishing rapidity; it takes something like only 23 seconds for all the blood to make the complete round of the circulatory system. Arteriosclerosis, or hardening of the arteries, is a disease of the blood vessels often associated with the process of aging. However, some doctors believe there may be a relationship between arteriosclerosis and excessive fats in the diet. Atherosclerosis is a form of arteriosclerosis.

THE RESPIRATORY SYSTEM

The process of breathing goes on automatically throughout life, whether we will it or no. It is controlled by the autonomic nervous system; it is capable of modification, however, by the power of the will or voluntary nervous system, as when we take deep breaths deliberately, or when we hold our breath. We cannot hold our breath long enough to suffocate, for a nervous impulse set up by the increased carbon dioxide in the blood will shortly force us to breathe, unless we are prevented by some mechanical outside agency.

The action of respiration involves the movements of the diaphragm and chest which expand the chest cavity, causing an inflow of air through the nostrils or mouth, then through the pharynx into the windpipe (trachea), thence through the bronchi (branches of the windpipe) into the bronchial tubes, and finally into an expansive array of tiny air sacs called *alveoli*. These small air sacs provide a surface area of about 1,000 square feet for *each* adult human lung where gas exchange takes place. In the pulmonary (lung) capillaries of the circulatory system of the blood, oxygen is exchanged for carbon dioxide through membranes just as the reverse process (oxygen absorbed by the lymph and then by the tissue cells, and carbon dioxide given off to the lymph and then to the blood) takes place in the many tissues of the body and their adjacent capillaries. Oxidation takes place chemically in conjunction with the action of oxidases; oxygen aids in the burning of fats, carbohydrates, and some proteins. Heat is produced, as in all oxidation, which helps to maintain the heat of the body at its normal temperature of about 98.6 degrees Fahrenheit. In addition, the energy required to do the work of the body results from oxidation.

When we inhale, the rib muscles contract, causing the ribs to move up and outward, and the diaphragm contracts, moving from its normal arched position to a flatter one. These movements increase the size of the chest cavity, causing air to rush into the expanded lungs. When we exhale, the rib muscles and diaphragm relax and return to their normal positions, thus decreasing the size of the chest cavity, causing the lungs to contract and expel the air. If the lungs cannot get the amount of oxygen required by the blood, asphyxia (as in exposure to poisonous gases) or suffocation (as in drowning) will ensue.

Everyday actions of the respiratory apparatus include what we call sighing (a long, deep inspiration, or breathing in, followed by a short, large expiration, or breathing out); yawning (the mouth is opened, and the air enters thereby instead of through the nose); hiccoughing (caused by contractions of the diaphragm); coughing (full inspiration followed by rapid expiration, often violent—the purpose is to remove from the windpipe or larynx any irritating matter, such as mucus or food swallowed "the wrong way"); sneezing (similar to coughing, except that the expelled air is sent through the nose, tending to remove irritating matter in the nasal passages); laughing and crying, which are physiologically much alike, and often pass into one another under emotional stress. These acts are primarily reflex; most of them cannot be induced voluntarily, although they can be very cleverly imitated. The tendency to yawn, cough, or sneeze can usually be successfully resisted. Hiccoughing is more difficult to resist, and has to be stopped by occupying the nervous system with some interfering action, as by deep breathing or swallowing water.

THE DIGESTIVE SYSTEM

Foods supply the body with the energy it requires to do its work—in the muscles, tissues, etc.—and with the nourishment necessary to maintain its structure and to repair the breaking down or wearing out of body cells. In children, foods do more: they contribute the nourishment necessary for growth. Normally, a person eats more than energy foods; he also takes into his stomach various accessory foods—water, of which the body requires a fairly large amount; salts; condiments (pepper, mustard, etc.); and the like. Some of these accessories contribute to bodily needs; others merely improve the taste or appearance of food and make it more palatable.

The body requires *vitamins,* which are present in various fruits, fresh vegetables, milk, butter, and, for growing children, in cod-liver oil; and also certain mineral salts, for the most part present in normal foods. A varied diet almost always provides the necessary substances.

TABLE SHOWING VITAMIN REQUIREMENTS
OF THE HUMAN BODY

VITAMIN	CHIEF SOURCES	DEFICIENCY DISEASES RESULTING FROM LACK OF VITAMINS
A	butter, milk, yellow vegetables, cod-liver oil, escarole, spinach, beef liver	eye disease, lack of resistance to infection, colds

B com- plex	whole-grain cereals (B_1, B_2), yeast, liver (B_1), eggs, enriched bread, oysters, turnips, prunes, green beans	nervous diseases, loss of appetite, skin eruptions, impaired growth (beriberi and pellagra)
C	citrus fruits, tomatoes, cabbage, horseradish, peppers, spinach	scurvy, loose teeth and swollen gums, general weakness and restlessness
D	fish-liver oils, sunshine, enriched milk, butter, eggs, oysters, sardines	soft bones and teeth, rickets
E	green leafy vegetables, wheat germ, milk, eggs, muscles of meat, fish	sterility, muscular atrophy (significance of Vitamin E in human nutrition not fully established)
K	green leafy vegetables, liver, cabbage, tomatoes	hemorrhages, inability of blood to clot

The strictly nutrient foods can be divided into three main constituents: proteins, carbohydrates, and fats. Few, if any, foods are made up of one of these alone—most carbohydrates are found in cereals and vegetables (including starch, dextrins, and sugars); fats are found in both meats and vegetables (including stearin, palmatin, and olein); proteins occur principally in animal foods, most of all in lean meats, but are also abundant in milk, eggs, cheese, and gluten of wheat, and much of the substance of beans and peas. Tea, coffee, cocoa, and chocolate, used as beverages, are valuable chiefly for their water content, and enjoyable for their pleasant taste; they are also mild stimulants to the nervous system and should be taken in moderation.

Opening at its anterior end in the mouth, the alimentary canal or food tract passes, in the form of a tube open at both ends, through the ventral body cavity, into the stomach, thence into the small intestine, and finally into the large intestine, which ends in the posterior opening called the anus. The canal is lined with mucous membranes at the two openings, where the membranes are continuous with the outer skin of the body.

The Mouth

The mouth cavity, or *buccal* cavity, opens between the lips and passes into the throat cavity (pharynx). The cheeks enclose the sides of the mouth, which has in its bottom the muscular tongue. In the roof of the mouth is the hard palate, which recedes into a soft portion, called the soft palate (the softening can be felt by moving the tip of your tongue backward across the roof of your mouth); from the back of the soft palate hangs that process called the *uvula,* which you can see at the back of your mouth if you examine the buccal cavity in a mirror. Inside the mouth is the apparatus with which you bite off, chew (masticate), and swallow your food. The biting and chewing mechanism consists of the teeth, set into the gums; they are activated by movements of the jaws. The teeth are of various shapes, *incisors, upper canines* (eyeteeth), *lower canines, bicuspids,* and *molars.* The 32 permanent teeth which grow into the mouth after the "milk teeth" of childhood are lost consist of eight incisors, four canines, eight bicuspids, and twelve molars, symmetrically arranged. The farthest back of the molars are popularly referred to as the "wisdom teeth," because they are the last to grow.

The tongue, being exceptionally mobile, plays its part in mastication; in it are embedded the nerve cells of the sense of taste. The tongue, too, plays a vital part in human speech. If your tongue has a "coat," or if you have a "bad taste" in your mouth, there is probably some digestive disorder causing it.

The moisture in the mouth is a secretion (called *saliva*) of several glands (salivary glands). Inflammation of the parotid salivary glands in front of each ear is called mumps (parotitis). The opening in the back of the mouth is technically called the *fauces;* at the sides of this opening are the tonsils, formed of lymphoid tissue and concerned with the lymph of the body. The normal person can easily do without tonsils: they are so frequently infected that they are often surgically removed.

The cavity in the back of the mouth is called the *pharynx.* Seven openings lead into it or away from it: the two *nares,* or openings to the nostrils; the two *Eustachian* tubes leading to the tympanic cavities of the ears; the *fauces,* from the front of the mouth; the opening to the larynx, or voice box, and windpipe; and the opening to the gullet (esophagus). The *epiglottis* is a plate-like formation of cartilage which acts as a lid to close the tube to the lungs when one is swallowing, keeping food from going down the windpipe. If anything swallowed goes down the windpipe, as sometimes happens, we speak of swallowing something "the wrong way." The gullet, or esophagus, is the tube which forms the upper end of the alimentary canal; it passes from the pharynx down through the neck and chest, through the diaphragm, ending in the stomach.

THE STOMACH AND THE INTESTINES

The stomach is a kind of bag into which the food passes almost directly from the mouth after being swallowed; food is carried down the gullet promptly, and literally dumped into the stomach. The stomach is located just under the lower ribs; what is commonly called the stomach, when referring to the exterior of the body, is properly called the abdomen. The size of the stomach varies to accommodate the amount of food deposited in it.

Through the *pylorus* or pyloric orifice the stomach opens into the

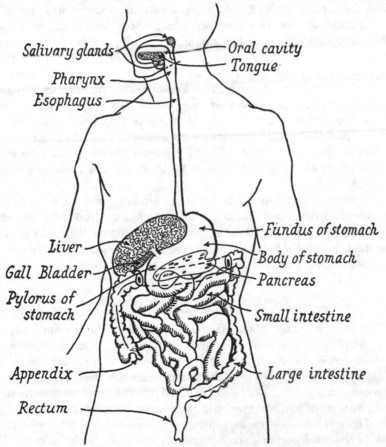

FIG. 16. The human digestive system.

small intestine. The pylorus is kept closed by a ring of muscle, called a sphincter, which opens only when food in a certain stage of digestion is ready to be passed along to the small intestine. The average length of the small intestine is about 20 feet; it is coiled upon itself in the abdominal cavity, forming, with the large intestine, what are vulgarly called the "guts." The small intestine is divided anatomically into the *duodenum* (the first foot of its length), the *jejunum* (the next seven and a half feet, or thereabouts), and the *ileum* (the remaining eleven feet or so).

The large intestine forms the posterior part of the alimentary canal. It is about five feet long, consisting of the following divisions: the *caecum*, the *vermiform appendix*, the *colon*, and the *rectum*. The small intestine passes into the large intestine a little distance from its anterior end; the closed portion above the small intestinal opening is called the caecum. From the caecum leads off the comparatively small vermiform appendix, a tube about the size of a lead pencil and about four inches in length. The vermiform appendix has no apparent purpose in modern man, though it may cause trouble by becoming inflamed (in appendicitis), requiring surgical removal. From the point at which the small intestine enters the large intestine, the latter is known as the colon, which is placed in the lower abdominal cavity in something of the shape of an inverted U. At the posterior end of the colon the rectum begins: this is the straight part of the large intestine which terminates the alimentary canal, ending in the anal opening (anus) between the buttocks (the great masses of muscle on which man rests his trunk when he assumes a sitting position).

Throughout their course, the intestines are lined with coats, including the smooth or unstriped muscular tissue which is controlled by the autonomic nervous system, and many glands which secrete the juices used in digestion. Into the duodenum of the small intestine open the ducts from the liver and the pancreas.

THE LIVER AND OTHER ORGANS

The liver is a huge gland—the largest gland in the human body: it may weigh as much as four pounds. Soft, reddish brown in color, it sprawls across the upper part of the abdominal cavity, just below the diaphragm, and is divided into lobes. In the liver is formed the gall (bile), important in digestion; this bile is secreted into the duodenum as needed; meantime, when not being secreted, its surplus is stored in the gall bladder. The condition known as gallstones arises when the bile crystallizes and (if the solid portions are not passed) the gall bladder is prevented from secreting its bile. The pancreas is soft, pinkish yellow, and long. It lies along the stomach. Its function is to secrete an important digestive juice, and also the hormone *insulin*, which vitally affects the metabolism of the body.

THE PROCESS OF DIGESTION

The process of digestion is the splitting up by chemical action (chiefly the chemical action known as hydrolysis) of the compound molecules of nutritive foods into simple molecules, which are soluble, and which can pass through the intestinal membranes to the blood in the intestinal capillaries and be carried to the parts of the body which need and can absorb them. Inorganic salts and some other substances are not digested because the body can make use of them in the state in which they are swallowed. Indigestible substances (such as cellulose) are passed through the intestines and excreted unchanged.

The saliva, secreted in the mouth by the salivary glands, is the first of the digestive juices. Besides keeping the mouth moist and dissolving salts and similar substances so that we can taste them, the saliva, due to the action of its enzyme *ptyalin,* has a primary chemical action on starch, converting it into maltose.

When it reaches the stomach, the swallowed food comes in contact with the gastric (stomach) juice, which includes two-tenths of one per cent of hydrochloric acid. Also present are enzymes, including pepsin and rennin, which change proteins to peptones. After undergoing the chemical changes brought about in the stomach, the food is passed into the small intestine, where it is further changed by the juice from the pancreas (which contains more enzymes), and by the bile (which aids in the digestion of fats). The intestinal juice secreted by the walls of the intestines contains the enzymes which bring about the last stages of digestion in foods which have not already been taken care of. The end products of digestion are amino acids from protein, glucose from carbohydrates, and fatty acids from fats.

In both the small and large intestines are colonies of bacteria which are not harmful to the body. These bacteria ferment certain carbohydrates in the small intestine; diarrhea sometimes results when this fermentation is excessive. In the large intestine the bacteria act on certain undigested proteins, causing putrefaction, bringing about the condition of the contents which appears when they are expelled through the anus as excrement (*feces*).

The digestive juices are powerful chemical agents, yet they do not digest the stomach or intestinal walls. Ordinarily, such strong chemicals would harm the cells of the structures which contain them; but it seems that, during life, other chemical factors are present which keep the digestive juices from destroying their glandular sources.

You take the food into your mouth and proceed to chew or masticate it by combined motions of the lower jaw against the upper jaw, causing a grinding and cutting action of the teeth. The food is kept under the teeth by motions of the muscular tongue. As a soft mass (*bolus*) thoroughly mixed with saliva, the food is swallowed. Swallowing, technically called *deglutition*, involves pushing the mouthful backward to the pharynx or throat cavity. The opening into the windpipe or trachea is closed (you can feel the cartilage called the "Adam's apple" rise in your throat as you swallow, helping to close the epiglottis tightly), and the muscles of the throat contract, forcing the food down the only opening left for it—that into the alimentary canal, of which the gullet (esophagus) is the first section.

The food is propelled along the gullet, downward toward the stomach, by a series of muscular contractions called *peristalsis*. These contractions are set up by reflex nervous action. Reaching the sphincter muscle which closes the opening into the stomach, the food is let into the stomach bag. This sphincter muscle guarding the stomach is usually closed, to prevent the acid contents of the stomach from "backing up" the gullet into the mouth. (However, this sometimes happens, as when you belch severely.) The food, together with other mouthfuls which distend the stomach, is now thoroughly churned and mixed with the gastric juice by a series of contractions. This food mass, called *chyme,* now is in a fairly liquid state.

By a finely adjusted chemical arrangement the food is let into the small intestine through the pyloric sphincter, a small amount at a time, when it is ready for the action of a new mixture of juices. It takes from four to six hours to empty the stomach of an average meal. The pancreas and liver empty their ducts into the small intestine. The food (chyme) is further churned and mixed, and is slowly passed along the intestine (almost five feet an hour) by peristaltic waves.

While passing through the small intestine, the nutrition available in the digested food is absorbed by the blood capillaries, sometimes through the agency of the bathing lymph. Most of the water is retained, however, so that when the remnants of the food mass are given into the large intestine (through the *ileocolic valve,* as it is called), the contents of the intestine are quite watery. Here, under a kind of reserve churning, the last nutritive elements and most of the water are absorbed for use in the body. The solid matter remaining is passed on into the further bends of the colon, and finally into the rectum, where it awaits excretion from the body. The packing of the colon is aided, and helps normal bowel movements, by the presence in food of "roughage," which consists of indigestible matter. The normal meal of mixed foods usually includes enough roughage for good health.

Excretion

Excretion of waste products goes on in various ways in the human body. Carbon dioxide is given off in the lungs and breathed out in exhalation. Some water vapor is also given off in the lungs, as can be seen when the warm breath is blown against a cool glass, or on a cold day when the water vapor immediately condenses into small visible globules like steam. More water and occasionally small amounts of other substances are given off by the sweat glands of the skin. The liver plays a part as an excretory organ, for the bile is primarily a waste product, although it has some influence on the digestion of fats in the small intestine.

The principal organs for the excretion of waste fluids, containing waste substances in solution, are the kidneys and their accompanying apparatus. Ducts called *ureters* lead from the kidneys to the bladder. In the bladder the waste fluid, called *urine,* accumulates until it is expelled through a tube called the *urethra,* which has its exit adjacent to, or in conjunction with, the reproductive organs. The average daily excretion of urine varies from 40 to 60 fluid ounces, is usually amber in color, and, normally, is 96% water.

Variation in the chemical contents of the urine indicates temporary or chronic bodily disorders. For this reason, the urine is an important aid in diagnosis, and the physician finds it desirable to have an analysis made of one or more specimens of urine from the patient.

The skin as an excretory organ is of great importance in standardizing the temperature of the body. Evaporation of water from the skin cools it, which explains why one perspires in warm weather.

The sweat glands are the excretory apparatus of the skin. There are some 2,500,000 sweat glands scattered over all the skin surface of the body. The sweat itself is watery, being transparent and colorless, and varying in odor (according to its composition) in different individuals. Dietary differences probably account for most variations in perspiration odor. Perspiration, in some degree, is constantly secreted; it becomes apparent only when it is sufficient to cause small globules of water on the skin. Because the various skin glands are always secreting substances, which dry on the skin, frequent bathing is necessary in personal hygiene.

Characteristically embedded in the skin, more abundantly in some regions than in others (as on top of the head), are numerous hair follicles, with hairs growing out of them. The color of hair is due to pigment contained in it. Accompanying the hair follicles are the sebaceous glands, which secrete a kind of oily fluid in small quantities.

The bodily temperature is maintained at a fairly constant warmth by specially devised nervous reflex mechanisms. The consumption of fuel (energy) in the muscles produces heat, which is dissipated by the blood throughout the body; similar heat produced by the internal organs is dissipated in the same way. The body cools itself by the evaporation of moisture from the surfaces of the skin. Clothing aids bodily warmth by retarding the surface evaporation. The normal temperature of the body varies somewhat in its different parts, between 96.8 and 98.6 degrees Fahrenheit, externally; a clinical thermometer placed under the tongue registers around 98.6 degrees Fahrenheit as the normal temperature of the mouth. Rectal temperature is normally about one degree higher. Above normal temperature occurs in fevers, which usually indicate a pathological condition.

THE VOICE

The human voice originates in the larynx, or voice box, which is enclosed in a kind of receptacle of cartilage in the front part of the neck, visible as a hump under the skin, popularly called the "Adam's apple." This projection is much more prominent in some people than in others. The larynx itself is situated just above the windpipe (trachea), so that currents of air from the lungs readily pass through it, setting in vibration the stretched vocal cords, giving rise to the sounds we know as speech.

The vocal cords themselves are bands of elastic tissue, so placed that they can be variously stretched and set in vibration by currents of air from the lungs. The pitch of the tones used in ordinary speech varies little, although the loudness, which depends merely on the strength of the blast of air used, may vary considerably. Proper pitch is important in singing, and often requires training and practice to maintain. The range of the human voice is normally about three octaves; famous singers have occasionally exceeded this range to a surprising degree. The limitations of individual range cause the division of singers into groups, as soprano, alto, tenor, and bass. The voices of children are pitched much higher than those of adults; in youth, the boy's voice becomes the deeper voice of manhood, and during the period of change his voice may often "break."

The vowel sounds are formed back in the larynx; they are fundamentally musical tones. Singing depends for its effect largely on the stress of vowels. The consonant sounds are made with the voice plus different positions of the mouth, tongue, lips, etc. A few sounds, called gutturals, are made in the back of the throat with the aid of the soft palate and the root of the tongue. Whispering does not involve the true voice; it is a noise made by irregular vibrations, and many of the sounds are necessarily imperfect.

THE REPRODUCTIVE SYSTEM

Reproduction is the general name given to the capacity of a living organism to reproduce itself—to give rise to another organism which will grow into a living thing exactly similar, in all important aspects, to its parent. Parenthood is an important factor in the civilized life of human beings; except for emotional, temperamental, and intellectual differences, all children are physiologically and anatomically very much like one or both of their parents, and, of course, like all other human beings.

THE MALE REPRODUCTIVE SYSTEM

The male reproductive organs are chiefly external. The *scrotum* is a kind of pouch of skin, in which are the *testicles* or *testes,* a pair of glands in which is formed the male sexual fluid, called the *semen.* Inside each testicle are coiled tubules, only 1/180 of an inch in diameter but

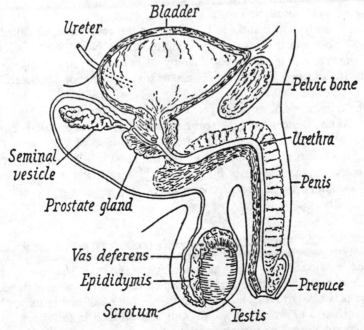

FIG. 17. The human male reproductive system.

about 27 inches long—about 800 in each testicle. These tubules connect with other coiled tubes, which finally empty into a common tube called the *vas deferens*. The vas deferens passes up the inner side of the skin of the groin, above the pelvis into the abdominal cavity, where it connects with the duct of the *seminal vesicle,* on the underside of the urinary bladder.

The seminal vesicles, two in number (one for each testicle), lie on each side of the bladder, and beneath it. Each is about two inches long and half an inch wide at its greatest dimensions. The duct from each seminal vesicle passes into the vas deferens, forming an ejaculatory duct, which one inch farther on joins the *urethra* (the tube leading from the bladder), through which urine passes when being excreted. The seminal vesicles serve as reservoirs in which the male semen is stored.

The point at which the ejaculatory duct enters the urethra is the region of the *prostate gland,* which sometimes gives considerable trouble in later life. It is about as large as a chestnut; through it pass both the urethra and the ducts from the seminal vesicles.

The urethra, which carries the male semen on occasion, leads from the bladder down through the *penis,* which is the male organ of copulation. The opening at the end of the penis is the *glans,* or tip, which is covered and protected by the *prepuce,* or foreskin, sometimes removed in the surgical operation known as circumcision.

The penis itself is composed principally of erectile tissue, so called because it possesses the faculty of gorging itself with blood, which is forced into tiny cavities in the penis, thereby distending it until the organ is rigid. The erection of the penis is a reflex nervous action, stimulated by sexual emotions.

The seminal fluid, or semen, is the secretion from the testicles, which is stored up at intervals in the seminal vesicles. The male sexual cells, or *spermatozoa,* form the main part of the composition of the semen. Each spermatozoon is about 1/500 of an inch in length; it is capable of great movement, which it achieves by "swimming" motions of its tail. In shape it is something like a tadpole, except that the head, slightly flattened, is more distinct.

THE FEMALE REPRODUCTIVE SYSTEM

The female reproductive organs are chiefly internal. The source of the female sexual cells is the *ovaries,* of which there are two, oval in shape, in the pelvic cavity. An ovary is about one and a half inches long, about three-quarters of an inch in width, and half an inch in thickness. In the ovaries are stored the ova or eggs; as they are ready for impregnation, the ova reach the surface of the ovaries, break through the enveloping fold of peritoneum in which the ovaries lie, and enter the *Fallopian tubes,* the ducts leading to the uterus or womb.

The *uterus* is hollow, formed of heavy walls of muscle. It is in the uterus that the impregnated female cell develops into the fetus and into the embryo, which, when fully developed, is born as an infant in the process of childbirth (parturition). Inside the pelvic cavity, the uterus lies between the urinary bladder and the rectum. At its anterior end the uterus has two "corners," so to speak, into each of which one Fallopian tube enters.

The lower or posterior end of the uterus is attached to and enters the anterior end of the vagina. During pregnancy, when the fetus is developing in the uterus, the walls of the womb (uterus) expand and bulge into the abdomen, forcing the abdominal organs more or less out of the usual positions.

The *vagina* is a passage entirely closed except for the almost microscopic opening in the posterior end of the uterus and the external open-

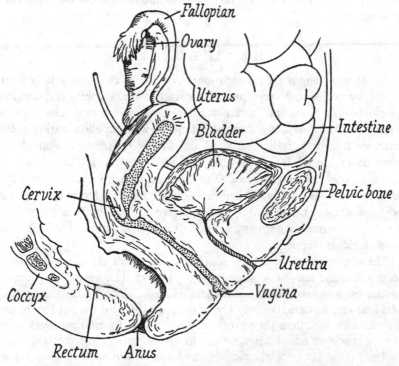

FIG. 18. The human female reproductive system.

ing between the anus and the small opening of the female *urethra*. It lies between the rectum and the bladder with its urethra. The lining of the vagina is a mucous membrane, continuous with the outer skin; the points at which the opening of the vagina reaches the outer skin are developed into folds, called the *labia majora* and *labia minora* (the large and small "lips"). The vagina receives the male organ during copulation. The semen is ejaculated into the vagina; the spermatozoa swim upward toward the uterus, and, if one of the spermatozoa finds an ovum or egg, the ovum may be penetrated by the spermatozoon, whereby conception takes place and pregnancy ensues.

The external female genital organs are collectively called the *vulva*. In front is an elevation of adipose tissue called the *mons Veneris*. Posterior to this is a small semi-erectile organ under the skin, called the *clitoris*. Between the labia are the inner lips, or labia minora, and between these is a kind of cavity, into which opens the female urethra, through which urine is excreted, and, somewhat more posterior in position, the vagina. In the virgin the external opening of the vagina is commonly partly closed by a portion of the mucous membrane called the *hymen*.

THE LIFE CYCLE

All human beings go through the same life cycle, unless it is interrupted by accident. Every one of us started when a sperm impregnated an ovum, and the impregnated ovum became an embryo and grew in the uterus until, as a full-formed infant, it was expelled during childbirth by the mother. In childhood the bodily functions are much the same as in the adult, except that the child has an additional activity which is very marked—growth. The child increases in stature and size until he becomes an adult, when such growth ceases. There are slow deposits of adipose tissue in most adults, increasing gradually in a man, and usually, in normal conditions, very gradually in a woman until after the climacteric or menopause.

The average span of a human life is a little over the proverbial three score years and ten—or between 70 and 80 years. The average expectancy of life, by which is meant a statistical average which takes into account accident and disease, is today about 69 years. People do not live to any grander old ages than they ever did, except that in modern times more people reach an advanced age than formerly. In old age the body is in decline; parts tend to become stiff, and senses diminish in their power —old people often see poorly, may be "hard of hearing," and are sometimes a little bent and walk slowly because of their stiffening joints. So old age gives way before the advancing younger generation, which is always more spry and more alert.

Death is the end of life. Unless it has been brought on prematurely by accident or fatal disease, death comes naturally when the decline of the body has reached a point where its co-ordinating parts can no longer sustain the complex activities of life. Sir Francis Bacon summed it up: "It is as natural to die as to be born." Certainly it is an inevitable physiological result of the living organism. Whether science can ever prolong the period of fully active life remains for the future to reveal.

HEALTH AND HYGIENE

As we have seen, the body is a highly complicated and intricately organized mechanism. Diseases and accidents are often unavoidable, and when they occur it is wise not to delay in consulting a doctor. Regular check-ups at the doctor's and dentist's offices, once every six months to a year, are recommended. There is much, however, which one can do in taking care of oneself and in preventing illness.

Every person should take daily exercise—walking, dancing, or a few minutes of calisthenics. This is necessary to keep all the organs and the muscles in proper function and to stimulate good circulation. It is necessary also to develop and maintain a good posture. Keeping oneself to the weight that is normal for one's height is most important. It is now believed that excessive overweight is unhealthy and may shorten one's life. If obesity is not glandular, it is usually caused by overeating and lack of exercise.

Proper nutrition is most important to health and the prevention of disease. We have already discussed the requirements of a well-balanced diet; a chart of the average vitamin requirements, their food sources, and the results of deficiency is on pages 1272–73. It is well known today that persons of normal weight may yet be undernourished; one must be careful to eat a variety of foods and to supplement with vitamins if necessary.

A number of minor accidents that occur around the home can be treated by oneself or may require attention before a doctor is available. One should know how to use a thermometer to determine whether fever is present, how to wash out cuts with antiseptic and bandage them, how to arrest serious bleeding, how to treat burns, etc. Often quick, simple, appropriate care of even a major accident will reduce the danger during the period before the doctor is able to come.

EXAMINATION QUESTIONS

1. How does physiology differ from anatomy?
2. What terms are used to distinguish the two ends of the body?
3. What are the names of the two layers of skin?
4. What is the center of intelligence?
5. What elements enter into the composition of the human body?
6. What proportion of the human body is composed of water?
7. What is the function of the blood?
8. Why do adults have fewer bones than growing children?
9. What is the sternum?
10. What are the seven neck bones called?
11. What is the inferior maxilla?
12. Why are the eleventh and twelfth pairs of ribs called floating ribs?
13. What is the upper bone of the arm called?
14. What are articulations?
15. How do the skeletal muscles differ from the visceral muscles?
16. What organ is the cardiac muscle?
17. What part of the body may be likened to a carefully co-ordinated telegraph organization?
18. What is the shape and size of the average spinal cord?
19. What is the normal weight of the human brain?
20. What sense do the olfactory nerves control?
21. What are ganglia?
22. How fast do impulses travel along human nerves?
23. Where are the cells which take care of complex activities such as "thinking," "memory," "will power," etc.?
24. What is a hormone?
25. What gland controls metabolism?
26. What physiological senses are there besides the commonly known five senses?
27. What is the usual range of vibrations to which the eardrum will respond?
28. What equalizes the air pressure on both sides of the eardrum?
29. To what is the apparent difference in the size of people's eyes due?
30. What is the lachrymal apparatus?
31. What are the chief colors which color-blind people have difficulty in distinguishing?
32. How many red corpuscles to the cubic inch has the average male in his blood?
33. What is the normal rate at which the heart beats?
34. What parts of the heart control the inflowing and outflowing blood?
35. In the beating of the heart, what are the terms used to designate the contraction and the relaxation?
36. What is the source of energy required to do the body's work?
37. What are the three main constituents of the strictly nutrient foods?
38. How many of each type of tooth are included in the thirty-two permanent teeth?
39. What is the duodenum?
40. What is the function of the vermiform appendix?
41. What is the largest gland in the human body?

42. What percentage of hydrochloric acid does the stomach juice contain?
43. What is the technical name of the act of swallowing?
44. What gas is breathed out in exhalation?
45. How many sweat glands are scattered over the skin surface of the body?
46. What is the normal temperature of the mouth?
47. What are the spermatozoa?
48. In what organ does the impregnated female cell develop into the fetus?
49. What is the process of childbirth called?

FOR FURTHER STUDY

FUNDAMENTALS OF PHYSIOLOGY, by Elbert Tokay. (Barnes & Noble, New York.)

THE HUMAN BODY, by Logan Clendening. (Alfred A. Knopf, New York.)

MAN: HIS STRUCTURE AND FUNCTION, by Fritz Kahn. (Alfred A. Knopf, New York.)

TEXTBOOK OF ANATOMY AND PHYSIOLOGY, by Kimber, Gray, and Stackpole. (The Macmillan Co., New York.)

XXVIII

Psychology for Beginners

WHAT IS PSYCHOLOGY?

THE SCIENCE of psychology endeavors to discover the roots of our behavior. It deals with aspects of behavior, as the basis of mental activity, habits and learning, intelligence and personality.

The word psychology comes from the Greek word *psyche,* meaning *soul,* and in ancient times psychology was the study of the soul. The soul included the whole personality. Later, "soul" was identified primarily with "mind," in the sense of mental processes; and this was the emphasis in nineteenth-century psychology. Today, psychology is concerned with human behavior as a whole, of which thinking, personality, and such physical factors as the brain and the nervous system are all aspects.

Psychology is thus seen to be closely linked with biology and physiology on the one hand and with philosophy (thought and its associations) on the other. Biology is the study of life and life processes, and physiology is the study of the structure and activity of the organism as a living thing. Life necessarily includes the brain and related parts, and their structure is necessarily a part of physiology. Psychology concentrates on behavior, and on human behavior in particular. Behavior, since we are more or less aware of it, and to some extent can control it (or so we think), is a manifestation of mental activity.

THE BASIS OF MENTAL ACTIVITY

The mind is dependent upon the body and its activities. Since the brain cells are of the same fundamental structure as other cells of the body, mental activity is basically as *physiological* as digestion.

In general, the *mind* is that which does our thinking, perceives our sensations, wills our actions, remembers our experiences. The mind is customarily associated with consciousness, with being aware of what is happening around us, and, to some extent, of what is going on inside us.

The highest manifestation of mind, and its associated attribute called *intelligence,* occurs in human beings. Intelligence as found in animals is less and less evident as we descend the scale of life. Yet, even in the simplest forms of life, something exists which is *akin* to intelligence. Under the microscope, unicellular (one-celled) organisms can be seen to live by meeting and ingesting (surrounding) food particles, and by eliminating or casting out waste particles; they maintain life by avoiding dangerous substances or dangerous spots. Since there is no "mind" as we know it, this activity is called irritability. As animals become more complex and composed of many cells, certain cells take on specialized irritabilities which serve the whole organism. In general, animals have developed their specialized irritabilities to a higher degree, for their food requirements have made it necessary for them to move around and to know what is going on about them in their environment. Plants have neither mind nor nervous system; plant cells, however, do have irritability, even in the lowest forms. The simplest plants are so nearly like the simplest animals that it is impossible to classify some microscopic organisms as strictly either plants or animals.

The degrees of specialization in irritability throughout the many forms of life are gradual. They grow slowly more complex in fishes, even more complex as one follows their variation among the animals immediately below man in the scale of life, and highly complex in man himself. Thus, in the human body, which is composed of millions of cells of many kinds, the nerve cells of the eye are irritated or stimulated by light rays, and those of the inner ear by sound waves.

As the organism grows more complex in the scale of animal life, it also develops a system of nerve fibers, ganglia, and centers of control and co-ordination. The greatest development of a center of control is the brain, which appears only in the higher animals, gradually becoming more complex, developing the cortex or complicated cellular structure forming the outer layer of the lobes, commonly called the "gray matter." What we know as intelligence is apparently an activity of the cortical cells.

METHODS OF PSYCHOLOGY

Psychology, following the procedure of all sciences, has developed by knowledge accumulated through observation and experiment. If you watch an animal or a person, you are using objective observation. You may notice that when a man touches a hot poker he jerks his hand away.

But suppose you observe yourself: when your own hand is touched by anything hot you have a sensation you call being burned—it is painful, you jerk your hand away, and perhaps suck the injured spot. Your examination of your own reactions, as nearly as you can make such an examination, is subjective observation. The self-examination of any conscious action, including how you think, how you notice things, and how you feel under the stress of emotion, is called *introspection* (looking within oneself). While analyzing thought, your mind is thinking—it can never dissociate itself from thinking long enough to perceive the thinking process as something apart. Here in this nebulous region true observation ceases and speculation begins.

By experiments on animals, children, and adults, psychology has discovered how they react to certain stimuli under certain conditions. In contrast with introspection, this is known as *objective observation of behavior*. After the rules for normal reaction have been laid down, various tests can be applied to individuals to determine how they may correspond with or be different from what is considered to be normal. Psychology may attempt to answer such questions as the following: Why does a baby look toward or reach for a bright object? What was the secret of Napoleon's power over his fellow men? Why does a person jump when he hears a sudden loud noise? What accounts for the mad actions of mobs?

Primitive man knew little of his actions and reactions—he could not guess, with any accuracy, why he did thus and so. There grew up, in his inherited traditions, notions of the supernatural—of something beyond the natural, beyond his understanding. Hand in hand with these notions went superstitions—things believed but not proved. Psychology is eliminating these blind gropings; from psychologists we hope to learn how to control ourselves, how to guide children in their best interests, how to find out what vocation we are best fitted for, and how to control or eradicate crime.

To illustrate the experimental method in psychology, the effect of verbal incentive on learning may be investigated. First, a large group of children may be given an associative learning test. Next, the group is divided into two equivalent groups of children matched for initial learning scores and in the same grades. After several weeks one group is praised for its initial performance and urged to do better and given the test again. The other (control) group is also given the test a second time, but without comment. Any increases in the scores of the experimental group as compared with the control are now taken as evidence of the effect of praise, since the other variable factors have been equalized.

In the case history or clinical method, the aim ordinarily is diagnosis and treatment of behavior problems. Here the procedure usually begins with an interview in which relevant biographical data is obtained, followed by aptitude, intelligence, and personality tests; reasons for past behavior are sought, and advice or treatment is offered.

RESPONSES TO STIMULI

The simplest response to a stimulus, a muscular action or "motor response," is called a *reflex*. The blinking of the eye as a particle of dust flies into it, or as an object swiftly approaches it, is a familiar reflex. Another example is the production of saliva upon the sight or smell of food. Such a stimulus-response action takes a fraction of a second. A reflex is an automatic, inborn response to a stimulus.

The speed of a reflex is accomplished by means of the arrangement of the nerve cells and nerve fibers which produce it. The sense stimulus is received by a sensory cell and conveyed almost instantaneously to an area in the spinal cord (or in the lower brain stem, depending on the part of the body involved); here the sense stimulus acts upon a motor nerve or nerves, sending impulses to the proper muscles, which move the part of the body concerned in the reflex. Such reflexes are elementary and do not have to be learned. Jerking the hand away from a hot object is another such reflex. (See Fig. 8, page 1255).

Next in complexity is the simple reaction. If you hear an automobile horn near you as you cross a street, you jump for the sidewalk; this is a simple reaction (response) to the motor horn. Your brain registers, through auditory nerves, the sound of the horn; your experience (memory) tells you that the horn means danger; your co-ordinating motor area (in your brain) sends down the spinal cord the required impulses, which act upon the proper motor nerves to produce the action which takes you out of danger. Such reactions are learned, though they may become almost automatic and approach the nature of reflexes.

Reflexes take place without the participation of the cells of the cortex of the brain. Simple reactions, as well as the more complex reactions, necessarily involve the brain cortex. Certain portions of that cortex comprise the motor area, for in that area occur the nervous activities which send out impulses causing muscular actions in the body. The cortex is further divided into centers: auditory, visual, motor, etc. In the motor area occurs the elaborate co-ordination necessary to bring about suitable actions of the body. The motor area can also control the body and prevent it from acting. It can even control reflex action, as when you persistently hang on to a hot dish that you do not wish to drop, even though the heat is painful.

Reactions that are not reflex derive from knowledge. The interpretation and use of knowledge takes place in the cortex. If you see a dog coming toward you, snapping and barking, you may run, lest you be bitten. Your brain cortex is utilizing the knowledge that you have acquired: that such an animal may bite if you let him get near you. But if, unnoticed by you, a dog nips your leg, you jump away and perhaps utter an exclamation of surprise or pain; the jumping is a reflex action, brought about by the pain of the dog's bite, no knowledge being required!

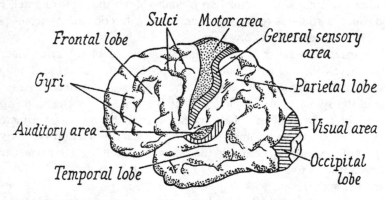

The localization of functions in the human brain.

Adjacent parts of the cortex, in conjunction with the motor area, determine the more skilled and complex muscular actions. Such actions, once learned, become less conscious or more automatic, as writing, throwing a ball, skating, or playing the piano. Simple movements do not require the attention of the cortex (apart from the motor area). Highly complex, indeed, is the center controlling speech, which is slowly trained in childhood; closely associated with it is the auditory center, for speech depends largely upon hearing, as is clearly evidenced by the imitative efforts of the child learning to talk. Visual centers control sight, and there is a small olfactory center which receives sensations of smell; the taste center has not been isolated.

Impairment of the motor area or of any of the cortical centers causes corresponding paralysis, either muscular or sensory. Impairment or lack of development of the higher co-ordinating cortex, adjacent to the various centers, deprives the individual of the more skilled reactions to stimuli. Variations in the cortex of the brain account for the differing abilities of various people in performing muscular acts, or in speaking or singing. An acrobat is necessarily equipped to perform highly skilled and closely co-ordinated muscular activity; his skill, of course, is due to practice, but the ability to profit by that practice must first be present. To this extent, an acrobat or a singer is born and not made.

Reflex action has no purpose or motive behind it. The reflex occurs in response to the stimulus, always the same, unless the higher brain centers inhibit it; in which case they may be said to exert a stronger stimulus than the stimulus which excites the reflex.

A stimulus acts either immediately, as in a reflex, or after a lapse of time when the person is prepared. A child may wait ten minutes after a signal before he starts to run, or may wait until he has counted to a certain number. The response can also be delayed by force, as when a child, anxious to follow some playmate, is delayed by his mother, but keeps in mind where his playmate went, so that he can follow in that direction the moment he is released.

The bloodhound following a scent follows that scent and that only, no matter how many other scents, perhaps stronger, may pass under his nose, and no matter what other stimuli may occur. A stimulus may therefore be continuous in its action: even if the bloodhound loses the scent, he runs around in circles in a strong effort to pick it up again. Though the stimulus is not present every moment, the response is continuous. It may almost be said that the bloodhound's behavior is motivated by that stimulus. There is something of a parallel between the bloodhound and the human being who is pursuing some particular object with absorbed attention. Anticipation of the goal is frequently the whole stimulus, or part of it, directing human reactions.

When a reaction to a stimulus is delayed, the person or animal is restless and dissatisfied, particularly if the stimulus is strong. Hunger or thirst is a strong stimulus, arousing the response to search for food or drink. If a person is hungry, he waits impatiently for lunch time, or for supper to be ready. The infant who is hungry is stimulated to cry in a complaining manner, and is prepared to begin sucking motions with his mouth as soon as he feels the nipple. Animals and savages seize food on sight if they are very hungry; but civilized people recognize, because of training, certain times for eating, and observe certain rules of etiquette in taking food and preparing it for the mouth with knife, fork, or spoon.

The sight of food not only stimulates the motor responses of the eating motions, but also stimulates the flow of saliva in the mouth—a glandular response. As the food is chewed, it further stimulates the secretion of saliva; when it reaches the stomach, it stimulates the flow of the gastric juices, which begin the work of digestion; in the intestines, it stimulates not only the needed secretions, but the rhythmical movements which pass it along from one part to another. Thus the body takes up energy and eliminates waste by an elaborate and co-ordinated system of stimuli followed by responses.

NATIVE AND ACQUIRED TRAITS

Traits of character and physical features are either native (inherited) or acquired. It is now generally believed that acquired characteristics cannot be inherited. Such things as stature, color of eyes and hair, the peculiar arrangement and size of features of the face, or the shape of the hands and fingers are native; they are determined to a large extent by inheritance. Scars, muscular development, and the like are acquired from the environment, by accident or by experience and training.

So it is with traits, many of which are so fundamentally native that we seldom think of them as such. The newborn baby breathes, cries, and makes muscular movements without being taught—such traits are native; they are common to all animals. The baby (according to the behaviorists, a particular school of psychologists) has three fundamental and native emotional reactions: fear, rage, and love. Fear is caused by two native or inborn tendencies to reaction, brought about by two stimuli: a loud noise or the sensation of loss of support (falling). Though we customarily speak of a child's learning to walk, a child would walk anyway when he reached the necessary degree of muscular and nervous development. Walking, like the flying of birds, is a native trait, and need not be learned. It may be retarded by barriers, or it may be encouraged by giving the child opportunity to try his legs.

The making of sounds is a native ability, but co-ordinated speech, in a particular language, is acquired by training. Children of all races and nationalities instinctively make the same sounds in infancy, but they learn whatever language they hear spoken around them. Vocal sounds are native, but speech is acquired. Native characters, such as the color of eyes, are not universal; but native traits, such as breathing, eating, making sounds, walking, and the like, are universal throughout the human race. Acquired traits are obviously developed in co-ordination with, and on the basis of, native traits.

Seeing, hearing, smelling, tasting, and the like, are native; but the interpretation of what we see or hear is an acquired trait. The baby naturally reaches for a bright object, but he gradually learns to tell one bright object from another, and that a burning flame or a red-hot ember should not be reached for. More succinctly, sensations are native, but the meaning of sensations is acquired.

MOTIVATION

In the early teaching of psychology strong *drives* with an inherited basis were described as instinct. This term is no longer generally used to describe human behavior. First, we find in man no such stereotyped pattern of behavior as is found in bees and ants. An insect can invariably be depended upon to do exactly thus and so when confronted with a particular set of conditions. In the higher animals instincts are more loosely followed. Human behavior varies greatly from person to person. The term instinct has been confused with learned behavior. For example, it has been said that some men play football instinctively.

A drive with some inherited basis, but whose expression is determined by environmental factors, is termed a *psychological motive*. Basic emotional drives and responses include anger→struggle; fear→escape; grief →weeping; love→affection.

Some psychologists assert that all drives are directly or indirectly concerned with either self-preservation or conservation and propagation of the species. Although some drives (psychological motives) can be readily so classified, others appear less associated with these fundamental impulses, and some appear to be altogether independent of them.

It must also be stressed that man is a social animal; he is gregarious, seeking the companionship of his kind. Some individuals enjoy a hermit's lonely existence, but man in general avoids solitude. For this reason many of man's activities have become social, as eating, drinking, and making a home. Most human recreations are social; to the majority of people a game of bridge is more enjoyable than a game of solitaire.

BASIC DRIVES

The sex drive is so basic that some psychologists (notably certain members of the Freudian school) explain mental illnesses as the result of inability to adjust the sex drive to other factors such as morality or unfortunate circumstances. A deep understanding of the various ramifications of sex attraction in all its stages is the basis of some psychoanalysis. *Psychoanalysis* is a branch of psychology which applies basic rules to a methodic analysis of a person's psychological make-up, called the *psyche,* in order to discover and prescribe cures for physical, nervous, or emotional disturbances whose causes are psychological. The Freudian school has been foremost in developing practical methodology, such as dream analysis.

Although many specific Freudian tenets have been disputed, there is no question about the soundness in pointing out the importance of sex in motivating human life: out of the gratification or repression of sex impulses, from childhood through youth to manhood and womanhood, come a great many of the acts, thoughts, and characteristics of human beings.

Some of man's love-making is native and some of it is learned or acquired. The ideals of romantic love are obviously acquired culturally. Assiduous attention to the loved one (courtship), strutting and display of physical charms and prowess, the whole game of pursuit-and-capture, are native in origin. Forceful capture, spurred on by the emotion of lust and followed by the unwilling submission of the pursued person, is primitive. Willing submission to an acceptable mate and consequent union by mutual consent (called marriage when the union is legalized) are more highly refined procedures; here the emotion is generally called love, or, when concentrated toward achieving sexual intercourse, passion.

The natural consequence of the mating drive and of sexual union is the conception and birth of offspring. The mother drive, so called, makes the mother care for her baby, feed it, cherish it, and protect it. The father drive is not often so strong. The force of the parental instinct varies in individuals, and in some seems to be almost totally absent. Frequently it takes some other form, as a fondness for pet animals, the care of plants, or social welfare and charity work. When a drive is satisfied in some learned or acquired way, it is said to be *sublimated*. Many desires which are not native, but are acquired from environment and training, can be sublimated.

In spite of the time-honored injunction that children should honor and obey their parents, there is no native tendency for children to do so. Their drive, on the contrary, is to take from their parents, as it is the parental drive to give to the children. A child may, however, acquire a respect for his parents and gratitude (usually) for what they have done for him, and may take a "mothering" attitude toward them as he grows older.

Many human drives tend toward play and recreation. The infant's purposeless movements and meaningless sounds are natural, arising from the sense of well-being, of just "feeling good," technically called *euphoria*. An active and noisy child is probably in the best of health. As the child develops he makes more purposeful movements, handling objects (toys), reaching for things, creeping and later walking toward things, exploring curiously here and there. Creeping, walking, and running are native; more skilled locomotion, as skating, skipping, and the like, is learned or acquired. The exploring drive often survives in adults, as witness the courageous explorers of the world's unknown regions, and the fun of touring in strange lands. The exploring tendency is counteracted or held in check by an almost native caution, which becomes more pronounced as the child grows older, and by an increasing satisfaction with things as they are. Children are naturally conservative, acquiring strong habits.

The impulse to laugh is fundamental, so much so that it is difficult to imitate genuine laughter. Yet what is the stimulus which produces laughter? An organic state, or emotion, called amusement or mirth, perhaps; yet this is not all. People laugh when they are tickled; children laugh for no reason at all, unless euphoria is a reason. Laughter is often a manifestation of cruelty, or at least an expression of superiority. The psychology of laughter and humor is not as yet fully understood.

Common social motives include: (1) *Self-assertion* and *the urge for mastery*. Pugnacity develops out of the attempt to defeat those people, institutions, etc., that may be restricting one's activity. In the case of the overanxious boy who reacts with hostility toward a stern father, severe punishment is likely to provoke even more anxiety and hostility based on fear. It is best to try to determine the cause of the boy's original anxiety and help to rid him of it. Self-assertion in childhood and adolescence often takes the form of rejecting adult aid and protesting against authority of parents and others whose domination is feared and resented. (2) *Achievement of prestige,* the desire to be praised and rewarded and given social approval, is a powerful social motive. The child seeks approval by performing and exhibiting, climbing, jumping, reciting, etc. If he does not receive attention he may try to obtain it through various anti-social or even criminal acts. (3) *Gregariousness* is the desire to be with one's kind, based on the need for security, sympathy, and understanding. (4) *Parental and filial drives* are strong urges to protect others in need, to take care of the helpless, or to be taken care of. (5) *Self-preservation* is a complex drive involving several emotions. For example, in face of danger, the need to escape is based on fear.

Man is a self-asserting, egotistic animal. He is the lord of the earth because of his native tendency to overcome all obstacles. This self-assertive drive reveals itself in games, whether physical or mental—the determination to win is just as strong in a tennis match as in a foot race or even in a game of chess. The determination to surpass one's fellows or to overcome a thing is the psychological explanation of the popularity of crossword and jigsaw puzzles, anagrams, quizzes, and similar tests of knowledge or mental ingenuity.

Ambition, zeal, determination, the will-to-power, enthusiasm, the desire to make money, all these are phases of native self-assertion. They are exhibited, in various forms, in most children and in all adults. Seldom is a state of discouragement and despair reached so hopeless that the individual cannot or will not assert his ego in some way. The disobedient child is asserting himself. To be sure, his self-assertion ought to be directed into useful channels, and child psychologists are seeking methods for accomplishing this. Hunting, driving a car, and using a camera are phases of self-assertion, for they give one a sense of power or achievement.

Next to striving to surpass is the striving to equal what someone else does, called emulation. If a boy performs a stunt, his playmates try to perform it also. The popular and neighborly pastime of "keeping up with the Joneses" is a pernicious form of this kind of self-assertion.

What happens when the self-assertive drive is thwarted? No doubt some persons are more easily discouraged than others, for individuals are variously endowed with nervous and physical energy, not to mention the capacity to become skillful in certain fields. When we do not succeed, in one way or another, we become sulky, resentful, ashamed, timid, bashful, stubborn, recalcitrant, gloomy, depressed. The "poor loser" exhibits such reactions when he is beaten, whether in a game or in the more earnest contest of business or politics. The child whose self-assertion is thwarted early in life may become shy, self-conscious, and in later years be completely baffled by life. On the other hand, he who has no real success to satisfy him may satisfy his ego by bragging and by bullying his inferiors.

EMOTIONS

Common emotions are hate, fear, anger, and love. The word *emotion* means a "stirred-up" state of being. It was once thought that each emotion had its particular organ or seat in the body; this idea explains the heart as a symbol of love. It is now known that the emotions are conditions of the individual as a whole, and not of any one organ or part.

Certain organic states are more or less localized: fatigue is localized in the muscles or nerves; hunger, in the alimentary tract; thirst, in the throat; drowsiness, in the eyes and muscles. These organic states modify responses to stimuli, but they do not come from the body as a whole, nor are they brought on by external stimuli. They are not, therefore, true emotions.

True emotions are brought about by something outside the body. The external stimulus may be a loud noise, someone's insulting voice, an overt act, or merely something which suggests cause for a particular emotion. Of course we do not perceive the cause for emotion and then proceed to "emote"! On the contrary, unless our feelings are very well controlled, the external stimulus sets up an emotional state in spite of us—and we are suddenly angry, afraid, or excited.

If you are very angry, you cannot benefit much from self-analysis by introspection. After the fit of anger has passed, you may perhaps think back to it and notice some aspects of it. But an observer can tell you things about yourself, when you were angry, that you were probably not aware of. You know that you have been angry, but do you know whether you clenched your fists, or breathed deeply, whether you spoke loudly, or whether your eyes bulged? These are common physical manifestations of anger. Also, the digestive processes may be arrested, and glandular responses take place of which one is not aware. It is unhealthful to become angry just after eating a hearty meal!

What distinguishes a "cool" person in the face of danger? If anything, probably the fact that he is not afraid in the emotional sense; that is, he perceives danger intellectually, not emotionally, and meets it with rational effectiveness. A person who experiences the emotion of fear is likely to react in a more primitive and possibly less effective manner. The emotion of fear is frequently followed by panic, for there are many causes of fear which cannot be effectively met by spontaneous reactions. For instance, flight is not an effective reaction to a fire in a theater.

The response to the stimuli of danger may be very swift—so swift, in fact, that the body has no time to reach the emotional state of fear. Immediately afterward, however, when the danger has passed, the person may tremble and exhibit all the signs of fear, and probably will feel afraid. "I wasn't afraid until it was all over," says the victim of an automobile accident, which may happen so suddenly that a passenger may not be aware of danger until he finds himself in the ditch. Here, also, the emotion is a result of the stirred-up state of the body, caused by awareness of danger even though it has passed.

Emotions can be rationally controlled to some extent. A person may feel an emotion without acting, for he can be angry and remain quite still. But an emotion usually is accompanied by an impulse to act, whether or not that impulse results in action. Such an impulse—for instance, to escape from danger when afraid, to injure an opponent when angry, or to caress and fondle the loved one when in love—is similar to an instinct. It is native and not acquired; the resistance to the impulse is acquired. But this emotional impulse differs from an instinct chiefly in that it is derived from a stirred-up condition of the body, and does not immediately follow an external stimulus, as does an uninterrupted instinctive reaction. Some drives are accompanied by emotion (as the mating instinct, accompanied by love).

CONFLICT

Except for an infant, life does not proceed for very long without presenting us with problems that we must overcome. To live harmoniously with society and to achieve our goals, we must continually make decisions and choices. In any case in which we cannot act spontaneously, but must make a choice between alternatives, we are said to be in *conflict*.

Conflicts are of three kinds. These are: the approach-approach conflict, the approach-avoidance conflict, and the avoidance-avoidance conflict. We shall discuss each in turn.

In an *approach-approach* conflict, one is torn between two or more mutually exclusive alternatives, each of which is desirable. Suppose you have been offered your choice between seeing the last performance of a fine play or visiting a friend who will be in town only on the night of the play. You wish to *approach* each of these alternatives; but you cannot choose both. Psychologists have noted that in such conflicts, the more one tends to choose *A*—that is, the closer one gets to approaching one alternative—the more attractive *B* suddenly becomes; and vice versa.

In *approach-avoidance* conflicts, the choice involves a single action which has both pleasant and unpleasant facets. Suppose you see a hat on sale at a time when your funds are low. You want the hat—that is, you want to *approach* it; but at the same time, you don't want to spend your last few dollars—you want to *avoid* that. Such conflicts are very difficult to resolve.

Avoidance-avoidance conflicts are the reverse of the approach-approach type. One is faced with two alternatives, both of which are unpleasant. Here the task is to decide which is *less* unpleasant. Suppose a teen-ager is to be punished, and his father tells him he must choose between staying in every night for a month, or giving up his allowance for the same period. He wants to *avoid* both alternatives—but he must choose one. Avoidance-avoidance conflicts are perhaps the most difficult type to solve.

Psychologists, who have studied conflict situations of all three types and how people solve them, tell us that no matter how difficult it is to reach a decision, invariably once we have *made* that decision, we tend to emphasize in our own minds the good points of our choice, and disparage or forget about the other choices we might have made instead—no matter how attractive they may have appeared originally.

FEELINGS AND SENSATIONS

You can always characterize your feelings by one of two adjectives, either *pleasant* or *unpleasant*. The two elementary feelings therefore appear to be pleasantness and unpleasantness.

The satisfaction of some drives is pleasant. You feel well pleased when you have made a difficult contract at bridge, or when you have made a profitable business deal. Such feelings, so called, should be distinguished from sensations, which are localized, coming from the "senses." What is pleasing to the senses contributes to the feeling of pleasantness, and vice versa. Sweet things are pleasing to the taste, and bitter things are unpleasant, even displeasing. Gratification of bodily needs (desires) helps to make us feel pleasant.

Associated with feelings are our likes and dislikes, some native, some acquired. The liking for sweets, fragrant odors, bright colors, and musical sounds is native. But persons sometimes have to learn to like certain foods or particular color combinations; and esthetic appreciation of colors (as in a painting) and sounds (as in a symphony) must often be learned. Natural likes and dislikes, together with those acquired from training or environment, are important factors to be considered in vocational psychology.

ELEMENTARY SENSATIONS

A sensation is a response to a stimulus, made by the sense organ stimulated, and recognized or interpreted in the associated brain centers. Thus the sensation of sight is caused by the stimulus of light acting upon the nerves of seeing in the retina of the eye, being registered in the visual center of the brain, and there interpreted or recognized. The five familiar senses are taste, smell, sight, sound (hearing), and touch; less commonly recognized are the senses of temperature, muscle, and pain. The "senses," so called, are native; they operate quite naturally, although what they report to the brain is interpreted and acted upon according to what the individual has learned.

The human skin is noticeably sensitive, having four kinds of "sense spots" on the surface, which receive the stimuli causing the sensations of touch, warmth, cold, and pain. These are the elementary skin sensations, of which other sensations are combinations. Moisture is a combination of smooth (touch) and cold (temperature) sensations. Extremes of heat and cold also stimulate the pain sense. The senses can be deceptive, for an extremely cold object will stimulate the warmth spots, giving a sensation of heat (warmth-pain combination). This deception is not serious when we see the object causing the sensation, for its appearance usually tells us whether it should feel hot or cold. The pain sense gives warning of danger—probable injury if the stimulus is not removed.

The sensation of taste seems simple, but is highly complex. It is compounded not only of taste proper, but of senses of touch, warmth, cold, and pain, for since the tongue has skin, sense spots are present in it. The "feel" of a morsel of food has a great deal to do with its taste: the taste is a combination of all the sensations the stimulus (food) causes. The muscle sense may also contribute, if the morsel is hard or gummy. Most tastes are partly smells, the odor reaching the olfactory cells of the nose through the back of the mouth. It is for this reason that you seem to lose much of your sense of taste when you have a bad cold in your nose.

The elementary tastes are sweet, sour, bitter, and salty. The taste of a cool glass of orangeade is a compound of sweetness, sourness, coldness, and the odor of the orange "flavor." Most tastes are *blends*. Their effect is total: it seems to be single, although it is really multiple.

The elementary odors are spicy, fragrant, flowery, fruity, resinous, foul, and scorched. As compared with that of animals, the human sense of smell is remarkably inefficient. But the human nose can detect surprisingly small quantities of odorous substances diffused in the air. Most odors, like tastes, are blends.

Sounds and sights may be blends, but they may also be *patterns*. A pattern, unlike a blend, depends on space or time. A musical composition, when played, is a time pattern of sound. A view of a crowded street is a complex pattern both in space and time, for many of the objects are in motion.

Some senses are more adaptable than others. The sense of smell fatigues rapidly, and a pronounced odor becomes less keen the longer it persists. Some tastes exhibit a similar fading. The senses become adapted to such prolonged stimuli, no longer responding to them. This adaptation is less noticeable in the sense of sight, though if you are in a room illuminated with yellow light, you are likely to suffer the illusion, after a time, of being in white light.

Sometimes sensations persist after the stimuli cease. This is especially true of sight. If you stare at an electric bulb, and suddenly shut it off, you will continue to see it for a moment afterward; this is the *after-image*. There may be a negative or opposite after-image, such as the black spots you see after gazing at a bright light like the sun. The persistence of sight sensation after the stimulus ceases is utilized in the familiar mechanism of the motion pictures, which of course do not move but appear to move because the eye carries over the impression of one picture to the impression of the next, which is projected on the screen too swiftly for the eye to perceive the jerk which actually accompanies the change.

Adaptation and after-images, together with contrast, help to make our eyes deceive us. A light color will appear lighter if placed in contrast with a darker, or with black; and the same color will appear darker if placed in contrast with a lighter, or with white.

Ordinary sounds which lack rhythm and regularity are noises. Music makes use of sound blends, together with pitch and the quality or timbre of the notes produced by different musical instruments. The human ear is limited in its capacity to perceive sounds, and the limitations vary with individuals and at different ages. Some persons can hear the squeak of a bat (they have exceptionally "good ears"); others cannot. The vowels of human speech are blends of sound tones, and, in most languages, the pitch of the sound does not change them (except in singing); the sounded consonants which are prolonged are also blends (like *m, n, r, f*), the other consonants being noises (like *p, k, g*). A noise is a blend of simple tones, but there is seldom anything like a tonal effect, and pitch is vague or lacking.

Though the eye can judge with fair accuracy the source of its stimuli (light rays), the ear can judge only slightly the direction or source of the sound waves which stimulate it, unless, as usually happens, it is aided by the eye.

There are also the senses of organic state, as hunger, thirst, and fatigue and the bodily senses. The bodily senses tell us whether we are moving and in what direction (when the eyes are closed), and the position of invisible parts of the body (which can be ascertained with fair accuracy by the muscle sense, especially if the part is moved slightly). The semicircular canals of the inner ear are not concerned with hearing, but have a great deal to do with maintaining our equilibrium (balance) and the efficiency of our motor mechanism, and they also tell us of movements of the head or of the body as a whole. In these canals the sensations of dizziness and falling are located, although they seem to come from the body as a whole. The muscle sense helps us to judge how much we move an arm in the dark, or, in conjunction with the sense of touch, enables us to judge the weight of an object by "hefting" it.

ATTENTION

Man has a noticeable capacity for attention, or concentration, which is an adjustment of the mental faculties, in co-operation with physical faculties, to the reception of certain stimuli in preference to all others. A student concentrating on his textbook is giving attention to his reading, and to his consideration of that reading, above everything else for the moment. His stimulus to such attention is perhaps interest in the subject, or the desire to profit by its study and mastery.

When we attend to what we are doing, we concentrate our faculties upon it. This means that we shut out, so far as we can, all distracting stimuli and adjust our muscles as well as our minds to the matter in hand. The muscular adjustment is particularly important in physical activity, but it is also a factor in mental work, for good light and a comfortable position are necessary.

The attention constantly shifts, in spite of all we can do. Our thoughts leap momentarily from one thing to another, or from one aspect of a subject to another. If you look at a pattern of wallpaper, you will seem to perceive one arrangement for a moment, and then the arrangement will change. If you look at a group of dots, your eye will arrange them first in one pattern or grouping, and then in another. If you separate your two eyes by holding a red glass in front of one and a blue glass in front of the other, you will seem to see blue for a moment and then red, and vice versa. It is impossible to look at any object steadily, for any length of time, without the attention fluctuating.

Strictly speaking, it is impossible to give attention to more than one thing at a time. When a person seems to do so, he is really shifting his attention rapidly from one thing to another and back again. The performer who juggles and recites poetry at the same time is partly letting learned actions take their own course while he gives attention to others. Juggling can become practically automatic. Similarly, the writer who rattles off his ideas on a typewriter is not paying attention to the mechanics of typewriting, for since he has those well learned, he can give his mind to the ideas which he wishes to express. We are limited in how much we can attend to at a moment; in a single glance we can notice only four or five objects, and then only cursorily. The taking in of a person from head to foot, including the pattern of necktie, the color of socks, number of buttons on the coat, and so on, is impossible in a fraction of a second. Some extended attention must be given if such details are to be noted. It is just as impossible to sweep the glance, for the eye does not sweep—it jumps in short, quick jerks from one focus to another. The eye can follow a moving object, but it cannot sweep steadily over a room.

HABITS AND LEARNING

THE LEARNING PROCESS

A fundamental principle of learning is exercise, or practice. Anything repeated tends to become easier to remember and more familiar. This is equally true of learning to ride a bicycle or to recite the multiplication tables. When a response follows a stimulus again and again, learning is the result. Since a recent response to a particular stimulus has more force than more remote responses, you may "become rusty" or "get out of practice." Since vigorous exercise is more helpful than indifferent exercise, the intensity with which you practice, or the amount of attention you give, modifies the value of the practice. Exercise may be voluntary, as it usually is when you set out to learn to skate or to memorize your lessons in school, or it may come about as a consequence of necessity, as when a hunter learns to walk quietly in the woods. Here the *effect* of responses to stimuli modifies the repetition of the responses, until only those are made which accomplish the desired result. As you learn by practice, you tend to eliminate waste motions, being guided by the desired effect.

Exercise does not completely explain learning. We learn by association, by noting similarity or contrast, or by noting things that are close together in space or time. A collection of several stimuli may arouse one response, so that later, by association, one of the stimuli alone may arouse that response. Thus there may be what are called substitute stimuli and substitute responses.

A stimulus may, after a process of learning or conditioning, arouse a response which naturally should follow a quite different stimulus. Suppose a baby is shown a toy rabbit just as a loud noise is made. The baby is frightened by the noise when he sees the rabbit. He is thus led to associate the fright with the rabbit. After a few times he may exhibit fright at the sight of the rabbit, without hearing a noise. The rabbit becomes a *substitute* stimulus for the noise (technically called a *sign*), arousing the response of fright. The child learns the names of things in a similar way: he hears the word spoken when he sees the object, and ultimately will repeat the word when he sees the object, substituting the *visual* stimulus for the original *auditory* stimulus.

We learn by observation. This means that a group of stimuli arouses a certain response, and that later one of those stimuli alone may arouse that response. Thus, as you become acquainted with a person, you learn how he looks. You may later be reminded of him by hearing his voice over the telephone, by seeing him from the rear as he walks down the street, or by seeing someone who resembles him slightly. Children often respond wholeheartedly to a partial stimulus by calling all furry animals "kitties"—making the kitten response to the single stimulus of fur. Irrational likes and dislikes of foods, of people of different backgrounds than our own may be due to a response to one or a few stimuli out of many originally presented.

It is thus seen that learning is combination; it derives from stimuli received at first as a group, and later singly, with the responses acquired by experience and exercise (practice). Emotions follow certain stimuli, but, as the child grows older, the stimuli which arouse his emotions change. What makes a child angry may not necessarily make an adult angry; what amuses a child does not always amuse an adult. Our emotions and their expression (response to the stimulus of emotion) become modified in socially acceptable ways. When necessary, we make substitute responses: we respond to an insult with sarcasm instead of with fisticuffs.

Everyone is greatly influenced by his early environment and childhood associations. Are you afraid of snakes or mice? Those fears have been built into you by substitute responses which you have probably been unaware of. It is wise to fear some snakes, but not all. It is absurd to fear mice. But you will find it extremely difficult to reason yourself out of fears which seem to you instinctive, although you may readily admit that they are foolish.

To a certain extent, early and often accidental associations also explain likes and dislikes.

Human beings, unlike animals, can perceive a problem at the start and formulate a plan of attack. Their movements, though they may follow the trial-and-error method, are directed more surely to the goal. But, like animals, human beings learn by doing. A man can learn to use a hammer without any instruction whatever, although instruction may speed up his progress toward skill. Human superiority depends on observing as well as doing; few if any animals are capable of true observation prior to performing an act. An animal cannot benefit by watching another animal perform a trick, but a human being readily profits by example.

Human beings have the further ability to note and remember: the child may imitate something he has seen his father do, but some time after his father acted. This ability is exclusively a human characteristic. When a man ponders a problem in his study, and works out a solution, he *thinks*. In thinking, imagination and association of ideas are involved. So far as psychological evidence goes, animals other than man do not think, though chimpanzees and gorillas have some power of association.

With learning come our habits, good or bad. We sometimes acquire absurd reactions, or "bad habits." A habit is rather difficult to break, but it can be done with proper determination—usually by setting up, through practice, a counter-habit, or substitute response to the stimulus which brought on the habitual reaction. Habits, obviously, are acquired and not native.

Memory

Remembering is a part of learning. Some things we remember consciously, as when we think or "reason out" a problem; other facts are remembered almost automatically, as when we make a response to a stimulus by habit. Some persons have better memories than others; a few are blessed with exceptionally good memories. A poor memory may be improved to some degree.

The most familiar exercise of memory is "memorizing" something—the multiplication tables, a poem, or a speech. The most obvious way to memorize is to repeat the thing to be learned, over and over, until it is learned. The process can be speeded up by noting similarities between units; memorizing a poem, for example, is easier than memorizing prose, for rhythm and rhyme aid the memory. Recitation aloud is a sound aid to memory.

A principle in memorizing is that of spaced repetition: if you are learning something by rote, it saves time and effort to go over it twice each day for twelve days rather than to go over it twenty-four times in one day or six times daily for four days. In studying, it is wise to read over your assignment, and then, when you take up the next assignment the next day, to read over the previous assignment before proceeding to the new lesson. Thinking back over what you have read, verifying from the text any doubtful points, is very helpful. Experiment has shown, also, that going completely through what is to be learned, taking it as a whole each time, is more efficient than learning it part by part and then putting the parts together.

The will to learn includes conscious observation combined with reciting (practice). Unless you train yourself to observe carefully, you will seldom remember anything that you see, hear, or feel, except what naturally arouses your interest. (A costume designer might remember that a fleeing criminal wore a necktie that did not go well with his hat, shirt, and coat, but the average person would not be likely to note that fact.)

We are likely to forget what we learn if we have no occasion to bring it to mind over a long interval of time. The degree to which we forget a fact depends on how well it is memorized or noted in the first place and on how frequently it is brought to mind or used meanwhile. Some psychologists assert that we never forget anything the nerve cells of our cortex have ever "recorded." Streaming through our consciousness at any moment are dozens and hundreds of impressions or responses out of the past, some dim, some vivid, some weak, some strong—all helping us to "think," as we say, and influencing what we are and how we act.

You remember, or are "reminded" of something in your memory, by a stimulus which arouses that response; it may be a substitute stimulus or a substitute response. You see a friend's face and remember his name, what he talked about when you saw him last, whom he married. You are continually being reminded of facts in your memory, of what you have read, seen, heard, smelled, or felt. The more recent impressions are usually the most vivid, though not always. Very recent impressions may obtrude themselves into the memory almost unconsciously, as when a tune keeps running in your head; this perseveration seems to act without a stimulus, though there may be a stimulus so vague that you are unaware of it.

Everyone experiences occasional difficulties in recalling a name or a fact which he knows very well. Fear, anxiety, doubt, embarrassment, surprise, or some distraction may inhibit recall. The best way is to think of all the similar or related facts, quite calmly, and the desired and elusive name or number, or whatever it is, may "pop into your mind." If you do not recall at once, abandon the mental search and return to it a little later, when the "interference" may have faded and you can remember without difficulty.

Recognition is a curious aspect of memory, for you may recognize a person or place without immediately recalling the attendant facts. You know your intimate friends spontaneously, without any effort at recall. In terms of stimulus and response, recognition is a learned response to a certain stimulus or group of stimuli.

MENTAL IMAGERY AND ASSOCIATION

We can call to mind, in varying degree, sensations we have experienced. These recalled sensations constitute *mental images*—the more vivid mental images are usually visual. A person capable of recalling visual mental images has in his mind's eye a picture of what he has seen. To a lesser degree, he can recall things heard, felt, smelled, or tasted.

Usually mental images are aroused unconsciously—that is, without conscious effort. But a person can often bring to mind a picture of a past experience at will. He can re-experience to some extent both the visual aspect and the action of the event. In general, we have mental images that are complete only in so far as we have observed and noted; it is impossible to bring to mind consciously portions of a scene which we have not definitely observed.

However, images come to mind, quite often, which we *do not remember* having observed. These may be free associations of details which were observed separately, or they may be images which we have entirely forgotten with respect to place and time, but which upon a certain stimulus are aroused. Such images, of course, are primary to what we call *imagination;* because of the tendency of mental images to simplify, elaborate, associate, etc., imagination differs from memory. You recall sensations which are sensory images. But you can also call to mind facts, which were perhaps noted originally in connection with sensations, and yet you recall them without the accompanying sensations. You know, for instance, that water is wet, and you can recall this fact without any mental image of water.

Association plays a great part in mental imagery. You may permit yourself to daydream, or you may fall into a reverie. Images rapidly follow one another in your mind, without any conscious effort on your part, following outside stimuli in some degree, perhaps, but following more closely your mental attitude at the moment. Controlled associations help us in most of our mental acts. In performing the operations of arithmetic, we control our associations of numbers so that we add, multiply, subtract, or divide, as we wish. In reading, we control our associations of words according to the context: we do not associate speed with the word *fast* if we read, "He was tied fast to the pillar." In speaking, we similarly control our word associations.

PERCEPTION

Every moment of your life you are perceiving facts and deducing from them. You hear a cat's meow, and you say, "I hear a cat." You do not—you hear the sound the cat is making. But you perceive that the sound is typically that which a cat makes, and you interpret it accordingly. You may say that a lemon smells sour—this is perception, for the sensation of sour is a taste, but you associate the smell of the lemon with the taste you have experienced, and you perceive that such a smell indicates a sour taste. The smell of the lemon is a sensation, followed by the perception that it suggests sourness; perception, then, is a *secondary* response to a stimulus.

Perception takes place in the brain, in the cortical areas adjacent to the corresponding sensory centers. If you feel a pencil in the dark, you perceive that it is a pencil, and perhaps you can "guess" or picture to yourself how it looks, except that you have no means of perceiving its color. Your sensory center of touch, linked somewhat with your muscle sense, gives you the sensations of feeling and weight. The adjacent parts of the cortex enable you to perceive that the object is a pencil.

A person does not always perceive correctly. As a joke, someone may give him a skinned grape in the dark, and tell him that it is an animal's eye. Helped by the suggestion that it is an eye, the victim is likely to perceive that it is an eye, for it feels about as he thinks an eye would feel if handled. You often make momentary mistakes in perception. How often have you gone to the window, thinking you heard rain, and discovered that the noise was something else?

Mistakes in perception create many of our illusions, ephemeral though most of them are. "Oh, I thought I heard you speak," you say in apology to someone walking with you down the street. Or you are thinking of dogs, and you mistake a piece of burlap lying in the road for a sleeping dog, until you look more closely. "Ghosts" are often seen in this way. Thus you perceive things, true or false, without any definite recall of an image formerly experienced when confronted with the same stimuli. You can hear thunder and perceive that it is thunder without picturing a storm in your mind.

To perceive, you must combine various stimuli and isolate them from their surroundings. What you perceive may therefore depend upon what you are looking for. You certainly would never find a needle in a haystack if you were not looking for it; but if you searched methodically you might find it. To see it, you would isolate it from the hay and perceive that it was a needle by combining the visual and other sensory stimuli which confirmed your perception.

What are objects of perception? You perceive things, happenings (events), qualities, characteristics (colors), abstracts (such as straightness and truthfulness), and other facts. But you can also perceive indirectly. For instance, you can examine the bottom of a muddy stream with a long rod and get an idea of whether it is rough or smooth. You seem to perceive through the rod; really, you perceive (or interpret) the sensations produced by the end of the rod, in your hand. Such perception is aided by deduction, a power of reason. Then you can perceive the passage of time, not always accurately, but you can usually judge fairly well the difference between one hour and two hours, or between one second and three seconds. Perception of time is most important in playing a musical instrument or in singing.

Sounds tell us little of the direction from which they come, or of the distance from which they come; a ventriloquist, suggesting where the sounds he makes come from, takes advantage of the fact that we customarily assume a faint sound to come from a greater distance than a loud sound, or from a more enclosed place.

Perception of space is largely visual, except as it may be referred to the position of the body or its parts. Our binocular (two-eyed) vision helps us in estimating distances and the relative size of objects; also, the fact that distant objects seem smaller than nearer ones (the principle of perspective used by the artist), and the familiar phenomenon of nearer objects seeming to rush by while more distant objects stand still or move slowly in the opposite direction, experienced while looking out of a train window (and also to a lesser degree when the eye is moved while one is quite still), both help us to judge distance. The perception of space is by no means perfect, for we may be entirely deceived by apparent distances.

Artistic perception may usually be developed, or acquired. It involves a capacity to feel emotions, to sympathize (to feel other people's emotions), or to have one's feelings aroused by substitute stimuli (as by a painting or a drama). Some esthetic perceptions, as those of symmetry and natural fittingness, seem to be native. Most persons have an inborn sense of balance and proportion in visual matters, and some persons have an inborn sense of rhythm in auditory matters.

ILLUSIONS

Some illusions are very familiar. A piece of marble feels colder than a piece of wood. If you come into a moderately warm room from the cold outside air, it may appear very warm indeed. An hour interestingly spent seems much shorter than an hour passed in boredom. Some of these errors are constant—we are always at their mercy, and cannot help making them. Other errors depend on circumstances or conditions which are temporary.

Generally speaking, a person makes more errors in perceiving small differences than he does in perceiving greater ones. This holds true of all relative or similar differences. If the room is lighted by one candle, and you light a second, the fact that the room is twice as bright is readily noticeable; the addition of a third candle is less noticeable, and finally, the addition of a hundredth candle to ninety-nine already lighted in a room is hardly discernible at all.

Preoccupation or mental attitude can cause illusions, such as hallucinations. If you are looking for a friend in a crowd, your mental attitude may cause you momentarily to mistake someone else for him, until your error is corrected by some additional stimulus. "Hearing burglars" in the house after reading of a midnight robbery in the paper is a familiar auditory illusion, due to preoccupation with a specific idea. "Seeing ghosts" is nearly always due to a mental attitude, which brings about mistaken perceptions.

Many optical illusions are utilized in puzzles and tricks with the pencil. The ancient Greeks recognized an optical illusion in modeling temple columns; they appear straight to the eye, but they are not straight; if they were straight, they would not appear straight!

INTELLIGENCE AND INTELLIGENCE TESTS

The student who learns his lessons easily, the mechanic who is handy with tools, and the salesman who sizes up customers quickly are all considered intelligent in different ways. Efficiency in the solution of everyday problems is a good working definition of intelligence. It demands both power and speed. For convenience, the psychologist distinguishes three areas of intelligent activity:

(1) Abstract—capacity for dealing with numbers, symbols, diagrams, ideas.

(2) Mechanical—ability to handle mechanical devices.

(3) Social—the knack of getting along well with people.

Psychologists have found that abilities are positively related. People tend to be more often above average in all of their achievements or below average in all their achievements than far above average in some and far below in others. A student is rarely very good in one subject and poor in all the rest, though he is likely to be better in some subjects than in others.

INTELLIGENCE TESTS

General intelligence tests widely used today are primarily measures of abstract intelligence. *Special tests* applying to mechanical intelligence, involving perceptual ability, motor skill, and ingenuity, have also been developed. Social intelligence is sometimes measured by tests, but frequently by rating scales and questionnaires and other methods.

I.Q., or intelligence quotient, is the ratio of a child's mental age to his chronological age. Thus a child of ten whose mental age is that of a fifteen-year-old has an I.Q. of 150. I.Q. is a measure of brightness or dullness.

It seems probable that intelligence is located in the brain and has something to do with the degree of complexity of the cortex, especially of that part of the cortex just behind the forehead. The exact relationship of intelligence to the brain is as yet unknown. Some men with rather small brains have been highly intelligent. Though some animals have large brains, they are not nearly so intelligent as human beings. But the frontal part of the cortex and the areas of cortex immediately adjacent to the motor and sensory centers of the brain seem to be the source of intelligence and skill.

REASONING

Reasoning power sharply separates man from other animals. In reasoning, you perceive facts and draw inferences from them. You perceive that a spark-plug wire has come loose, and you infer that that is the cause of the engine stopping dead. Your bank informs you that your account is overdrawn, and you infer at once that one of three things must be true: (1) the bank has made a mistake, (2) you have made a mistake, or (3) a check has been raised or forged. By examination of your figures and of the canceled vouchers, you can arrive at the correct explanation. But if, while thinking it over, before you examine any figures, you suddenly remember that you wrote a check a week ago without putting it down in your checkbook, you infer immediately that your neglect caused the error.

Reasoning is subject to false inferences, or fallacies. The loose thinker is more prone to become a victim of fallacies than the careful reasoner. Deliberate misleading of unwary thinkers is called sophistry. The analysis of reasoning and its fallacies is called *logic*.

Reasoning answers such questions as why? how? what? by whom? We are in a difficulty—how are we going to get out of it? We need money—how are we going to get it? My friend avoids me—why? Given enough relevant facts, the answer can be "reasoned out."

Rationalization is not reasoning, but rather a form of self-justification. If a husband is unkind to his wife because of what has happened at the office, he may justify himself by seeking some other "reason" for, or cause of, his behavior. Children are often particularly expert at rationalizing their conduct—not always from a wish to deceive, for they may not know the real reason themselves.

IMAGINING AND DREAMS

Man is undoubtedly an imagining animal: he is continually bringing images to mind, and drawing conclusions from them, or acting upon what they suggest to him.

The child manipulates his toys and, by imagination, is able to build his blocks into towers, to arrange dolls like real people, to construct machines from his building outfits. Curiosity and exploration, memory and reasoning, perception, all enter into it. Ultimately, imagination tends to create something new out of what one has already learned. Play and recreation depend a great deal on imagination. Games may be looked upon as fantasies acted out—they satisfy self-assertive or other instincts, because we imagine them to be real. We make substitute responses, or we are reacting to substitute stimuli, but our mental life during the process is imagination.

A particular aspect of imagination is called *empathy*. If you watch a bird flying, and enjoy the sight because you seem to imagine yourself smoothly flying through the air, that imaginative self-projection is an instance of empathy. Empathy partially explains our enjoyment of such things as art, literature, and contests of skill (when we watch them). Self-projection into the personality of another person, to feel how he feels, is much like empathy, but it is called by the familiar name of sympathy.

Daydreaming is a form of imagination which enables us to enjoy something that is not happening at the moment or is impossible to us in real life. We may imagine ourselves to be conquering heroes, or masters of industry, or Don Juans in love. The daydream is a mild form of mental dissipation; usually it has no practical result.

Worry and anxiety are brought on by imagining what one does not want to have happen, but what one thinks might happen. In extreme instances of worry, the imagination is given full rein and allowed to bring to mind all sorts of terrors.

Freud held that when a person sleeps, his unconsciousness obtrudes into his consciousness, giving his dreams a basically sexual coloring, to be found in symbolic substitutions which are explained in psychoanalysis and "dream interpretation." Psychoanalysts consider dreams to be disguised wish fantasies. Interpretation of dreams is an important part of modern psychotherapy.

When you dream, you are probably not deeply asleep. Dreams seem to take place when you sleep lightly, or just before you fully awaken. That is, those dreams which you remember after you wake up take place in light sleep. Some authorities believe that you always dream, but that you forget the greater part of your dreams—that is, that they make no impression on the waking mind.

Dreams are not prophetic. They are born of the past, and may be prophetic only in so far as they may indicate tendencies or wishes that may sometime be fulfilled. Apparent contradictions of this truth can usually be explained if all the attendant facts are known.

Controlled imagination, directed toward some result in reality, has practical value. The inventor who produces some new machine or chemical process does so by means of controlled imagination. His inventive imagination is constantly subjected to the criticism of what he already knows to be true or false. He continually tests his idea by asking such questions as the following: Will it work? Will the public find a use for it? Can it be manufactured cheaply enough to be commercially profitable?

Art is a product of the imagination. The artist makes use of his imagination (as well as his intellect and learning) as he composes a symphony, paints a picture, writes a novel, or models a piece of sculpture. He gives expression to a conception which he has in his imagination. That conception is new to him—it is some novel expression of a life-truth which he feels should be given form, and which, in the degree in which it is art, will be admired and appreciated.

To enjoy art, the individual must be imaginative along lines similar to those which produced the work of art, though not necessarily in the same degree. Appreciation of art, involving both empathy and sympathy to its parts and a detached comprehension of the whole, is not vicarious living.

No matter how far your imagination reaches, it can never conceive anything which is not made up of what you have perceived, what you have experienced, what you have learned. The products of the imagination are new combinations of old facts.

PERSONALITY

Personality is derived from inherited physical factors as well as environment. Physical factors influence personality in a number of ways. First, psychologists have made classifications of physical "types," based either on physique or on glandular activity. A person of a particular type shows a propensity toward a certain type of emotional reaction.

Less direct though perhaps more understandable physical influences on personality are those produced by physical handicaps. These often produce a sense of inferiority.

The theory of personality arrived at by Sigmund Freud in his research on psychoanalysis is as follows: the fundamental energy in a person is called the *libido*. The libido is basically a sex urge, or, more broadly, a love urge. A person's mental health and balance depend in great part on how the libido is released, to what "objects" it attaches itself, etc. The *Id,* referring in large part to the unconscious life of the individual, strives to satisfy the libido. The Id is primitive, non-moral in nature. The *Ego* is the rational, civilized part of the individual. It acts as a control on the Id, often "repressing" (either consciously or unconsciously) its urges. These repressed desires become unconscious. A further factor in personality, according to Freud, is the *Super-ego,* which corresponds closely to what we call conscience. This factor acts as a control over both Ego and Id, imposing on them moral ideas. Basically we may see that the Super-ego (conscience) and the Id (primitive nature) are in constant conflict, which the Ego (reason) tries to resolve. This basic outline of personality is accepted by many psychologists today.

There are numerous social influences on personality. The first influence on anyone's personality comes from parents and other persons in the home. How the adults behave and how they behave toward the child have a strong influence on his later development. This is particularly so because of the child's ability to imitate others, even identify himself with others. It is rare that an unharmonious home with an atmosphere of conflict and animosity will produce a well-balanced child. A child who has not known tenderness and affection may grow up with neurotic problems or even delinquent traits. Overaffection is likely to be less harmful, although it "spoils" the child and retards maturity. Parents should seek a happy medium in this matter. Likewise, between rigorous discipline and overprotection on the one hand and neglectful submission to the child's whims on the other hand—a happy medium must be sought.

Relationships among brothers and sisters in a family and with other children and teachers at school have also a strong influence on the growing child's personality. Many problems are involved in this area, among them: feelings of inadequacy on the part of the duller child or the less popular child; individual conflicts; struggles for superiority; etc.

Finally, the individual's position in the community as well as his social and economic standing may be major determinants of personality—not so much in themselves as in the way that the individual responds to these situations.

MENTAL HEALTH AND MENTAL ILLNESS

Statistics indicate that one out of every ten Americans today suffers from some sort of mental illness; of course, one must recognize that there are many, many varying degrees of mental illness. Perhaps, before considering these, it might be wise to ask: What is mental health?

Mental health can be satisfactorily defined only in terms of adults; children and adolescents, just as they are growing physically, are also growing emotionally, and in the process they undergo psychological stages and changes which are transitional, and not necessarily indicative of their "true selves." For the adult, however, mental health may be defined as a combination of three basic emotional and psychological capacities: a capacity for working creatively, a capacity for relaxing and playing with zest and pleasure, and a capacity for enjoying mature sexuality.

When one or more of these capacities fails to develop or becomes deadened in an adult, he is likely to become unhappy with himself, with his life, and with society; he may become mentally ill. Mental illness may be little more than a sense of depression that seems to linger much longer than it ought; or it may become so severe that the victim becomes unable to function in society and his personality disintegrates. When the mental disorder is of a type that does not seriously alter the victim's life, it is called *neurosis.* A major mental disorder which causes radical disturbances in the individual's personality and behavior is known as *psychosis.*

Some of the symptoms of neurosis are: *anxiety,* which seems to have no motive; *compulsions,* which drive the sufferer to perform certain meaningless actions repeatedly; *obsessions,* specific but irrelevant ideas which continually intrude in the conscious mind; *amnesia,* loss or severe malfunction of memory; *fugue,* which drives the victim to flee from unnamed terrors; *phobias,* irrational fears of various kinds; and *hypochondria,* which shows itself in the victim's conviction that he is suffering from physical diseases of which he is actually free. Persons who suffer from one or another of these symptoms may continue to live and function within society quite successfully; but they endure much needless agony if they do not seek treatment.

Among the psychoses are: *schizophrenia,* characterized by emotional withdrawal from reality; *catatonia,* characterized by complete physical immobility; *hebephrenia,* characterized by silliness; *paranoia,* characterized by hallucinations and feelings of persecution; *megalomania,* characterized by feelings of grandeur; and the *manic-depressive syndrome,* characterized by alternating moods of extreme elation and despair. All psychoses require prolonged treatment if they are to be cured.

TREATMENT FOR THE PSYCHOLOGICALLY ILL

Just as there are many different types and degrees of psychological maladjustment, so there are a number of different methods and techniques for helping people resolve their psychological and emotional problems, and different professional groups administer different techniques. Professionally trained *psychologists* usually administer tests to their clients, discuss problems with them, and make certain recommendations. *Psychoanalysts* are medical men who have made a study of the bases of emotional disorders in the light of certain special techniques which are useful in effecting cures. *Psychiatrists* are physicians whose specialty is treatment of mental disorders.

Among the various therapeutic techniques widely practiced in the solution of psychological and emotional problems are the following:

Counseling. The counseling technique is used primarily when problems arise in specific terms, generally in the realm of social adjustment. Very often, the problem treated by a psychological case worker involves more than one person. Among the types of problems usually dealt with are those pertaining to marriage, vocational choice, religion, and family life.

Psychotherapy. Psychotherapy has proved of great value in the treatment of a patient's subjective emotional problems. Through discussions with the therapist, in which the patient reveals his inmost thoughts, anxieties, and fears, he gains an understanding of why he feels as he does, and gains help in learning to think and act more effectively.

Group Therapy. In group therapy, a number of patients, each with his own problem, meet regularly for discussion. Under the supervision of a trained therapist, the patients gain new insights into their own problems from the experiences and attitudes of the others in the group.

Psychoanalysis. Psychoanalysis is the form of therapy originally devised by Sigmund Freud. It is thorough and extended treatment, in which the patient, meeting with his analyst on a regular basis over a considerable period, reveals his thoughts and memories in a stream-of-consciousness manner. Recognizing the symbolic value of words, details of dreams and fantasies, odd slips in speech and writing, and set behavior patterns, the patient and doctor together explore the deepest bases of the patient's personality, in an effort to restructure his personality along more meaningful and satisfying lines. Psychoanalysis has proved of great benefit even in cases of very severe disorder.

MODERN SCHOOLS OF PSYCHOLOGY

All modern schools of psychology and methods of psychotherapy have been influenced by Sigmund Freud (1856–1939), founder of psychoanalysis. Freud was the first to theorize on and practice the analysis of dreams as an access to the subconscious mind, and to use this method and that of free association, in which without planning the subject recalls experiences, ideas, and objects which are related in his mind. These techniques have replaced the older method of investigation under hypnosis. Freud concentrated his theories at first primarily on the sex urge. He found that repressions due to social mores or parental instruction may cause substitute desires or may lead to a rejection of reality.

Alfred Adler (1870–1937) was a student of Freud. He concluded that the primary drive of all individuals is not the sex urge but the will to power, and in this connection he developed the concept of the inferiority complex.

A third important psychological school stems from Carl G. Jung (1875–1961). Jung is often considered the most spiritual of the three. He devoted much of his life to a study of mythology and religions, in an effort to account for man's persistent search for concrete images of spiritual power. His studies are dominated by the theory of archetypes, such as the father image, the mother image, the hero image, etc., which have recurred in the beliefs of mankind throughout history. They are for him expressions of the subconscious spiritual complex, just as the respectable man, the virtuous man, the man of social prestige, are expressions of the complex of surface personality. Among these generalized forms of expression, the individual seeks to find himself, as a personality and as a spiritual being. Thus Jung placed an emphasis on the expression of the whole individual. In practical psychotherapy, the theories of single dominant drives are often more readily related to the patient's problems.

The discovery of a relationship between mental disturbance and blood composition has reaffirmed the importance of viewing mind and body as one unified complex. The interaction of mental states and bodily states becomes increasingly apparent to many people, particularly to physicians who practice in fields in which psychology and medicine come into close contact. The important work of Adolf Meyer (1866–1950) in Baltimore has been developed further in this area, which may be referred to as psychosomatic medicine.

APPLICATIONS OF PSYCHOLOGY IN DAILY LIFE

Psychology and its findings can be of great help to us in many areas of everyday life. Vocational guidance, personnel work, individual adjustment, family relationships, mental health are only a few of the fields in which trained psychologists are equipped to provide valuable assistance to both young people and adults.

In the vocational field, those who are seeking the sort of employment for which they are best qualified often find that their decision is made easier if they avail themselves of the services of an organization which specializes in giving vocational tests. Such organizations are to be found in the larger cities, and in most communities individual specialists in vocational counseling may be consulted. Vocational tests would usually include I.Q. (intelligence quotient) tests and aptitude tests of various sorts.

Without doubt one of the primary factors in everyone's life is his vocation. A steady job occupies most of one's time, and it is of the first importance that it be appropriate to one's interests, intelligence, and aptitude.

In making a choice, one must also take into consideration such factors as one's ability to get along well with others (of prime importance in sales, public relations, etc.), one's capacity to work under supervision, and the type of life one wants to lead. Work as a newspaperman or in the theater, for instance, generally requires a certain physical endurance, a capacity for a very active life, a readiness to travel, etc.

Guidance and counseling are available not only in the vocational field but also in areas of personal adjustment. Problems that arise in marriage and family life may often be resolved more easily through conferences with professionally trained psychologists, who practice guidance work in many communities. Work in counseling, psychoanalysis, and psychotherapy have been discussed above under Treatment for the Psychologically Ill.

Apart from its usefulness to the individual, psychology also has many applications in the business world. Advertising, for example, relies largely on analyses of psychological reactions to the manner in which it presents products and services through various media. And in large industrial organizations such questions as qualifications of applicants, effectiveness of work, and suitability of working conditions are studied by a special personnel staff, which constantly makes use of the findings of psychology.

EXAMINATION QUESTIONS

1. What does psychology deal with?
2. With what other sciences is psychology closely linked?
3. Why do we say that mental activity is basically physiological?
4. What function akin to intelligence exists in even the simplest form of life?
5. What is subjective observation called?
6. What are we learning from psychologists?
7. What is the simplest response to a stimulus called?
8. What is the name of the response when you jump out of the way on hearing an automobile horn?
9. What is the center of the brain that receives sensations of smell?
10. Has the taste center of the brain been isolated?
11. Is the reflex occurring in response to the stimulus always the same?
12. When the flow of saliva in the mouth is stimulated by the sight of food, what is the response called?
13. What three fundamental and native emotional reactions do the behaviorists say that babies have?
14. Is walking a native or an acquired trait?
15. Differentiate between the ability to make sounds and to use coordinated speech.
16. What is a psychological motive?
17. Is the father drive usually as strong as the mother drive?
18. When is a drive said to be sublimated?
19. Is there a native tendency for children to honor and obey their parents?
20. What is euphoria?
21. What is gregariousness and on what is it based?
22. What are four common emotions?
23. Are emotions conditions of any one part of the body?
24. When is it particularly unhealthful to become angry?
25. Why is the emotion of fear often followed by panic?
26. Why are some impulses similar to instincts?
27. What distinguishes a "cool" person in the face of danger?
28. Name a drive that is accompanied by emotion.
29. What are the three types of conflict?
30. What is a sensation?
31. By what is the exploring tendency held in check?

32. What is the psychological explanation of the popularity of crossword puzzles?
33. What are the five familiar senses?
34. What are the elementary tastes?
35. What are the elementary odors?
36. Give an ordinary example of a sensation that persists after the stimulus has ceased.
37. How may habits be broken?
38. What is the principle of spaced repetition in memorizing something?
39. What factors may inhibit remembering?
40. Explain the statement that a lemon smells sour.
41. What is the mistake if you think a piece of burlap lying in the road is a sleeping dog?
42. Explain "hearing burglars" in the house after reading of a midnight robbery in the paper.
43. What three areas of intelligent activity are distinguished by psychologists?
44. Does the size of the brain have anything to do with intelligence?
45. What is the analysis of reasoning and its fallacies called?
46. What is rationalization?
47. What aspect of imagination is called empathy?
48. What is libido, according to Sigmund Freud?
49. What is the primary drive of all individuals according to Alfred Adler?
50. What discovery has reaffirmed the importance of viewing mind and body as one unified complex?

FOR FURTHER STUDY

BASIC TEACHINGS OF THE GREAT PSYCHOLOGISTS, by S. Stansfeld Sargent. (Dolphin Books, Doubleday & Co., New York.)

GENERAL INTRODUCTION TO PSYCHOANALYSIS, by Sigmund Freud. (Liveright Publishing Corp., New York.)

THE HUMAN MIND, by Karl A. Menninger. (Alfred A. Knopf, New York.)

INTRODUCTION TO PSYCHOLOGY, by John F. Hahn. (Doubleday & Co., New York.)

THE PSYCHOLOGY OF ADJUSTMENT, by Laurance F. Shaffer. (Houghton Mifflin Co., Boston.)

THE WHOLESOME PERSONALITY, by W. H. Burnham. (Appleton-Century-Crofts, New York.)

XIX

Sociology Simplified

WHAT IS SOCIOLOGY?

IN THESE DAYS of world-wide political, economic, and social change, we are aware as never before that the evolution of mankind is not the story of single nations or states but of society as a whole. We may contrast one country with another, one race with another; we may note different customs and different traits; we may stress the special characteristics of Western civilization as compared with the Orient. But underlying all these variations we find an essential similarity. Men and women, no matter where or how they live, are concerned about a few major matters: about their families, their work, their government, their religion. Their conceptions of love, their marriage customs, their attitude toward the home, may be widely unlike, as may also their versatility and skill in industry, agriculture, and commerce, their standards of living, their interests in culture, in education, art, science, and literature, their sense of justice, their observance of law, their convictions concerning war and peace, their creeds and faiths.

Yet, despite striking differences in attitude and method, human life and human nature in all parts of the world are faced with the solution of the universal, elemental problems of mankind: the problems of home and family, of work and wealth, of education and culture, of law and order, of right living, and of religious beliefs. And it is these fundamental interests and activities and problems which constitute the subject matter of the science which deals with society (using the word "society" to mean "mankind as a whole"), the science of Sociology.

The sociologist examines the conditions of human life as they are today in civilized communities and in more primitive groups, and contrasts modern society with the life of ancient times. The sociologist is concerned with the things men do in groups, large or small groups, but in groups rather than as individuals. Psychology studies the individual mind and the behavior of individuals. Sociology does not deal directly with the mind or with behavior; it studies the institutions which man has evolved in the process of meeting the major problems of life, and it observes the variations in custom and practice associated with these institutions in all parts of the world and through the ages.

Sociology and psychology supplement each other in their approach to the ways of men. If a man rises to great power in his country and reveals a genius for statesmanship, psychology is interested in his intellectual and emotional make-up, sociology is interested in the changes in social institutions, in the methods of handling the problems of industry, trade, finance, in the methods of insuring justice, which characterize his administration. If a man commits a serious crime, psychology is concerned with his mentality, sociology is concerned with the effect of the crime upon the community and the means devised to prevent repetition of the crime. If a man becomes destitute and dependent on charity for his support, psychology seeks to discover the traits in the man himself which have handicapped him, sociology seeks to discover the conditions in the community which have made progress difficult for him and looks for plans for providing improved opportunities.

Thus far we have considered only the social groups, the social institutions, which constitute what may be called the structure of society. But sociology is concerned equally with the dynamic aspects of society, with the way in which society evolves and changes, with the social forces constantly at work, social forces which are far greater, far more irresistible than the power of any of the countless men and women whose lives they influence, forces which make for war, for revolution, for crime, for economic depression and poverty, forces which make for peace, for stability, for security, for prosperity and progress.

To a certain extent we plan what we do on a given day or any day, to a certain extent our activities are planned by others, to a certain extent things merely happen. If a man could plan his life with a view to making it well-ordered, secure, and happy, what would he do? In order to answer this question, it is necessary to have a knowledge not only of man's psychological nature but also of the effect upon him of traditions and social institutions.

CIVILIZED AND PRIMITIVE PEOPLES

At first sight the life of our modern civilized communities seems wholly unlike the life of primitive peoples. The tribes which inhabit more remote parts of Asia, Africa, and Australia, and some of the islands of the

Pacific, the Eskimos and such of our American Indian groups as still preserve their native traditions, live in accordance with customs which are strikingly different from our own. Yet, if we think in terms of the fundamental problems of society, our civilization differs from the life of primitive peoples principally in its degree of complexity. Most of the daily duties of a primitive man or woman can be carried out without moving very far from home, whereas most of the daily duties of civilized communities involve the use of one or several of our modern mechanical means of transportation. Primitive peoples use only the simplest utensils for tilling the soil and caring for their crops, for hunting, for cooking, for the preparation of their garments and the construction of their shelters. Men and women in modern civilized communities are for the most part dependent on a complex system for supplying them with food, clothing, and housing. Although the life of the farm in its direct contact with nature corresponds more nearly than the life of the city with the simpler ways of primitive groups, the increasing use of intricate mechanical instruments in agriculture and the ease of modern communication and transportation are greatly increasing the complexity of rural life. Nevertheless life in the country is much simpler than it is in a modern city.

It is not only in its relative simplicity, however, that the life of primitive tribes differs from civilized life; primitive life is essentially cruder. Most primitive tribes know little about sanitation or medicine, are more hampered by fears and superstitions, and not infrequently resort to violence. Formerly primitive peoples were always thought of and spoken of as savages, and were pictured as war-like and given to uncontrolled violence. This conception has been much modified in recent years by the work of anthropologists who have lived long among primitive peoples. To be sure, there is much that is brutal in primitive life, and there may well have been much more brutality in earlier times. However, most primitive peoples nowadays live according to laws of their own devising, which are often entirely just, even according to our standards, and are enforced by methods which when understood are seen to be reasonable and fair.

THE ORIGIN AND EVOLUTION OF SOCIETY

The culture of civilized nations today consists of an aggregation of traits that originated in peoples of all races, living in all parts of the world. Archaeological investigations have enabled us to trace the development of culture in Europe for the last one hundred thousand years, a development which began slowly and which proceeded at an ever-increasing tempo. Until modern times the most important factor in this development has been the acquisition of traits from neighboring cultures by the process of *diffusion:* in modern times, with European civilization spreading over the greater part of the globe, the greater number of additions to our culture come from inventions which occur within the civilization itself. The investigations of anthropologists into the lives of contemporary primitive peoples enable us to appreciate both the widely varying customs under which man may live and the underlying principles which remain the same even under differing circumstances, thereby giving us a more vivid insight into life in simpler circumstances than our own, life such as our own ancestors must have lived.

Associated with the evolution of culture is the question of the origin of society. Did men live alone as individuals before they lived semi-organized in groups? We have no definite evidence with which to answer conclusively, but the psychological nature of primitive and civilized man and the social organization of allied forms of life are such as to indicate that an elementary form of society must be older than the human race.

Perhaps the strongest clue to the origin of society is found in the two fundamental human urges, self-preservation and self-perpetuation, which determine the basic outline of human life and create the basic structure of human society. Of these two needs, the need for food and the need for sexual satisfaction (perpetuating the race), the sexual need is very definitely social. Man may seek food alone, but in his need of a mate we find one of the beginnings of society. Of course these motives take many forms, some of them not obviously related to the basic urges; as, for example, the desire for prestige, which is the predominant desire of man in his social organization. As the group in which man lives advances in degree of civilization, other interests take their place beside these most fundamental desires. With increasing civilization, man's approach to all his activities becomes increasingly complex, his interests more and more specialized; yet beneath the changing surface of human life, the two elemental needs remain unchanged in their importance.

THE CLASSIFICATION OF HUMAN GROUPS

Fundamentally, there are two radically different ways in which human groups can be classified: according to their race or according to their customs. But as there are many different customs that may serve for classificatory purposes, there actually seems to be an unlimited number of ways in which classification may be performed. Besides race, the commonest methods are classification by language, by nationality, by religion, and by cultural origin. Each method is important in its own field, but it is indeed unfortunate that there should be a great deal of popular misconception whereby classifications which are really linguistic are confused with those that are racial, and so on.

There are three obvious divisions of the human race: the Caucasians, Mongoloids, and Negroids; to which anthropologists usually add a fourth, Australoids. These divisions correspond roughly to the popular classification by color, Caucasians being "white," Mongoloids "yellow," and Negroids and Australoids "black" or "brown." Actually, other biological characteristics, particularly the cross section of the hair, are much more revealing than color, and play a more important role in racial classification. Within each major group there are a number of subdivisions, more or less important according to the amount of divergence found in that group. Within the classification of Negroids there is one highly differentiated group known as the African Bushmen, or Pygmies. The Mongoloids include the Eskimo and the American Indians, as well as the "yellow" races of Asia, the peoples of North and South China, Mongolia, Tibet, Japan, and Indo-China, and the Malayan peninsula. The subdivisions of the Caucasian race are not as distinct from one another. They are the Nordics, Alpines, and Mediterranean. The Armenoids are sometimes distinguished from the Alpines, the Hindus from the Mediterraneans. Besides these main races and principal subdivisions there are several racial groups that are apparently mixtures of the principal races; thus the Polynesians of the northern Pacific area are a mixture of Mongoloid, Caucasian, and Negroid; while the Melanesians further south are probably a similar mixture with Negroid predominating. Race is in itself unimportant to the sociologist. Differences in the skills of the major races are so slight that they cannot be demonstrated beyond question.

That man may be classified by nationality or religion is obvious to everyone. The linguistic classification is not so clear. French, Spanish, and Italian are all "Latin" tongues, so that speakers of those languages are sometimes known as Latins. The Latin languages, together with the Teutonic, Slavic, and Greek, are derived from a language once spoken in northern India and known from the region of origin as "Aryan." The Aryan group of languages is the largest in Europe; the Semitic and Hamitic groups are of much less importance. In other parts of the world there are other linguistic groups. Thus, in North America, Algonquian was the most important linguistic stock of the Indians, while Siouan, Athapascan, Shoshonean, and many other stocks also existed.

THE PRINCIPAL SOCIAL INSTITUTIONS

The chief divisions of sociology correspond to the fundamental interests and activities of mankind, and more specifically to the social institutions which are the expression of these interests and activities. Let us see more precisely than we have thus far what these institutions are and how they are related to one another; and, after defining the range of each institution and our approach to it, we shall study each in turn in some detail. In naming these major institutions we find a lack of adequate terminology. The institutions are more definite than the phrases by which we designate them:

(1) *The Family* as a social institution includes the intimate family group (husband, wife, and children), the larger family group (the relatives of either husband or wife or both), and the customs and practices associated with the family and with marriage and divorce.

(2) *Classes* and *Social Associations,* such as clubs and secret societies, are other important personal groups which, despite their differences in inclusiveness, may be considered together.

(3) *Work,* in the sociological sense, is man's daily means of earning a living, including all branches of industry, the professions, and wealth and property—all of man's economic activities.

(4) *The State,* as a sociological institution, includes the national and local administration of justice, preservation of law and order, all government regulation of domestic and foreign affairs, all political activities.

(5) *Education* consists of the processes by which men and women seek to fit themselves and their children for the various activities of life, including their knowledge about health and their ethical conceptions, their standards of right living.

(6) *Culture* is perhaps the best word we have for the various avocational or leisure interests of men and women—art, music, literature, and drama, recreation and sports, all phases of knowledge as a background for living.

(7) *Religion* includes the faith of men and women in the spiritual things of life, their convictions concerning Divinity, fate, and immortality, and the role of the church and other religious organizations in human life.

The social groups corresponding to these seven great social institutions are obviously not mutually exclusive. Men and women may be and usually are identified with most or all of these groups, but identified with each in a different way. A man is likely to be the father of a family, a worker in industry, a citizen of the state, a graduate of a school or college, a theatergoer, concert-goer, or sport enthusiast, and he will belong to a certain class, be associated with a certain club or social circle, and be a member of a religious organization. Consequently each of the major social institutions touch his life very closely, and all of the institutions taken together constitute a full range of his activities and interests.

Sociology gives us a very inclusive survey of the aspects of society. Sociology presents the larger, more universal, more human view of each of the social institutions. There are, however, individual social sciences which deal with the detailed workings and practical applications of the individual institutions. The most fully and systematically developed of these are *economics* and *political science*. *Anthropology* deals especially with primitive man. *History* views the sequence of human events chronologically, whereas sociology views not individual events, but movements and changes in their larger, more fundamental aspects.

THE FAMILY

The family is the most universal, most fundamental of all social groups; based as it is upon man's simplest social needs, it is the earliest social institution; and to this day the family, as a group, is the child's first social contact, his introduction to society.

Has the nature of the family changed since its primitive beginnings? If so, how? Is the family changing at the present time? If so, why? The family has changed and is still changing, and it has existed simultaneously in different forms in different parts of the world. We shall want to see how these forms differ and to compare them with the family as we know it and as we feel that it ought to be.

Whether man in early times took a mate for life or not, it is impossible for us to know definitely. But there is every reason to believe that he did. For a partnership of male and female for the protection and education of the young is a common enough trait of mammals generally, and with the increased dependence of human offspring upon their parents, partnership would doubtless be intensified rather than diminished. Even with the lower mammals and with birds there is a tendency for the same couples to mate year after year; when the period during which the offspring are dependent upon their parents overlaps the birth of further offspring, a semi-permanent marriage relationship would be almost necessary. Thus there is good reason to believe that marriage, or the relatively permanent union of man and woman, is older than the human race. In fact, the apes and some other animals have a family life not altogether unlike our own.

MARRIAGE AMONG PRIMITIVE PEOPLES

Marriage as we think of it today is a life partnership between a man and a woman, based on the love and admiration of each for the other, and including the establishment of a home and family, and the joint responsibility of the parents for the care of the children.

What other conceptions of marriage are there? As contrasted with *monogamy*—the marriage of one man and one woman—which is the only legally recognized form of marriage in most civilized countries, there is today, and there has been in the past, the practice of *polygamy*. The more common type of *polygamy*, one man having several wives, is specifically known as *polygyny*, and the less common type, one woman having several husbands, is known as *polyandry*. Polygamy of one or the other type is most likely to occur in communities where there is a wide difference in the number of men and women. In the natural course of events, approximately the same number of boys and girls are born and grow to adulthood in any given community. Among primitive peoples, however, as, for instance, among African tribes and certain groups of American Indians, numerous groups are or were dependent for their sustenance on the skill of the men of the tribe in capturing wild animals, and for their protection on the strength and bravery of the men in their encounters with hostile tribes. Clearly where many men are lost in the perils of daily life, there will be more women than men in the community. In order that the women may all realize motherhood, it becomes necessary for such a group to recognize the right of one man to have several wives.

Polygyny exists also among peoples where there is great inequality of wealth or property, or great inequality of power. In certain Asiatic countries a man of wealth or power is likely to have many wives because he can afford or demand them, whereas one wife is all that a poor man can obtain!

Polyandry, on the other hand, usually occurs in communities where the environment is itself unfavorable; for example, among the Eskimos of the frozen Arctic it is sometimes considered necessary to permit some of the female infants to die of exposure in order to avoid a greater population than the region can sustain. In these communities there are more men than women, and several men therefore share one wife. The wife in many instances lives part of the year with each husband, though among some groups the home is shared by all.

The investigations of sociologists and anthropologists definitely indicate that, despite numerous exceptions, the tendency among even the most primitive people is toward monogamy, and that the alternative practices are found principally where economic and environmental conditions are such as to make monogamy difficult. Tradition plays an important part, however, and communities which in early times or under unfavorable conditions recognized polygamy may continue to practice it long after it is really necessary.

There is another important aspect and explanation of polygyny; namely, that in communities (as in parts of the Orient) where all the household work is done by the women of the family, the first wife herself may welcome additional wives as aids. Ordinarily the first wife takes precedence over the others and has a certain amount of authority over them.

One other form of marriage is sometimes found among primitive peoples—group marriage. Group marriage is not, however, precisely what the name implies. It consists of the marriage of more than one man and more than one woman, any man being a recognized husband of any woman. But this group does not live together in a sort of limitedly promiscuous relationship. Group marriage usually occurs when men are forced to travel a great deal, and therefore share wives in several localities. In fact, the situation is not unlike the traditional situation of a sailor's having a wife in every port, it being understood, however, that the group wives, in turn, have a husband on every ship.

MARRIAGE RESTRICTIONS

There are certain degrees of blood relationship which are considered too close for marriage. The most primitive as well as the most civilized people forbid marriage between brother and sister, father and daughter, son and mother, and look upon sexual relations between men and women bound by these closest ties of blood as *incestuous*. Among some peoples marriage between first cousins or even more distant cousins is forbidden, although the marriage of cousins is more often permitted than forbidden; and even brother-sister marriage is accepted in some primitive groups. Just why the rules against incest should be so nearly universal is not at all clear. Because of our own traditions in the matter, we are apt to believe that the reason is an attempt to avoid certain dangers of inbreeding. But these dangers have never been proven. The real biological objection is that inbreeding standardizes human nature, and thus prevents rapid evolutionary development; but this point can hardly be the motive in the case of primitive societies. Two possibilities remain: the occasional appearance of undesirable recessive traits in the progeny may lead to the view that all intercourse of close relatives is bad; or the real objection may lie in the social injustices that would occur if a man were permitted to marry women who were under his control because of other relationships than those of marriage.

The degree of kinship which is considered too close for marriage varies greatly among different peoples. Usually the determination of whether two persons may marry or not depends upon the groups to which they belong. Certain groups are known as *exogamous;* that is to say, a person belonging to the group may not marry another member of the same group. Family groups, both in the limited sense and in the larger conceptions of the unilateral family, such as the gens and clan, are usually exogamous. So also are certain other groups found among primitives, such as the moiety and marriage class. Other groups are commonly *endogamous;* that is, one member of the group marries another member of the same group. The tribe itself is endogamous, and where classes are distinct each class is usually endogamous. The local group is sometimes endogamous, sometimes exogamous, sometimes neither. Consequently we see that in many instances a man belongs to groups of both types, and the possible ways in which he may marry are limited by his obligations as a member of a group.

Thus, whether two relatives may marry depends more upon their group affiliations than upon their biological closeness. The family group is regularly exogamous, and brother and sister belong to the same group whether relationships are bilateral, matrilinear, or patrilinear. Therefore brother and sister are regularly forbidden to marry each other. But certain exceptions occur. In a class system the members of the highest classes are frequently so limited in number that brother and sister are the only members of the highest endogamous class. In such cases the rule of endogamy has often superseded that of exogamy. Thus the Egyptian Pharaoh married his own sister, and the Incas of Peru also followed this custom. Frequently Polynesians of the highest rank are reduced to brother-sister marriage for the same reason.

When we come to the marriage of cousins, the situation is more complex. The children of a brother and a sister belong necessarily to different groups, whether the groups be matrilinear or patrilinear. Consequently there is ordinarily no objection to their marriage, and it is even encouraged in a large number of tribes. This relationship is known as that of cross-cousin. But children of two brothers in a patrilinear group belong to the same group, and children of two sisters in a matrilinear society belong to the same group: two parallel cousins often may not marry.

Marriage Customs

Several other marriage practices of primitive peoples are of great interest in indicating the extent to which the institution of marriage varies from place to place and from one type or degree of civilization to another. Thus the rule known as the *sororate* requires a man to marry the eldest of a group of sisters, and the younger sisters to become his subordinate wives. The term *levirate* is applied to the inheritance of a man's wife or wives by his younger brother or nearest male relative upon his death.

The custom of *marriage by purchase,* found among the majority of primitive peoples, is an example of the conception of marriage as an act of the group rather than of the individual. In order to marry a certain girl, a man or his family must pay the family of the girl a sum, known as the bride price, in terms of produce, cattle, or other valuables, and when complete payment has been made, the girl becomes to some extent a member of the man's group. Among the most primitive tribes the young wife loses all connection with her own family, but this does not happen among more advanced tribes. Among other tribes we find that payment is made by an exchange of women, so that each of two families or other groups receives a woman in exchange for the one it gives away. Sometimes the payment is made by the husband's working for the bride's family, or performing some ceremonies in their behalf. Very commonly the payment for the bride is purely nominal, and is made only as a ceremonial token of marriage. Another common custom is *dowry,* where the bride's family makes the gift to the husband. The custom of dowry is not intrinsically different from that of bride price.

Marriage by capture is and always has been an uncommon event. It occurs when the more powerful individual or group seizes women by virtue of their power. Its importance is limited, but its hold on the imagination is so great that it is frequently used as a symbolical gesture in the ceremonies of marriage that are not at all marriages by force. The term "marriage by capture" is thus applied to the practice whereby the prospective bridegroom must engage in wrestling and other feats of skill with the bride's relatives prior to the consummation of the marriage.

Our survey of the most important marriage customs and practices among primitive peoples would be incomplete if we did not mention a custom practiced at times among all primitive peoples and among all civilized peoples as well—the custom of *elopement.* In all times and places some young men and women are unwilling to accept the traditions of their group with regard to marriage. A marriage in defiance of group traditions involves much the same problems among primitive as among civilized peoples.

MARRIAGE IN MODERN LIFE

We speak of a "love match" as the finest and truest marriage, a marriage in which a man and woman feel drawn to one another by personal attraction and look forward to the establishment of a jointly directed home in which the children will grow up under the guidance of parental love. Nevertheless, in some parts of the western world, marriages which appear desirable from the economic or social point of view are arranged.

In countries where marriage is by arrangement, the ideals of marriage may be just as high as in those countries in which marriage is based on mutual attraction, and if the husband and wife prove congenial, their home may be just as happy, and the devotion between them and between them and their children just as great as in marriages founded on falling in love.

Actully, marriage of mutual attraction and marriage by arrangement are not as different in practice as their designations would indicate. Thus most young Americans grow up with the intention of marrying when they reach marriageable age, and with the expectation of marrying someone whose social and economic status and background are approximately the same as their own. The specific choice of a marriage partner is ordinarily determined by attraction, but for the most part the range of choice is limited by various other factors. On the other hand, where young men and women reach marriageable age after having grown up with the thought that a suitable marriage will be arranged for them and that they can find their happiness within the institution of marriage and the family, they are ready to call forth the best qualities in their partners in marriage. The principal difference between these two approaches to marriage is that one emphasizes the importance of individual choice and action, the other stresses the importance of marriage as an institution. The arranged marriage, called a "marriage of convenience," is becoming less frequent, particularly as class barriers and class traditions are becoming less marked.

DIVORCE

There have been divorces since the earliest times, but statistics show that voluntary or legal termination of marriage is far more common today than ever before in the history of modern civilization. Does this indicate that the institution of marriage is not as well suited to the conditions of modern life as it was to the life of earlier times? Or does it indicate that it is our modern life and not the institution of marriage which is out of gear?

Two factors, essentially opposed to one another, combine in accounting very largely for the increase in divorce: they are the greater frankness and the greater selfishness of our modern life. Greater frankness, as compared with former times, is in itself a great gain. For happy marriages do not have to conceal their strong foundations, and wholly unhappy marriages only sink into deeper misery as a result of secrecy and unwillingness to face the facts. Divorces resulting from an honest recognition of the complete lack of any true basis for the continuation of a marriage are socially and personally beneficial and desirable.

Society, after all, has no interest in continuing a marriage between two persons when they are unable to live happily together. When there is a third party to the situation, a child, then society has a right to demand that the parents stay together, even if it is a sacrifice for them, for the sake of the child. But it is not at all certain that society would be wise to insist upon this right: a child is usually handicapped by the divorce of his parents and by being deprived of a normal home environment with two parents; but it might easily be worse for the child to be brought up in a home where its parents were maladjusted and unhappy.

But the other explanation of increased divorce, greater selfishness, works differently. For willingness to see the point of view of one's partner in marriage, eagerness to harmonize one's own point of view with that of one's marriage partner wherever possible, and readiness to respect the other point of view where the two are at variance, are essentials to a happy marriage; and, more than that, they are essentials which marriage as an institution has a right to expect, for they are not merely essentials of marriage, but essentials of right living generally. If they are lacking in a marriage, the fault lies not in the institution of marriage but in the parties to the marriage. The institution would not be worth continuing if it were not now proving to be, as it always has been, on the whole, the best basis for individual contentment. If it is true that the strains and stresses of modern living wear one ragged, make one irritable, and if society expects one to bear up reasonably well in public, it is nevertheless far from sensible to concentrate in the privacy of one's home the accumulation of dissatisfaction which is the result of lack of headway in the other daily problems and contacts of life. Under such conditions marriage is called upon to bear more than its rightful burden.

A third factor, purely economic, may have contributed to the increasing number of divorces. Women in the past few decades have achieved a degree of economic and political independence which rivals that of men. Women are no longer obliged to be married and to remain so to enjoy a comfortable existence.

THE LARGER FAMILY GROUP

When a man and woman marry, their marriage is the starting point of their own intimate family. But at the same time each of them remains a member of a larger family group. The parents and brothers and sisters of the husband and his more distant relatives and more remote ancestors are all part of his family; and, likewise, the corresponding immediate and more remote relatives of the wife are all part of her family. In this larger sense the family is the whole group of blood, collateral, and adopted relatives.

In modern society the paternal and maternal branches of the family are equally important, and the modern family is consequently said to be *bilateral*. Nevertheless, in modern communities the family name is always that of the male line. (In Spain this custom is modified; the family name of the father and mother are used jointly.)

Among primitive peoples the paternal and maternal branches are commonly not looked upon as equal in importance. Some groups give precedence to one, some to the other. Where the male line determines relationship, the family is said to be *patrilinear;* where descent is traced primarily through the mother's family, the family is said to be *matrilinear*. Early sociologists, drawing their conclusions from the history of modern civilized groups, assumed that the patrilinear family was almost universal, but later students, making extensive researches among the existing primitive peoples, found the matrilinear family exceedingly common. Where the family is reckoned on one line of descent only, it is known as a *sib*. Where the sib is matrilinear, it is known technically as the *clan;* where patrilinear, as the *gens*. Whether a tribe is organized into clans or gentes or into bilateral families, the general rule is that the men have the power and control over the group. In this case, and particularly when the ruler is the oldest man of the family group, the group or tribe is called *patriarchal,* and the system a *patriarchate*. In the very unusual cases where women have the major power, as among the Iroquois Indians, the group is called *matriarchal,* and the system a *matriarchate*. With the matrilinear clan system there is no tendency for women to rule, but sometimes authority over a family is vested in the mother's eldest brother or other male relative, rather than in the father. Such a system is known as an *avunculate*. In most matrilinear communities men live with their wives' families: such residence is *matrilocal*. Where men bring their wives to live in the vicinity of the men's families, the residence is *patrilocal*. It is possible, though uncommon, for a community to be at once matrilinear and patrilocal.

The word *taboo,* or *tabu,* which came originally from the Pacific regions, means the prohibition of an act or object. There are tabus on all subjects, but some important ones deal with the relationships of relatives to each other. The prohibition of incestuous marriages is a tabu, and so are many prohibitions of sexual and non-sexual intimacies between brother and sister. The parent-in-law tabu is one of the most common, prohibiting a person sometimes from even looking at his parent-in-law. Of the four possible types of parent-in-law tabu, the most common is that between a man and his mother-in-law. The reason for the prevalence of this tabu is undoubtedly to prevent a conflict of authority between the husband and parents of a young woman.

The Family Unit Today

In modern society the larger family group does not function as a unit to any great extent. Members of the same larger family group often live far from one another, and are closely associated with the customs, practices, and interests of their own locality rather than with those of the more scattered family group. Most of the responsibilities assumed by the larger family group among primitives are functions of the state in modern society.

Among primitive peoples the traditions of the family, traced back to remote ancestors, are of great importance in determining the practices of the family group. Until very recently the ancestral tradition was the guiding influence in the life of the Chinese people. Yet, in modern society, family tradition does not carry the weight which it once did, and ordinarily it does not extend back very far.

The influence of the larger family group has lessened, and with increasing divorce and with occasional experimentation in the rearing of children away from the home, the family in the narrower sense—the small, immediate family group—is having to prove its right to existence. Nevertheless, the indications are that the intimate family group has a unique function to perform which no other group can manage, and that, buffeted though it is by the rigors of social change, it will remain the basic social institution, the cornerstone of human society.

CLASSES AND SOCIAL ASSOCIATIONS

Next to the family, the most personal of the social institutions are the groups of people not necessarily related by birth yet connected through belonging to the same class of society, or through the closer bond of membership in the same circle of friends, or in the same club or other social association (using the word "social" in its narrower sense, referring to companionship in recreational activities).

Society in practically all parts of the world is divided into classes representing different social levels, although usually there are no clear lines of demarcation between classes. In feudal times the social classes were very sharply differentiated into the nobility, the clergy, the middle-class small landholders, and the serfs or laborers. In India, class distinction until recently existed in extreme form, constituting what is known as a caste system. A man was born into a certain caste; and, with certain exceptions, changes in wealth or accomplishment could not change his caste, and he was expected to marry within his own caste. There were various gradations in the caste system, from the highest Brahmans to the Pariahs (the outcasts beneath any of the classes of the caste system), each caste having its own work to perform and its own manner of living.

Among more democratic peoples, class distinctions are also clearly recognized. Where the government is monarchial, royalty and nobility constitute social classes, and there are upper and lower classes among the commoners, wealth and achievement being the basis for inclusion in the upper classes. In a republic, although titled classes do not exist, social leaders constitute an upper class into which their children are born, and which may ordinarily be entered by others only through the acquisition of great wealth or by outstanding accomplishment of some sort. Nevertheless, in countries of relatively recent traditions, people advance from one class to another with comparative ease or are permitted to drop to a lower class if they are unable to maintain their position.

Under socialistic and communistic doctrines, the distinction between the bourgeoisie or capitalistic middle classes and the proletariat or laboring classes is emphatically stressed, and the differences between the bourgeois property owners and the proletarian workers are held to be so fundamental as to make class conflict inevitable. In putting Marxist doctrines into practice, Soviet Russia has abolished class distinctions by recognizing the existence only of a working class; yet power is actually in the hands of a small minority. Even a legally established equality is difficult to maintain, since differences in individual ability exist in all groups, and greater ability almost inevitably leads to greater recognition, greater authority, and, in time, ordinarily to higher social standing.

From the sociological point of view all class distinctions which separate people into higher and lower ranks are undesirable. Social groupings based on common interests are natural and desirable; classes based upon rank divide society into antagonistic levels. Social groupings based on common interests enrich the interests by the encouragement which the group gives to its individual members; and each enriched social group contributes its share to the enrichment of the life of society as a whole.

CLUBS AND "SECRET SOCIETIES"

The typical secret society of primitive culture is very different from the type of organization among us that bears the same name. The most common primitive secret society is the group that consists of all adult men in the community. Such a group is usually politically important, governing the whole community and managing religious affairs. The group is not exclusive; every boy joins the society as a matter of course when he reaches the age of puberty. At that time the society functions to teach him many things: about sex and marriage, about the tribal religion, about ways of curing the sick, about governmental functions. A frequent function is to initiate the boys into the society in such a way as to impress upon the boy the tribal morality and its importance, emphasizing courage in war-like communities, the financial virtues in trading communities, and many other virtues in communities where they are especially important. Occasionally there are similar societies for women.

Frequently there are other societies among primitives, whose membership is less than the whole group of men and which function for particular purposes. Such are the medicine societies and war societies among American Indians, and religious societies in parts of Africa. But anyone who wants to may join these groups.

A third type of society among primitive peoples is the age group. The oldest men, or the young warriors, or the unmarried men may belong to separate groups that play important parts in communal life. The group of unmarried men is very common; sometimes they live together in a *men's house* which frequently becomes an important center for the community.

In our modern society, organizations such as the churches, political parties, YMCA, Boy Scouts, and many other organizations correspond in certain respects to the secret society of primitive cultures. They may have elements of secrecy, but membership is essentially open to anyone of the proper sex and age, and with an interest in the particular functioning of that organization. Most of our clubs are of this pattern; a few, such as our Greek letter fraternities, are genuinely secret, and membership is not available to everyone. This type, which is infrequently met with among primitives, is of much less social importance than the other varieties.

Other Organizations

Mankind sometimes divides itself into groups of types other than those we have already discussed. Sometimes a community is divided into two parts, called *moieties,* which take opposite sides in games and contests, and may also assume differing functions in ceremonies and dances. Sometimes a community is divided into more than two such divisions, which are then called *phratries.*

In Australia, *marriage classes* are common. A man belonging to one marriage class must marry a woman from a particular marriage class, not his own. The marriage classes are not family groups.

Commonly, human groups of any sort are symbolized, frequently by animals. Sometimes the belief is held that the group is descended from the animal used to symbolize them. This use of symbolism, known as *totemism,* is found in our own society as well as in primitive ones. When we symbolize a nation by a flag or bird, political parties by animals, colleges by various devices, professions by barber poles and similar signs, and so forth, we are practicing the same sort of totemism found in more primitive cultures.

THE CIRCLE OF FRIENDS

The most intimate personal group apart from the family is the circle of friends and close acquaintances. Friendship, among primitive peoples, among ancient civilized peoples, and in our own society, is one of the strongest of social bonds. A circle of friends is a social group of the utmost importance for society as a whole, for the co-operative spirit which may develop in small, intimate gatherings carries over into the larger groupings. Friendship is not necessarily based upon similarity of views, but it is based upon mutual respect and consideration. Without agreeing about specific problems, friends are nevertheless ordinarily in harmony about major matters. It is often remarked that the rush and confusion of modern life interfere with the full development of friendships, and undoubtedly this is true; yet it is a condition which society as it advances must rectify. For the friendship of a group of men and women is the surest indication that understanding, sympathy, and co-operation can increasingly become the determining factors in the evolution of society.

WORK AND WEALTH

Why do men work? Primarily to earn a living, undoubtedly; and earning a living means acquiring the wherewithal to supply oneself and one's family with the necessities of life and a reasonable share of the luxuries, conveniences, and pleasures of life. Nevertheless, men do not work only to earn a living. Some men work because they want to express the abilities which are in them, because they have natural or acquired skill which will not remain unused, because working is not merely a means of earning a living, but is in itself a manner of living. Welcome as leisure, idleness, and rest may be at times, few human beings can devote themselves entirely to play. Human nature is made for work, for the experiences, the attempts, the achievements which come in the course of working.

WORK AMONG PRIMITIVE PEOPLES

The instinct of self-preservation, the need for sustenance and shelter, compel primitive men and women to work. They undertake the tasks which are necessary in order to provide themselves with food, clothing, and housing of some sort. In very primitive societies each group of families is ordinarily an independent economic unit, its members working together to supply the needs of the community without joining with the economic activities of other communities.

The division of work between men and women was rather clearly defined even in the early stages in the development of society. At first men were principally hunters, women doing such simple agricultural work as necessary and preparing the food; men constructed the shelters, and women made the clothing.

There are various typical ways in which communities obtain food. The simplest and perhaps the most primitive type is that in which men live upon whatever their environment has to offer, *collecting* such objects as seem useful for nourishment—gathering eggs, insects, wild plants, fruits, and berries for food. Besides this method of subsistence, *hunting* and *fishing* may be the main sources of food. Hunting communities are extremely common; fishing communities are rather rare. When man learns to plant crops he comes soon to depend largely upon agricultural products, and we have *agricultural* communities. Sometimes a community will rely largely upon domestic animals for their food, and we have *pastoral* communities.

With more advanced cultures, the major occupation need not be the provision of food, so we have *commercial* and *industrial* communities.

Of course these types are not mutually exclusive. A hunting community may do some gathering and fishing on the side, as well as a certain amount of trading and perhaps some agriculture; and the modern industrial community gets its food from agriculture, the keeping of animals, and fishing.

In tracing the development of culture in Europe, we find that European man was first a hunter. Then he learned both agriculture and the domestication of animals at about the same time, becoming primarily agricultural about eight thousand years ago. In fairly modern times European man became commercial, and finally industrial. At no time, as far as we know, were Europeans chiefly a gathering, fishing, or pastoral community.

PROPERTY AMONG PRIMITIVE PEOPLES

Men work primarily in order to provide themselves and their families with the necessities of life. Some of these necessities, among them the most indispensable, such as food, are perishable and must be used promptly; others have permanence and may be kept almost indefinitely, such as materials from which a man constructs his shelter, and especially the land upon which he builds. Very early man had a sense of ownership, a feeling that what he had acquired belonged to him, was his property. At first his property was the product of his own work or his wife's, or of his neighbor's and acquired by exchange; or the land which he had cleared and settled upon. Later property of all sorts began to have a definite value placed upon it, to be reckoned in terms of exchange, to represent wealth—thus the conception of money as tokens of value developed. Capital as we know it today has evolved from the concrete types of property of primitive peoples.

Most peoples of ancient times and most primitive tribes of today recognize private ownership; all men recognize the semi-exclusive right of an individual to his tools, his clothing, and the other products of his industry; commonly property rights are recognized in names, dances, and other intangible objects; even land is frequently looked upon as the personal possession of the individual or the family who develop it. Not only do primitive peoples recognize a man's claim to his own property, but, in many groups, inheritance of property is an accepted custom. Besides individual property, primitive communities often recognize the ownership of property by families, sibs, societies, and by the community as a whole.

LABOR IN EARLIER TIMES

Fairly early in his evolution man must have discovered that he could compel other men to do his bidding, for indications are that slavery is a very ancient practice; but in very simple cultures the life of a slave is hardly to be distinguished from that of his master. In fact, in a very simple community master and slave of necessity engage in the same activities in order to support life, and the existence of a slave or so does not free others in the community from the search for the major part of their own necessities. Even in the early days of Greece and Rome a slave more often than not was practically a personal friend of his master. But advancing civilizations often demanded a large number of slaves, and their condition became much worse, as it did in Egypt, North Africa, later Greece and Rome, Europe, and America.

Through long periods the custom of enslaving men as a result of superior strength or conquest prevailed in many parts of the world and, in our own history, persisted beyond the middle of the nineteenth century. In Europe, slavery as a widespread practice gave way to serfdom during the Middle Ages. Under the feudal system a serf held his own small piece of land, subject, however, to the authority of his overlord, who in turn was a vassal or subordinate of a still more powerful noble, and so on in stages up to the king. The serf was obliged to give his overlord half of the produce of his land and to devote half of his time to his overlord's interests, including warfare.

WORK IN MODERN LIFE

The modern system of wage earning is based upon the assumption that each man can earn according to his ability. Under an economic order affording equal opportunities to all, this system might very well work out fairly. Yet the relation of an employer and an employee constitutes a distinction equivalent to that between classes, and men who live on an income from stocks and bonds and mortages set themselves apart from those who are dependent entirely on their daily earnings.

Modern industry produces more than modern man can possibly use, yet modern society fails to distribute its industrial and agricultural products so that all men can benefit by the increased facilities for production. Modern machinery constantly changes the qualifications expected of workers and reduces the number of workers required to meet the needs of industry. Consequently there are many men and women to whom little opportunity for advancement is offered, and even little opportunity for work.

The difference between primitive and civilized society is very evident in the evolution of work. Primitive peoples work to provide themselves with the necessities of life; their own abilities determine their success, for, allowing for differences in climate, each man has the same factors to contend with, the same assistance and the same opposition on the part of Nature.

Think of the life of the farmer in the days when sun and rain and his own endurance and that of his animals were the determining factors in the progress of his work. Think of a modern city, where food, clothing, and all the supplies needed for living can be bought in stores; some food, to be sure, sold in the natural state in which it came from the soil, but much in packages, in cans, in boxes, in bottles, in containers of one sort or another. Are the packaged, bottled, frozen, processed, canned foods as good as, less good than, or better than the natural foods? And does the housewife find her tasks simplified, her labor lessened, her home improved by the use of mechanically prepared foods in place of natural foods? There is clearly no simple, single answer to these questions. Modern methods have brought gains and losses with them.

TYPES OF WORK

Men choose work for which they are qualified, and in so far as they can, they qualify themselves for work which is to their liking. Whether a man shall be a mechanic, an electrician, a carpenter, a mason, a farmer, a printer, a salesman, a merchant, an engineer, an architect, an author, an artist, a musician, an actor, a financier, a lawyer, a doctor, a teacher, a minister, or devote himself to any of the other vocational or professional occupations, is often decided, however, by circumstances rather than by choice. A man may be trained for the trade or profession which his father has followed, or one which is the principal activity of the community in which he lives, or he may be headed toward a career determined for him by the ambition of his parents or friends.

As society adjusts itself it should provide all men and women with ample opportunity to acquaint themselves early with the various trades and professions, to try out their abilities and skills while they are quite young, so that they can decide for themselves the vocation which suits them best, which makes most use of their equipment for work, and which affords them the greatest satisfaction.

Labor Organizations and Labor Unrest

Yet it is not enough for men to be able to choose the work for which they are fitted. Men must have conditions for work which are conducive to good work. The tendency toward the organization of workers in unions has become marked in many fields in recent years, partly because the workers have found that only by joint action can they make their voices heard and bring their needs forcefully before their employers, partly because many of the workers have no interest in their work other than as a means of livelihood, or gain no personal satisfaction from their labor. With conditions such as they are, it is readily understandable that labor unions should be organized solely for the protection of the workers' rights. Yet under a more equitable opportunity for work, labor unions might well become groups for the advancement of the workers' interest in the field of their activity.

Strikes, lockouts, bargaining for adjustment of wages, and other manifestations of labor unrest are symptoms of social change, indications of an age of social instability, an age which has not succeeded in adjusting itself to the needs of human life. Clearly, the Industrial Revolution, the introduction of machinery into industry, brought about changes so far-reaching that its effects have increased and multiplied down to the present day. Economically, socially, and psychologically, the advent of the machine has complicated man's life, and as yet man has been unable to find a new equilibrium within this new complexity.

Wealth, Poverty, and Unemployment

Men must work and must benefit from their work in the satisfaction of their needs. The acquisition of wealth is often looked upon as an indication of success in life. To a certain extent it may be an indication of success in work, but it is far from being an indication of success in living. Even with regard to work it indicates little, for, where opportunities are unequal, accomplishment cannot be measured in terms of the amassing of wealth.

There can be no justification for great wealth for some, where there is poverty for others. If equality is impossible and undesirable, surely a minimum of comfort and security is the social right of everyone. Throughout the ages there have always been people dependent upon the charity of others. But society itself must be to blame for the existence of poverty. Poverty may be due to inability to work, to unwillingness to work, or to the lack of opportunity for work. If the inability is caused by illness or by lack of training, if the unwillingness is caused by shiftlessness, the problems must be solved by society through its handling of matters of health and education, by its better care for the individual. But if there is lack of opportunity for work, if there is unemployment because of overproduction resulting from the needlessly vast capacity of machines, then the problem involved cannot be solved by caring more adequately for individual health and education. Unemployment on any considerable scale is an unmistakable sign of social maladjustment, a clear-cut call for a readjustment of economic life. In a stable, ordered society, work must be expected of all, there must be opportunity for all to work, and work must bring a full measure of satisfaction to all.

THE STATE

Why does man feel the need for a state, for some form of government? Governments provide men with the necessary setting for life, giving them a sense of security, a sense that justice and personal safety are assured. The state is man's own creation, to which he surrenders many powers of regulation and control, feeling that the good of the whole is more important than the advantage of the individual. The state, at its best, expresses the will of the majority and yet gives full opportunity for the expression of the individual will as well.

GOVERNMENT AMONG PRIMITIVE PEOPLES

The instinct of self-preservation which compels primitive men and women to work for the necessities of life also compels them to band together for protection from common natural dangers and for protection from strangers who are potential enemies. From joint activity for purposes of protection and economic activity, primitive peoples progress in time to formal organization of the community, the better to achieve the advantages to be gained by co-operation in joint endeavor.

Among many primitive peoples the older men are the leaders of the group; they are recognized as having the right to make rules which the others in the group must follow, and in their authority and their deliberations we find the beginnings of the state. Among other groups the men as a whole rule the community, or sometimes the young warriors. More frequently there is a chief, who owes his position to his outstanding personality, his wealth, or his supposed magical powers. Some tribes have several chiefs, each one ruling the community in those activities that he knows much about. Later the chieftainship sometimes becomes formalized, a man inheriting the right to rule, and thus becoming a king.

As we have seen, the larger family group is in effect a political unit among many primitive peoples. But most communities include several family groups, and in time the need for some recognized controlling power superior to that of the family becomes evident. One of the earliest powers of the state is undoubtedly the regulation of the use of force. The political organization which governs a community determines to what extent force may be used by individual members of the group, eliminates conflicts within the group in so far as that is possible, and organizes the use of force against hostile communities when that becomes necessary.

Justice and Law among Primitive Peoples

The state is for the most part not highly organized among primitive peoples; nevertheless there is a very definite sense of right and wrong. Primitive standards differ from our own standards in many respects, but the accepted customs and standards are more fundamentally just than would be generally assumed. Among many tribes a definite system of fines, payable in animals or other produce, is in use in place of violence for the settlement of disputes.

Tribes in which group sentiment is not highly developed permit individuals to obtain justice for themselves in their own way. On the other hand, tribes which recognize the importance of the community assign the responsibility to the leaders. Among the peoples who are conscious of the unity of the group, there are two very different conceptions of leadership. The tribes of Africa are strongly monarchial, the authority resting in a powerful king, whereas among the American Indians we find an essentially democratic sentiment, the chief sharing his power with others.

FORMS OF GOVERNMENT

The state has taken on increasing authority in its evolution through the ages, coming in time to be thought of as having something of an existence of its own apart from that of the individuals who compose it.

With more frequent and more rapid communication, travel, and contact between neighboring or widely separated nations, each state has necessarily thought of itself as the representative of its people in dealing with other states. States have developed a conception of sovereignty, of state authority and power, to be respected by other states. In some parts of the world and in some generations, the state, which was developed to exist as an aid to men, has insisted that its citizens existed for it, that the state or nation is greater than the sum of its individual members.

The specific form which government takes among a given people is determined by many factors, including the traditions and temperament of the people themselves, the tendency of the age in which they live, the extent to which they are influenced by the convictions of individual leaders. Democracy, monarchy, fascism, nazism, socialism, communism are all modern conceptions; in earlier times there were autocracy, despotism, feudalism, the city-states, and leagues of free cities. Some nations have been content to remain within their own boundaries, while others have embarked on expansion into far corners of the globe, following the way of imperialism. Some nations have magnified their own importance at the expense of others, have stressed the claims of individual statehood, of nationalism; others have recognized clearly the need for constant active co-operation between nations, paving the way for internationalism. The United Nations (UN) is the furthest step which has yet been taken toward bringing the nations of the world into harmony with one another.

THE STATE AND THE INDIVIDUAL

The state is ordinarily evident in daily life chiefly in the protection which it offers to the individual; and as his expression of citizenship a man pays taxes, votes, and recognizes the right of the state to call him to arms in the national defense. In recent years the state has been authorized to intervene to a greater extent than ever before in the economic life of its inhabitants; man's status as a worker, as a producer, as an owner, has become so uncertain that the state has had to extend its authority to the economic sphere, to legislate about matters of industry, agriculture, and commerce, about investment and property.

Many who believe that individual initiative is the basis for work feel that the government should not intervene; others who believe that the state must provide a sure means of livelihood for all would like the state to go further, to take over the ownership of industry itself. There can be no doubt that in times of stress and change, individuals and the state must co-operate at all points and to the fullest extent, and that the assistance which the state can render in the economic field must be welcomed whole-heartedly. On the other hand, when society finds itself in a condition of relative equilibrium, of comparative stability, the functions of the state and the functions of industry may well be clearly distinguished from one another; the tendency will be to separate the economic and political aspects of life while still keeping them closely correlated and in harmony with one another.

CRIME

The state in its administration of justice finds itself called upon to handle the problems of crime. The criminal is an offender against society —a danger to society and a maladjusted member of society. Those guilty of corruption in the conduct of industry or government are criminals as truly as those guilty of individual crime. It is the function of the state to punish offenders, protect individuals, and make all its members well-adjusted citizens. Until recently the principal problems in handling crime were the establishment of guilt and the meting out of punishment. To these have now been added the important task of aiding the offenders to gain full control of themselves and to become useful and dependable members of society, and even more fundamental, the prevention of crime by the sympathetic study of individuals and their adjustments to society.

Heredity and environment are both important factors in laying the foundation for crime. Many criminals are found to have grown up in an environment of low moral standards, where instances and examples of crime were common.

Heredity and environment may afford explanations, but they cannot remove the responsibility from the individual. For those whose development is stunted so that they have no true sense of right and wrong, the problem is one which must be treated as an illness. For those who deliberately plan and carry out a crime knowing fully its significance, the community reserves its most severe punishments.

Some form of confinement and supervision of those guilty of crimes is absolutely essential for the protection of society, but sociologists are convinced that the life of a confined person must have the essential elements of living if there is to be any progress toward permanent improvement in the confined person's attitude toward and qualifications for life. Solitary imprisonment may produce remorse, but it does not increase a man's capacity for leading a life which will be a benefit to society. More and more those who have committed crimes are being permitted to work and study during their confinement, and they are also being aided to see life rightly. Even those who are imprisoned for life are being given opportunities for work and study, so that within their prison walls they may benefit others and themselves.

When a mob in its fury seizes a man guilty of a crime and sets about obtaining justice in its own way, to punish by lynching, the authority of the state is challenged. The mob in its passion for revenge may inflict punishment, but in defying the state the mob itself is committing a crime. The state exists to preserve law and order, and must be made to administer justice promptly, but an angry mob only endangers justice, only invites more widespread indulgence in crime.

The state must act promptly and firmly. It must keep under constant supervision anyone who has shown inability to live in accordance with the just standards of society. It must make certain that a man can be so confined as to make escape impossible, so that society's protection will be complete. If the state can demand that a man offer his life on the battlefield, it can certainly demand that a man who deliberately has taken the life of another should forfeit his life in atonement; but a world which is seeking to eliminate war altogether may well consider whether the state, in administering justice, should inflict capital punishment by putting an end to a human life.

War and Peace

War is the most destructive force with which society has to contend. Disease, accidents, disasters due to earthquake and volcanic eruption, claim heavy tolls, but man is learning steadily how better to combat disease, he is working steadily to make accidents less likely, he is even learning to build for greater security against the vast natural catastrophes which at times shake part of the earth and in the presence of which he is largely helpless. But war is a man-made disaster, a catastrophe of society itself, to which man must put a final stop. There are several types of wars, each presenting its own problems.

First there is warfare between neighboring nations, intended to solve some disagreement between them. It has often been pointed out that just as men once tried to settle their personal grievances by duels and in time recognized that personal justice could never be obtained by the use of sword or firearms, that the law courts must be the place for obtaining justice, that so, too, nations must in time recognize that their differences must be settled before a justly constituted and justly organized international court.

Civil war is the second type of warfare. Here the conflict is ordinarily a spontaneous, sudden uprising, a clash between temporary opponents belonging to the same group. Some deep emotional dissatisfaction causes part of a nation to band together to overthrow the existing order, and the supporters of the existing order fight back. The causes of civil war lie far deeper in human nature than do the traditional causes of war between neighboring nations, but as society adjusts itself increasingly well to human needs, the possibility of revolutions and civil wars will inevitably grow less.

World wars, wars involving many widely separated nations, constitute the third type. Superficially, they may seem to be merely wars between neighboring nations on a larger scale. But actually their significance is quite different. For distant nations are not readily drawn into wars unless "the time is ripe" for war. And the time ripens not because of any specific conflict of sovereignty, but because of some deep-seated condition in the world's population. It is not personal emotion, like the cause of civil wars, but an actual pressure of overcrowding populations against one another, which causes world wars. Not that there is insufficient room in the world for its populations, as the English economist Malthus predicted there would be, but that from time to time populations in the more crowded parts of the world seem to have growing pains, to feel the need for expansion, to be restless, ready to endanger the long, hard-won civilization of the years of peace. When this mood is upon great groups of men, war is difficult to avert.

Some sociologists have called war a crude safety valve, a way in which society restores equilibrium in a world in which population is out of balance. This conception of war as a blind force in society seems to remove it from the realms of human control. But even sociologists who recognize how elemental this stirring of population may be would hardly conclude that society is powerless to devise some method by which these strains can be released without recourse to war. Woodrow Wilson, Franklin D. Roosevelt, and other world leaders felt that a great world forum where nations could present their cases, make known their urgent needs, would provide a means of ending the possibility of war. At the end of the First World War the League of Nations was formed to accomplish this purpose, yet it failed to prevent another conflict. At the close of the Second World War the United Nations was established to provide a new and more effective instrumentality for the preservation of peace.

The preparation of atomic and hydrogen bombs and long-range missiles of various types has revealed man's terrifying capacity for unlimited destruction. The horror which the use of these weapons would produce acts as a powerful deterrent.

More fundamental is the realization that when human nature matures to the point where war is recognized as the denial of all that society aims to be, then war will be permanently eliminated from the ways of men. Then the deep stirrings of population will direct themselves toward peaceful solutions of their problems and will turn their powerful energies to the upbuilding of society in all parts of the world on a firm foundation of uninterrupted peace.

EDUCATION

From the point of view of society, education is not limited to schooling; it includes all of man's means for equipping himself for life. We hear much nowadays about adult education, courses and books designed to carry a man or woman's education through life; about health education, aiming to aid men and women in the treatment of and preventing of disease and accidents; about moral education, seeking to develop in all men and women a clear, strong, permanent sense of right and wrong. The acquisition of knowledge and the preparation for a vocation are fundamental, but in addition to these sociology is concerned with the other aspects of education.

FORMAL AND INFORMAL EDUCATION

Primitive peoples learn more by doing than by hearing about things; there is work which must be done, and means must be found to do it. In primitive groups, boys and girls are expected to lend a hand; they work in the fields or in the house; they help in so far as they can in all the daily tasks. With increasing practice and experience they acquire notable skill. They have no formal education; they learn while working, while playing. They hear tales of prowess, stories of the earliest adventures of their tribes; they listen to the recollections of their elders, and they learn from what they hear, but only as a supplement to what they have learned by doing.

In modern civilized communities, education is largely *formal,* administered by schools and universities. The fields of knowledge have been organized for systematic presentation; and for students who are academically minded, formal education has an endless wealth of material to offer. But many students are essentially practical in their approach to life, do not learn as well from books as from experience. Those who do learn well from books need the steadying, the stabilizing, which comes from learning in the midst of working and playing, and from learning to do things when knowing how to do them is essential for progress in the task at hand. From this concrete approach to knowledge most boys and girls, young men and young women, will in time want to reach out to the learning which is found principally in books.

It is only very recently that educators and teachers have begun to realize that in coming as far as we have from the ways in which primitive peoples learned, we have lost as well as gained. It is not only in the long jump from primitive to modern society that we have lost fundamental physical endurance essential for ease in doing the things which need to be done all about us; it is true that in the transition from the country to the city we have lost many indispensable abilities and that in moving from individual homes to apartments with central heating, cooling, lighting, and other services, we have been spared still more tasks and lost still more qualifications for daily living.

It is for this reason that many educators feel that what was once learned in the course of actual daily duties—was learned, that is to say, *informally*—must now be made part of our schooling so that these fundamental abilities will not be lost altogether.

SCHOOLS

There is no question that society has benefited greatly by the emphasis laid in recent years upon the necessities of formal schooling for all. Many who would have lived lives of drudgery have been fitted for better work by their schooling; many who would have few interests apart from their work have become interested in cultural aspects of life and have rounded out their lives by deriving tremendous enjoyment from their new interests.

The schools offer to children, and indirectly to their parents, the great treasures of human knowledge; and they provide them with a background for earning a living. These two functions raise schooling to great importance. Yet there is a weakness in our school system, a tendency for it to become stereotyped, rigid, and inflexible, to repeat itself rather than to adapt itself to changed conditions, to expect all students to fit into a common mold rather than to recognize the qualifications, background, needs, and future plans of the individual student. Clearly it would be a great deal to ask of our schools that they meet the special requirements of each student, but this must come in time. Meanwhile it is important for parents to see education in this newer light and to supplement the work of the schools, in so far as possible, toward this newer goal.

HEALTH

Knowledge about matters of health and hygiene is an exceedingly important part of education. The great advances of medicine in recent years in the control and cure of disease have been due in considerable part to the greater alertness of the public, the greater readiness of the public to co-operate with physicians in matters of vaccination and inoculation against diseases, recognition of symptoms, quarantine during illness, and scientific care during convalescence. Clearly the guarding and improving of health is in the very forefront of the needs of society.

ETHICS

Do men and women instinctively distinguish between right and wrong? Or have our moral standards evolved through the ages? There was a widespread sense of justice and fairness among primitive peoples. We cannot say that this was the expression of a moral instinct, but human beings must have recognized early the necessity of standards for behavior, the necessity of encouraging certain types of conduct and prohibiting others. These standards, enforced by universal support, have become the guiding ethical principles of society.

In times of social change, moral standards are frequently challenged or disregarded by individuals, and are often upheld less strictly by society as a whole. In such times there may be less restraint in speech and dress; but such symptoms are likely to be temporary. Unless they are accompanied by a deeper disregard for moral standards, society need not concern itself greatly with minor habits, but it must at all times preserve the fundamental standards of right and wrong—it must make right living the guiding principle of every human life.

CULTURE

Culture is a general term which brings together all the leisure interests of men and women, all the activities which enrich life by giving it variety. Although the cultural interests are less concretely practical than the activities called for in earning a living or governing a community, they are no less essential to life. For a life which is lived from day to day with no thought other than the necessity of providing sustenance and protection is wholly meaningless; and furthermore, industry and government themselves are handled more successfully, more effectively, more efficiently, by men who have the ability to see beyond their immediate tasks, to recognize and to adopt improved methods as a result of their more varied background.

For most people the cultural interests—literature, drama, art, architecture, music, the outdoors (nature, gardening, sports), scientific knowledge, and philosophic thought—are definitely leisure interests, activities to be pursued when time permits and inclination prompts. For some, however, they are of the utmost practical concern; they constitute the means by which the author, painter, sculptor, composer, and scientist earn their livelihood. For those whose daily work is within the cultural activities, as well as for those who turn to cultural interests only at times, culture is something added to life.

CULTURE AMONG PRIMITIVE PEOPLES

The beginnings of culture are clearly present in the lives of primitive peoples. Language and handicrafts are among the most fundamental cultural expressions, and the origins of language and crafts go back to the very beginnings of human life. Among animals there are, of course, very definitely developed and recognized cries, calls, songs, and other means of communication, so that human beings must always have communicated with one another and must very early have elaborated their system of communication and set in motion the evolution of language. Writing, the recording of language, came later, first in the form of drawings of the objects referred to—writing and painting have a common origin. Dancing, also, must have been a very early trait, and song scarcely less so. In their crafts, the making of clothing and cooking utensils, primitive peoples showed early an interest in adornment, in decoration; many arts go back to the primitive use of color and design. The necessary task of providing shelter is the forerunner of architecture and of branches of engineering. The primitive uses of tools, of fire, of water, are the simple forerunners of physics and chemistry.

CULTURE IN MODERN LIFE

Culture, in its beginnings so intimately bound up with the daily tasks of primitive life, so deeply cherished at many high points in the history of civilization, tends to be set aside amid the confused duties which characterize our complex modern age. Yet, if it is true, as it very apparently is, that with the aid of machines all the work required to meet the needs of the community as a whole can be done in a comparatively few hours a day, provided some work is done by everyone; and if work is distributed wisely and fairly, so that all can work, and can work at tasks for which they are qualified, then everyone will have more leisure than heretofore, as well as more energy to devote to leisure interests. Where for a long time cultural activities have been thought of as at best diversion, amusement, recreation, they are already taking their rightful place as true and valuable interests for all. Men and women are discovering once more how indispensable the expression of individual effort in some form of artistic and scientific endeavor is in the rounding of every life.

RELIGION

Religion is man's faith in his own highest spiritual nature and in the spiritual power which transcends human life—the power called God. Religion is man's approach to the whole of life and to the great unsolved problems of life; problems which lie beyond the realm of science—problems of life after death, of the nature of Deity.

PRIMITIVE RELIGIOUS BELIEFS AND CUSTOMS

Among primitive peoples, Nature, inanimate Nature, was strange, unknown. Sun, moon, and stars—darkness and wind and rain—thunder and lightning—fire, streams, rivers, and the sea—the tops of mountains and the depths of caves—were filled with mystery. Primitive man found Nature uncertain, now helpful, now hostile, and beyond his power to control. He sought to understand Nature, but its meaning lay far beyond his knowledge. He felt that the unknown powers of Nature must be beings greater than himself; he looked upon natural objects as powers in themselves; the forces of Nature he believed to be controlled by deities which did not reveal themselves but merely revealed their power. Among some primitive peoples these mysterious powers are all thought to be manifestations of one great vast spirit pervading the whole universe. When peoples held individual objects in Nature to be powerful in themselves, such objects were treated with awe and reverence and became fetishes of the tribe. Yet whether they attribute superhuman powers to one or to many spirits or objects, all primitive peoples believe that there is some unrevealed explanation for happenings which they cannot understand, and it is in this belief that we find the beginnings of religion.

Primitive peoples dread things which they do not understand; consequently fear and superstition are closely bound up with the earliest religious feelings, and many primitive religious practices were for the purpose of winning favor and protection of the mysterious Spirit or the lesser deities, or atoning for some act which was believed to have aroused the anger of the higher powers. Storms, floods, gales, plagues were looked upon as signs of the displeasure of the great forces of Nature, and such a rare phenomenon as an eclipse of the sun, with its awe-inspiring fascination for us today, has at all times been looked upon by primitive peoples as an indication of the might of the unknown powers.

Primitive man must have discovered very early that his views about Nature, his beliefs and his fears, were shared by the others in his tribe, discovered also that one or more men in the group had confidence in their ability to approach the mysterious spirits and to seek their help or forgiveness. Such men would be looked upon as leaders in dealing with all that was not easily understood—with the calming of fears, the healing of wounds, the curing of sickness, the recognition of death, with the hopes of men for increased fertility of the soil, with all questions concerning the hidden spirit or soul in man himself, with the fate of the soul after death, and the nature of the great spirit or spirits which guided the universe. Such an early religious leader, medicine man or shaman, was at once priest, doctor, and magician. Skilled beyond others in his group in many ways, and helpful according to his skill, he oftentimes claimed for himself powers far beyond his abilities, magical powers which called for elaborate rituals for worship, fasting, punishment, sacrifice, gradually making him a mysterious figure, partaking somewhat of the mystery of the unknown in life, which it was his task to explain. Mystery has combined with ecstasy in the religious celebrations of many times and places: in the spring revels of the ancient Celts and Slavs, the Bacchic orgies of the Greeks, the mystical exaltation of the medieval saints, and the revivalism of later days.

THE CHURCH AND OTHER RELIGIOUS ORGANIZATIONS

A man's religion may be the creed of the religious organization to which he belongs and whose views he accepts. How closely he associates himself, if he does, to an established creed depends partly on his own individual conclusions concerning life and the unsolved problems of his relation to the universe. Men whose beliefs are identical naturally group together, naturally turn for guidance to leaders whose views represent their own. Faith is heightened when it is shared with others, and joint faith can offer its benefits to many who would not be reached or touched by individual convictions. The followers of the primitive medicine men constituted the first religious groups; and as society advanced in complexity, churches and other religious organizations came into being in simple form and evolved into the great religious institutions of our own day.

The history of religion is a story of contrasting beliefs in different parts of the world, of beliefs taking precedence one over another, of beliefs modified, re-enforced, reconsidered, changing to meet new conditions. And the history of the churches and other religious organizations through which man has expressed his views and his aspirations is also a story of great variety, a story of the upholding of faith in periods of doubt, and of the personal courage of many religious leaders.

We cannot attempt here to indicate the difference between the various great religions, between Christianity, Judaism, Mohammedanism, Buddhism, Brahmanism, Confucianism, Zoroastrianism, the polytheism of the ancient Greeks and Romans, and other cults. Each has its elements of greatness in satisfying human religious needs, each has made vast contributions to the welfare and progress of mankind. Yet each has at times revealed weaknesses—limitations in adapting itself to changed conditions. Religious churches have risen to great heights of temporal power, have fallen again, have sometimes gained, sometimes lost in eminence.

It is important to recognize that many of the great benefits of the religious organizations to mankind have been in such fields as education, welfare and health, morality and standards of conduct. Sociologically these fields are the concern of social institutions other than religion. Consequently the churches are more than religious organizations. They perform great social services of varied nature. In many communities the church is the meeting place of many interests and many activities. In periods of political uncertainty and instability, the churches are often the strongholds of sane thinking in political matters, though at times they are found on the side of reaction. This wider role of the churches must be differentiated from their function as the expression of the strictly religious aspects of the lives of men and women.

RELIGION IN MODERN LIFE

One hears fairly often nowadays that religion is losing its hold, that the churches are not satisfying individual needs as fully as they formerly did. Is this true, and if so, to what extent, and why?

In a time of great social unrest and social change, man is hard put to meet the demands of daily life. Most of his efforts, his energy, his attention, is devoted to the mere business of living. Reflection and contemplation have little place in a world in ferment. Some people, to be sure, seek to escape from the uncertain realities about them, to lose themselves in the great eternal problems which are untouched by material changes. Yet true religion is not an escape from the realities of daily living. It has a most important place in a well-rounded life, lived in full acceptance of all the demands of living. Yet when daily life becomes too demanding, requiring all of a man's time, religion may be crowded out.

Again, approached from another angle, religion recedes at certain points before the advance of science. Some of the tenets of established religion are challenged by geology in its study of the evolution of the earth, others are challenged by biology in its study of the evolution of life, still others by psychology in its study of the evolution of the mind. Often it is held that science and religion are diametrically opposed to one another; but there may be problems which science can never solve, problems which must always rest for their solution on human faith. There can be no question that there are problems which lie beyond the realms of science, problems which men can approach only through reflection, through philosophy, and possibly through sensing the spiritual quality in each other which is the essence of religion.

TEMPORARY SOCIAL GROUPS

We have now considered the chief divisions of society, the permanent social institutions. There are, however, certain temporary social groupings which are of extraordinary interest to sociology; they are mobs, crowds, audiences, rallies—brought together largely by chance. In studying them we are concerned with behavior rather than with institutions. We are in reality in a field which lies between sociology and psychology and is known as social psychology.

People in certain group gatherings, such as audiences at theaters and concerts and sports events, remain essentially themselves, though their reactions are heightened by the presence of others, their pleasure intensified or their disappointment increased.

Individuals who become a part of a mob behave differently; they lose their own personality in the drive of the group; they are motivated by a herd instinct, derived from the instinct of gregariousness in animals. More often than not they are moved by an unreasoning urge to carry out the momentary will of the mob. Mobs are more easily swayed emotionally than individuals are; inhibitions are removed, repressions released; and in action, mobs inflamed by revolutionary spirit or by desire for vengeance are destructive, having no respect for property or life.

Crowds, on the other hand, driven to action by common danger, by fire or explosion, behave differently from herd-like mobs. In panic and fright they may cause destruction, but it is the disorder and not a released herd emotion which is the cause.

Group feeling has its influence upon people brought together in a common setting: at a hotel, on a ship or train; in a hospital; and there are the worshipers at a religious service; there are officers and men in war, in the midst of battle; and there are workers banded together in mines and plants in the industries of peace.

SOCIAL FORCES AND SOCIAL CHANGE

In discussing the principal social institutions we have noted many forces at work, many changes during the evolution of society. Sociologists define social forces in many ways. For our purposes we shall use the term *social forces* to apply to those great movements within society which bring about social change. Some of these build up society, others tear it down.

The need for sustenance and the need for sexual satisfaction, increases in population, cycles of prosperity and depression, revolutions in methods of industry or in forms of government, tendencies toward nationalism or imperialism, war, movements for international solidarity and peace, are all forces working in harmony or in conflict with one another within the framework of society. These social forces are of such magnitude that individuals seem powerless before them. Great wars, great depressions, apparently run their courses despite the efforts of men to limit them or to end them; great periods of prosperity and progress seem to advance to their zenith unhampered by the mistakes of men. Yet men are not wholly helpless before social forces; very slowly, but cumulatively over long years, men can modify these forces, can turn them more nearly in the direction that they want them to go.

Less vast than the social forces in their irresistible power, yet more continuous in their influence, are the *social habits,* the *folkways* and *mores* of society, to use the terms of one of the most penetrating and original of American sociologists, William Graham Sumner. *Folkways* are the customary ways of doing things within a given group, the usual practices with regard to marriage and the family, work, property, government, and the other social institutions. When they develop into firmly established local customs and conventions enhanced by local tradition, they become *mores.*

Social forces and social habits between them determine *social selection.* To a certain extent social forces resemble natural forces; yet because of the modifying influence of social habits, social selection does not proceed as natural selection would toward the "survival of the fittest" in the physical sense. Society aims to provide the weak and the strong equally with opportunities for life. In its care of those who are sick in body or mind, or guilty of crime, society in its humanity aids those whom Nature would not aid; yet for its own protection it necessarily prevents them from endangering the health, welfare, and security of mankind. Social selection aims at social fitness, and in testing for this fitness it considers intellectual and emotional as well as physical qualifications. Survival in society calls for a balance between strength and ability.

Social evolution is the general movement of social change. We have studied the evolution of various social institutions, but as yet we have scarcely noted their relation to one another. We have stressed the fact that in the development of society, when changes take place, economic changes occur first, political changes after them, educational and cultural changes later still, and religious changes last of all. Let us see how this works in actual life today. Social forces are clearly at work bringing about social changes. The changes are apparent first as disturbances in our daily work, as upsets in wealth, property, and employment. Without as yet having arrived at a new stability in the economic world, these social forces are now reaching out to the sphere of political activity and calling upon governments to adapt themselves to changing economic conditions. Education and culture and religion have hardly been able to keep pace with these changes, and are only now beginning to sense the new roles which they will play when society is once more in comparative equilibrium.

These stages of social change mark every period of social evolution and, omitting the immediate family because it is a personal rather than a general institution, the economic needs are, at all times, the groundwork for the whole social structure. This conception is basic in Karl Marx's economic (or materialistic) interpretation of history. According to this view, it is not kings, not parliaments, not ideas that are the basic determinants of the course of history, but the need of each group of people for the simplest things of life, for food and shelter, for an opportunity to work in order to provide for oneself and one's family, that on a larger scale it is commercial, agricultural, or industrial rivalry between nations, which makes the succession of events in history what they are. Such a view is, of course, very incomplete. Fundamental as the economic factors may be, they are no more than the foundations. It is the political, social, cultural, and personal superstructures which are the richer and fuller expressions of human living.

SOCIETY TODAY

We are living in an age of such rapid, such thoroughgoing, such universal social change that sociology is, as never before, the science of the moment. There have been earlier periods of tremendous social change: the transition from the autocracy of the late Roman Empire on one hand and the tribal government of the Teutons on the other to the feudalism of the Middle Ages; then the transition to monarchy during the commercial revolution which accompanied the Renaissance; then to democracy during the industrial revolution, commencing toward the end of the eighteenth century.

Whether the changes which are now taking place all about us are as momentous as these earlier great transitions, it is still too early to say. The likelihood is that we are indeed on the threshold of a new era, economically, politically, and socially. Seldom have people been so aware of being in the midst of great social changes as we are today. Society, having evolved to its present complexity, is at last beginning to submit itself to study. While men are learning to understand something about the nature and structure and forces of society, its structure is rapidly changing, its forces are rapidly at work. Life today, with all its hardships and uncertainties, is more thrilling than ever before; for man, with his first glimpse at the nature of society, has his first opportunity to set himself to modifying the forces of social change, his first opportunity to assist at the birth of a new social order, his first opportunity to be himself the founder and designer of a new and more human society.

EXAMINATION QUESTIONS

1. How does sociology differ from psychology?
2. What is the principal difference between primitive cultures and our own?
3. What, until recent times, has been the most important factor in the development of our civilization?
4. What are the four principal races of mankind?
5. What differences are there between human races?
6. What is marriage, actually and ideally?
7. What is the most common form of marriage?
8. What is polyandry?
9. What reasons can be given for the occurrence of polyandry?
10. What reasons can be given for the occurrence of polygyny?
11. What is group marriage?
12. Is there a biological objection to inbreeding?
13. What groups are usually endogamous?
14. What groups are usually exogamous?
15. What is meant by the term "cross-cousin"?
16. Show that cross-cousins belong to different groups.
17. What is sororate?
18. What is the significance of the method of marriage which is most common among primitives?
19. What is "marriage by arrangement"?
20. Has divorce always existed?
21. Are divorces socially desirable?
22. Why do we call our family system bilateral?
23. What is a gens?
24. What is the distinction between these three terms: patrilinear, patrilocal, patriarchal?
25. What is a tabu?
26. Between what sets of relatives are social tabus frequently found?
27. What is the reason for the commonest of tabus?
28. What was the caste system of India?
29. Why is it difficult to maintain a classless society?
30. Are class distinctions necessary and desirable?
31. Among primitive societies, what is the commonest form of "secret society"?
32. How does it differ from what we know as secret societies in our own culture?
33. What are the functions of the primitive secret society?
34. What are a moiety's functions?
35. What is the social importance of friendships?

36. Could it ever be possible for the average working time to be reduced to a few hours a year?
37. Is the conception of property a modern development?
38. When was the state first organized?
39. Should the state interfere with the conduct of business?
40. What principles should govern the treatment of confined criminals?
41. What is meant by "informal" education?
42. What are the two functions of education?
43. What are two fundamental cultural expressions?
44. What was the earliest form of writing?
45. What is the commonest form of religious belief among primitive communities?
46. What is fetishism?
47. Do religions change and develop?
48. How does a mob differ from a crowd?
49. What are "social forces"?
50. What was the basic doctrine of Karl Marx?

For Further Study

AMERICAN WAY OF LIFE, by Harry Elmer Barnes and Oreen M. Ruedi. (Prentice-Hall, New York.)

INTRODUCTION TO SOCIOLOGY, by Joseph S. Roucek and Roland L. Warren. (Littlefield, Adams & Co., Paterson, N.J.)

MIDDLETOWN and MIDDLETOWN IN TRANSITION, by Robert S. and Helen M. Lynd. (Harcourt, Brace & World, Inc., New York.)

SOCIAL INSTITUTIONS, by Harry Elmer Barnes. (Prentice-Hall, New York.)

SOCIOLOGY, by Emory S. Bogardus. (The Macmillan Co., New York.)

SOCIOLOGY, by John F. Cuber. (Appleton-Century-Crofts, New York.)

Answers to Examination Questions

(For instructions see page xvi)

I. ANCIENT HISTORY

1. Until he began to record his activities. (page 1)
2. The period in history before men learned to work in metals. (page 1)
3. Messenger. (page 2)
4. 5000 B.C. (page 3)
5. The Pharaohs built them for tombs. (page 3)
6. Cleopatra was an Egyptian queen who was the last of the line of the Greek Ptolemies. (page 3)
7. The Sumerians impressed their records on clay tiles, while the Egyptians wrote on papyrus. (page 5)
8. Hammurabi. (page 6)
9. In Arabia. (page 7)
10. For their activity as navigators and traders. (page 8)
11. Monarchies (ruled by one man), oligarchies (ruled by a select group of a few men), and democracies (ruled by all the citizens). (page 12)
12. 776 B.C., the year of the first Olympic games. (page 13)
13. Periods of four years between the Olympic games. (page 13)
14. The Assyrian empire. (page 6)
15. An enslaved class of farmers and soldiers. (page 14)
16. Solon. (page 15)
17. In the island of Lesbos. (page 15)
18. Heavily armed infantry. (page 17)
19. A messenger who ran 150 miles to get reinforcements for the battle of Marathon, and later, mortally wounded, ran ahead 22 miles to Athens to announce the victory. (page 17)
20. The pass of Thermopylae. (page 17)
21. Pericles was an Athenian leader of the fifth century B.C. who consolidated the empire. (page 18)
22. Phidias. (page 19)
23. Socrates, an Athenian philosopher of the fifth century B.C. It was a method of asking pertinent questions which would lead those who answered them to discover the truth of the matter under discussion. (page 20)
24. The Peloponnesian War. (page 20)
25. Philip II of Macedon. (page 22)
26. Alexander the Great. (page 22)
27. Alexandria. (page 23)

28. To the Punjab region of northern India. (page 23)
29. Ptolemy, one of Alexander the Great's generals. (page 24)
30. From Greece. (page 28)
31. Twenty-three years. (page 29)
32. Rome was the only power, imperial or military, in the Mediterranean world. (page 33)
33. All Spain, northern Africa, Italy and adjacent islands, Macedonia and Greece. Western Asia, including Syria, was a Roman dependency. (page 33)
34. Rome sold the right to collect taxes (from dependencies) to the highest bidder, who made what profit he could for himself in the transaction. (page 34)
35. Pompey. (page 35)
36. In 59 B.C. (page 35)
37. At the battle of Pharsalus, in Thessaly. (page 36)
38. By assassination. (page 36)
39. Officers of his guard slew him. (page 37)
40. Nero. (page 40)
41. Flavius Vespasianus (Vespasian). (page 37)
42. In 79–81 A.D., during the reign of Titus. (page 37)
43. Because they would not honor the Roman gods. (page 38)
44. The barrel vault, which permitted the construction of arched edifices. (page 38)
45. Theodosius. (page 40)
46. Constantine. (page 40)
47. Alaric and his Gothic hosts. (page 41)
48. From the steppes of Asia. (page 41)
49. Siddhartha Gautama, who was born in India around the middle of the sixth century B.C. (page 42)

50. Shi Hwang-ti. (page 43)

II. MEDIEVAL HISTORY

1. In 476 A.D. with the deposition of the last Roman emperor. (page 46)
2. The period commencing in the fifth century (fall of Rome) and ending in the fifteenth century, or somewhat earlier in parts of Europe. (page 46)
3. In the reign of Justinian, 527–565 A.D. (page 49)
4. The Franks were Germanic tribes from the lower Rhine. (page 49)
5. Clovis, who was a Salian Frank. (page 49)
6. Forty-six years, from 768 to 814 A.D. (page 50)
7. He was a Christian. (page 51)
8. Between the ninth and eleventh centuries. (page 56)
9. In the fifth century A.D. (page 53)
10. The Christian missionary who came to England in the sixth century. (page 53)
11. Until 1453 when the Turks captured Constantinople. (page 55)
12. Constantine. (page 54)
13. From the early Greek city Byzantium on the site of which Constantinople was built. (page 55)
14. Out of Arabia. (page 56)
15. They developed agriculture to a science, effected many improvements in manufacturing, and made great advances in chemistry, mathematics, and medicine. (page 57)
16. Scandinavia, comprising Norway, Sweden, and Denmark. (page 58)

17. The sea-going warriors of Scandinavia. (page 58)
18. Normandy. (page 59)
19. Canute. (page 59)
20. In 1066. (page 59)
21. The Kingdom of the Two Sicilies. (page 60)
22. From the ninth to the fourteenth century. (page 60)
23. The feudal system was based on land. (page 60)
24. A trial in which the accused and the accuser fought with each other, and the winner was recognized as the choice of God. (page 61)
25. The privilege of clergymen to be tried in an ecclesiastical court. (page 62)
26. The clergy. (page 63)
27. Innocent III (1198–1216). (page 64)
28. A period of nineteen years (1254–1273) during which Germany was without a ruler. (page 64)
29. 1095–1291 A.D. (page 66)
30. Saladin was a famous Moslem monarch and the first sultan of Egypt. (page 66)
31. The reign of William the Conqueror in the eleventh century. (pages 67–68)
32. The Magna Carta, or Great Charter. (page 68)
33. The House of Lords and the House of Commons. (page 69)
34. The power to grant funds to the king. (page 69)
35. The nobles, the clergy, and the commons. (pages 69–70)
36. The longbow. (page 70)
37. France and England, 1337 to 1453. (page 70)
38. She was only seventeen. (page 70)
39. Rodrigo Diaz. (page 71)
40. The Hapsburgs. (page 72)
41. To the Slavs. (page 73)
42. A chieftain who became the builder of the Mongol Empire. (page 73)
43. A famous Venetian traveler who visited the Mongol realms during the reign of Kublai Khan. (page 73)
44. The empire of the Mongols, or Tatars, in Russia. (page 74)
45. The Janizaries were a specially trained body of Turkish troops, led against Constantinople in 1453 by the sultan Mohammed II. (page 75)
46. Apprentice, journeyman, master. (page 76)
47. A trade protectorate formed by northern German cities. (page 77)
48. Dante (1265–1321) and Chaucer (1340–1400). (pages 78–79)
49. Architecture. (page 78)
50. It revolutionized warfare and rendered obsolete the existing methods of offense and defense. (page 80)

III. MODERN HISTORY

1. He believed that he would reach the Indies. (page 83)
2. The invention of printing and the use of paper. (page 85)
3. By the end of the Middle Ages. (page 86)
4. The leading spirit of the Reformation was Martin Luther. (page 88)
5. Cardinal Wolsey, who became the British Chancellor, was Henry VIII's right-hand man. (page 90)
6. Forty-five years, from 1558 to 1603. (page 91)
7. The defeat by the English of the world's greatest fleet, the Spanish Armada. (page 93)
8. Cardinal Richelieu was adviser to King Louis XIII of France. (pages 93–94)
9. Charles II, with whom the Stuart line of monarchs was restored to the throne. (page 97)
10. William and Mary, of the House of Orange, were summoned from Holland by Parliament. (page 98)
11. An edict which granted freedom of

worship and full political rights. (page 100)

12. The wife of Louis XVI of France and the sister of Joseph II of Austria. (page 105)

13. Twelve years, from 1792 to 1804. (page 107)

14. Napoleon Bonaparte was born in 1769 on the island of Corsica, a French dependency. (page 108)

15. The Russians retreated, luring Napoleon farther and farther away from his base of supplies—at the same time laying waste the surrounding countryside so that it could not support Napoleon's men in the cruel Russian winter. (page 110)

16. Robert Fulton built his steamboat in 1807. (page 115)

17. With the scientific advance in knowledge and the invention of complicated power-driven machines. (page 115)

18. In 1837, at the age of eighteen, upon the death of her uncle, William IV. (page 127)

19. Louis Napoleon, a nephew of the Emperor Napoleon. (page 121)

20. Count Camillo Benso Cavour, Giuseppe Mazzini, and Giuseppe Garibaldi. (page 122)

21. Benjamin Disraeli was made Lord Beaconsfield. (page 127)

22. About 12,000,000 square miles of land surface throughout the globe. (page 128)

23. Nicholas II, who was murdered in the revolution of 1917. (page 128)

24. France, Russia, and Great Britain comprised the Triple Entente. (page 140)

25. The general armistice came on November 11, 1918. (page 142)

26. On December 7, 1941. (page 148)

27. The United Nations, plans for which were drafted in 1944. (page 153)

28. General Dwight D. Eisenhower. (page 156)

29. On June 25, 1950, the North Korean Army made a sudden attack on South Korea. (page 159)

30. Dienbienphu, in what was formerly Indo-China, was the fortress.

31. The year was 1973.

32. In 1971, the country's name was changed to Zaire.

33. The separation policy is called *apartheid*.

34. It identifies the underdeveloped countries of the world, many of them former colonies. The name distinguishes these countries from the First World and the Second World—the United States and its Western allies and the Soviet Union and its satellites.

35. At Chernobyl, in the Soviet Union, in 1985.

IV. UNITED STATES HISTORY

1. North and South America were named after Amerigo Vespucci, a Florentine explorer. (page 168)

2. They were predominantly English, with some other nationalities, notably Dutch and Swedish. (page 169)

3. They landed at Plymouth Rock in Massachusetts, in 1620. (page 170)

4. Henry Hudson was an English explorer, working for Holland. (page 170)

5. New York City (modern Manhattan) was settled by the Dutch, who called it New Amsterdam. (page 170)

6. The French and Indian War began in 1755. (page 172)

7. The Boston Tea Party was a protest against the duty on tea staged by a group of Bostonians disguised as

Indians who boarded a British vessel and dumped its tea cargo into the harbor on December 16, 1773. (page 176)

8. The American Declaration of Independence (July 4, 1776). (page 177)

9. Privateers were vessels fitted out by private enterprise, which cruised about much like pirates, although licensed in their activities by the exigencies of the American Revolution. (page 179)

10. Cornwallis surrendered to General Washington on October 19, 1781. (page 179)

11. The American statesman, Benjamin Franklin. (page 180)

12. To put an end to the piracy of Tripoli and the other Barbary states (Morocco, Algiers, and Tunis) in the Mediterranean. (pages 182–183)

13. $15,000,000 was paid for the Louisiana Territory. (page 183)

14. The Mexican War began in April, 1846. (page 190)

15. *Uncle Tom's Cabin,* by Harriet Beecher Stowe, which achieved wide success in the North. (page 194)

16. About 4,000,000 people were recorded in the first census. (page 191)

17. Fort Sumter was bombarded in April, 1861. (page 195)

18. The *Monitor* and the *Merrimac* were the first armored war vessels. (page 196)

19. 23,000 Union soldiers and 20,000 Confederate soldiers fell at the Battle of Gettysburg. (page 198)

20. Custer made his famous "last stand" in the Sioux War in 1876. (page 202)

21. In 1883 Congress created the Civil Service Commission provided for in the Pendleton Act, and this ef-

fectively ended the "spoils system." (pages 202–203)

22. The blowing up of the U.S. battleship *Maine* in the harbor of Havana, Cuba, precipitated the Spanish-American War. (page 204)

23. They were established during William H. Taft's administration. (page 206)

24. General John J. Pershing commanded the American Expeditionary Forces. (page 207)

25. Roosevelt's program was known as the New Deal. (page 210)

26. The United States, Great Britain, and the Soviet Union comprised the Big Three. (page 212)

27. The establishment of the United Nations. (page 215)

28. The European Recovery Program was designed to stimulate prosperity in the countries of Western Europe and ensure their remaining outside the Soviet orbit. (page 218)

29. The Korean War ended in 1953. (page 219)

30. President Eisenhower broke diplomatic relations with Cuba in 1961.

31. The first humans on the moon were Neil A. Armstrong and Edwin E. Aldrin, Jr., both American astronauts.

32. Panama will take control of the Canal, by treaty, at the end of 1999.

33. The Department of Education was created during President Carter's administration.

34. The crisis began with seizure of the U.S. embassy in Tehran, Iran.

35. The Strategic Defense Initiative came to be called "Star Wars."

V. CIVICS AND THE UNITED STATES GOVERNMENT

1. Civics is the science of civil government. (page 224)

2. By naturalization. (page 224)
3. By returning to his country of origin and residing there for two years or more, or by becoming a resident of some other country and residing there for five years or more. (page 224)
4. The majority of the people. (page 225)
5. Three-fourths. (pages 225–226)
6. The central or federal government. (page 226)
7. "To form a more perfect Union, establish justice, insure domestic tranquillity, provide for the common defense, promote the general welfare, and secure the blessings of liberty to ourselves and our posterity." (page 227)
8. It is generally accepted that the one most recently passed or made shall be binding. However, a treaty always takes precedence over a state law. (page 228)
9. The legislative, executive, and judicial. (page 229)
10. The House of Representatives is apportioned according to the population; while the Senate is made up of two members from each of the states. (page 229)
11. Six years each. (page 230)
12. Income taxes, customs duties, and excise taxes. (page 231)
13. The Federal Trade Commission. (page 232)
14. The carrying of first-class mail. (page 232)
15. The Democratic and Republican. (page 233)

16. With a reading of the President's message suggesting desirable legislation. (page 234)

17. When the President fails to take action on it within ten days after he receives it from Congress. (page 235)

18. A person must be a native-born citizen of the United States, at least 35 years of age, and must have been a resident of the United States at least 14 years. (page 236)

19. By national convention of the various political parties. (page 237)

20. On the 20th of January following the November elections. (page 237)

21. The President chooses the members of his cabinet, and the Senate customarily approves the appointments. (page 240)

22. No. Nor is he subject to the mandates of any court, high or low, while he is in office. (page 239)

23. The Secretary of State, Secretary of the Treasury, Secretary of Defense, Attorney-General, Postmaster-General, Secretary of the Interior, Secretary of Agriculture, Secretary of Commerce, Secretary of Labor, Secretary of Health, Education, and Welfare. (page 240)

24. Under the Department of State. (page 240)

25. The diplomatic service, which is an arm of the Department of State. (page 240)

26. The President. (page 241)

27. It looks after the welfare and improvement of conditions of wage-earners and supervises aspects of immigration related to labor statistics and employment. (pages 241–242)

28. The Civil Service Commission. (page 242)

29. The Supreme Court of the United States. (page 242)

30. For life, unless they resign, retire, or are impeached and tried by Congress. (page 243)

31. By impeachment. (page 244)

32. A writ compelling the civil authorities to give any person an immediate preliminary hearing before a court, in order that he may know why he is being held. (page 244)

33. The legal rights of a citizen. (page 245)

34. The first ten amendments to the Constitution. (page 245)

35. To the states, or to the people. (page 247)

VI. GEOGRAPHY

1. Writing about or description of the earth. (page 249)

2. The rocky envelope of the earth. (page 249)

3. Triangular. (page 250)

4. About 25,000 miles. (page 250)

5. About 13,000 feet. (page 251)

6. Because they ebb and flow twice in every 24 hours and 51 minutes. (page 251)

7. An imaginary line drawn around the earth, equally distant from both poles. (page 251)

8. The distance of a point north or south from the equator. (pages 251–252)

9. The animals which inhabit a particular region. (page 254)

10. Europe, Asia, North America, North America, South America, and Australia respectively. (pages 273–306 *passim*)

11. The total land area of the United States is 3,628,150 square miles. (page 258)

12. The five Great Lakes are: Lake Superior, Lake Michigan, Lake Huron, Lake Erie, and Lake Ontario. (page 258)

13. The Upper Mississippi, the Missouri, and the Ohio. (page 258–259)

14. Cotton and tobacco. (page 264)

15. Chicago is the center of the meat-packing industry. (page 265)

16. Alaska is the most sparsely populated state. (page 267)

17. Alaska. (page 267)

18. The British Commonwealth includes over 700,000,000 people. (page 269)

19. Ottawa. (page 270)

20. Nicaragua is the largest Central American republic. (page 272–273)

21. Sugar is Cuba's chief product. (page 273)

22. Venezuela is the leading South American producer of petroleum. (page 278)

23. Brazil's chief product is coffee. (page 278)

24. Argentina is South America's leading importer-exporter. (page 280)

25. Santiago is the capital of Chile. (page 276)

26. The Netherlands (Holland) is ¼ below sea level. (page 283)

27. Vatican City is the world's smallest independent state. (page 284)

28. The Rhine, the Elbe, and the Oder. (page 286)

29. Sweden is a kingdom. (page 287)

30. Russia's official name is the Union of Soviet Socialist Republics. (page 289)

31. About 218,000,000. (page 290)

32. Jerusalem. (page 293)

33. China's population is over 700 million people. (page 297)

34. An archipelago of over three thousand islands makes up the Philippines. (page 299)

35. Canberra is Australia's capital. (page 306)

VII. Economics

1. Economic wealth consists of those things that man uses either in production or in consumption, and which are not freely found in the environment in the form in which man uses them. (page 311)

2. Ownership was originally determined by creation, discovery, and use. (page 312)

3. Exchange and inheritance are two additional factors of ownership found in modern society. (pages 312–313)

4. Capital consists of all goods required to assist in the production of wealth. (page 313)

5. Workers are paid in wages out of the original capital before the joint product of labor and capital is sold and money received. (page 314)

6. Those elements of wealth used in production but not consumed by the production are known as capital investment; such elements are land, factories, machines, patent rights, etc. (page 315)

7. The loss of value of capital investment as it wears out or be-

comes outmoded must be passed on to the customer by being added to the price of the articles produced by that capital investment. (pages 315–316)

8. There must be a greater risk that the "B" stock will not be paid than exists in the case of the "A" stock; therefore the "A" stock must have preference over the "B" stock as to assets or dividends or both. (page 316)

9. Yes. (page 317)

10. It is not subject to deterioration or great seasonal fluctuations, and its use is not important to the community. (page 318)

11. Because it is only valuable when and if someone else is willing to accept it in exchange for commodities; and its real value fluctuates according to the quantities of commodities that it will buy. (page 318)

12. The amount and quality of necessities and luxuries consumed by the average person. (pages 320–321)

13. In 1946 a dollar bought less of some simple foods, less labor, and less of most commodities where hand-work plays a large part of the manufacture. In many respects, however, the dollar bought more in 1946 than in 1846 due to decreased costs of manufacturing. (pages 320–321)

14. As the total amount of monetary wealth in the world is but a fraction of the amount involved in commercial transactions, these transactions must be completed in terms of bank credit. (pages 321–322)

15. Because in the great majority of cases the bank merely establishes a credit which is never converted into cash. In addition, a bank can operate upon the capital of other banks by rediscounting its own loans. (pages 323–325)

16. In both cases, the value of the currency depends upon the habitual willingness of people to accept the currency in exchange for commodities. (page 325)

17. Monetary inflation is the decrease of the value of currency. (page 326)

18. By devaluing currency in terms of gold or by increasing the supply of currency without a corresponding increase in gold reserves. (page 326)

19. Credit inflation occurs normally with periodic prosperity. Its effects are not as severe or dangerous as those of currency inflation. (pages 326–327)

20. No. (page 329)

21. The law of supply and demand is the fundamental one. (page 329)

22. The marginal cost is the cost of producing a further unit quantity of any product beyond the quantity already produced. (page 328)

23. In the long run they are equal. (page 328)

24. The two laws are actually one, since marginal cost is the measure of supply and marginal utility is the measure of demand. (page 328)

25. Profiteering takes place in the interval between an upset in the equilibrium of prices and the time when economic forces establish a new equilibrium. Such an upset occurs when demand

suddenly increases, as for certain products in wartime, or when supply is suddenly curtailed, as in crop failure. (page 329)

26. Because the supply of labor is inelastic: the number of laborers available is practically a constant. The supply of trained labor within a special field, and the supply of professional men in the professions, is inelastic in that it takes a long time to prepare other men to enter the field. (page 330)

27. For two principal reasons: because the high price might attract competition, and because demand at the higher price might be so low that total profits would be less. (page 331)

28. When an individual company or group of companies constitute the whole market for a given product. (page 331)

29. By a bargaining process. (page 332)

30. Because the depression is apt to continue until reduced consumption overtakes reduced production and consumes the inventories on hand. (page 333)

31. Yes. (pages 333–334)

32. Division of labor has brought it about that many persons are engaged in the production of luxuries, and their living is consequently dependent upon the continuance of trade. (pages 333–334)

33. Yes, because unemployed workers in an undeveloped country can usually find agricultural employment or make new homesteads for themselves on previously unoccupied land. (page 333)

34. Socialism is the view that wealth should be distributed to each individual in proportion to the amount he contributes to society by his productive efforts. (page 335)

35. Socialism would prohibit the inheritance of any large quantity of wealth. (page 336)

36. The economic creed of communism is that wealth should be distributed according to need. (page 337)

37. No. (page 337)

38. Karl Marx. (page 338)

39. The glorification of the state, the abolition of democracy, militarism, and economic isolation. (page 338)

40. If the population should continue to grow at an increasing rate a time might come when there would not be enough food, but there is no danger of this for several centuries. (pages 338–339)

41. A greater amount of leisure time is made possible by increased efficiency in production. It is necessary to have a greater amount of leisure time as luxuries are produced which must be consumed at leisure. (page 339)

42. If the number of hours in the working week are more than the number which should exist to accord with the efficiency of production, chronic unemployment will result. (pages 339–340)

43. Production of goods is increased. (page 340)

44. Reduction of working hours, as in the case of women entering industry. (page 340)

45. Since the industries of different regions are in competition, employers of a given region cannot

pay their employees much more than employees are paid in other regions. Hence the existence of poorly paid workers in any region constitutes a drag upon the workers of all other regions. (page 340)

46. By withholding half the supply from the market, Brazil hoped to raise the price sufficiently so that the value of half the crop would be greater than the value of the whole crop. (page 341)

47. The keen competition for markets that are not unlimited. (page 342)

48. Governmental control of production based on anticipated consumption. (page 343)

49. The law of diminishing returns states that after a certain optimum size of a business has been reached, any further increase in size is attended by a reduction in the rate of returns. (pages 343–344)

50. By the use of new methods, materials, and processes in industry and agriculture. (page 344)

VIII. GOOD ENGLISH

1. We visited my two *sisters-in-law* last night. (page 355)

2. Two *calves* occupy the rear stalls in the barn. (page 356)

3. Some bacteria *are* helpful to man. (page 356)

4. *Charles'* (or *Charles's*) books arrived. (page 357)

5. Someone has lost *his* coat. (page 358)

6. Everyone had better hold on to *his* tickets. (page 358)

7. The rain got into our very bones, *causing us great annoyance.* (page 359)

8. *We* girls were the first ones here. (page 360)

9. It is *he* I like most. (page 360)

10. We greeted Ed, the lawyer's son, and *her.* (page 360)

11. Between you and *me,* he is completely wrong. (page 360)

12. Do you know *who* she was? (page 361)

13. *Whom* did you give it to? (page 361)

14. Choose *whoever* wants to go. (page 361)

15. The book is losing *its* interest for me. (page 361)

16. *Who's* going to the party? (page 362)

17. Fresh coffee tastes very *good* to me in the morning. (pages 363, 364)

18. Running at full speed, *he tripped over the chair.* (page 365)

19. My brother and cousin, whom I haven't seen in several months, *are* coming for dinner. (page 366)

20. Mathematics *is* one subject that I find uninteresting. (page 366)

21. The committee *were* in violent disagreement. (pages 365–366)

22. There *are* a chair with a straw seat and a day bed in my room. (page 366)

23. He *has been* in this country for two years now. (page 367)

24. Norman *laid* the book on the table. (page 370)

25. I *lay* in bed all day because I had a sore throat. (page 370)

26. He has *lain* there since early afternoon. (page 370)

27. Won't you *sit* down? (page 371)

28. The water main has *burst.* (page 372)

29. The prisoner *fled* from the jail in the confusion. (page 372)
30. The picture was *hung* in the living room. (page 372)
31. Have you ever *trod* the light fantastic? (page 374)
32. I'll take two of *this* kind. (page 375)
33. Did you sleep *well* last night? (page 376)
34. Which pair do you like *better*—the black or the brown? (page 378)
35. I think that my typewriter is better *than* his. (page 379)
36. You should read Anthony Trollope's *Barchester Towers*. (page 381)
37. Theodore Dreiser is, I believe, a powerful writer. (page 382)
38. We are coming home tonight; we will leave tomorrow. (page 384)
39. "I'm so tired," Ellen cried, "that I think I shall be very bad company." (page 384)
40. Do you feel *all right?* (pages 385, 394)
41. His remarks were *sacrilegious*. (page 387)
42. Don't *lose* your temper now. (page 386)
43. Keep a steady *rhythm* while dancing. (page 387)
44. A mirage is an optical *illusion*. (page 394)
45. You will have to choose *between* him and me. (page 394)
46. What makes you so *angry with* him? (page 394)
47. *Besides,* I have nothing to do now anyway. (page 394)
48. Blood from a person of one color or religion is no different *from* blood from a person of another color or religion. (page 395)

49. *Almost* all of us ski in winter. (page 396)
50. The accident *happened* on the busiest street in town. (page 396)

IX. EFFECTIVE SPEAKING

1. A pleasing personality and presence, the ability to cultivate friendships and improve his acquaintanceships, and to make the most of his social contacts. (page 399)
2. Yes, provided that he does not antagonize the audience. (page 399)
3. Self-consciousness. (page 400)
4. Seize eagerly all opportunities for speaking that may come your way. Force yourself to ignore your own fear. Cultivate self-confidence. (pages 400–401)
5. The sense which enables a speaker to know whether his audience is interested or bored, sympathetic or antagonistic. It enables a speaker to know when he has spoken long enough. (page 401)
6. Introduction, body, and conclusion. (page 402–403)
7. To open with a funny story if it is appropriate to the occasion and the subject. Sometimes praise of the audience's intelligence is a good opening. (page 402)
8. The *body* of the speech is its main substance. (page 402)
9. Your own life and experiences, and your reading. (pages 403–404)
10. Particularly in the daily press, magazines, and in special speakers' anthologies. (page 405)
11. It may be used as a textbook to illustrate the elements of different

sorts of speeches that may be followed in planning his own speeches. (page 405)

12. The relations between men and women—love, romance, courtship, marriage, etc.; self-improvement—in education, health, business, and sports; money—how to get it and invest it. (page 406)

13. On a broad human level. (page 406)

14. By meeting the audience on a common ground. (page 407)

15. By the vocabulary of your audience. You must avoid words that they are not likely to understand. (page 409)

16. Because long sentences are more difficult for the audience to follow. (page 409)

17. By learning it as a whole instead of sentence by sentence. (page 410)

18. It helps the speaker to develop appropriate gestures. (page 411)

19. By restating it in different language. (page 412)

20. Specific instances or definite, concrete examples are more convincing. (page 412)

21. The quotation of authorities or of experts in their fields. (page 413)

22. In the rebuttal, each debater attacks the arguments previously advanced by his opponents and attempts to destroy them by bringing forward arguments against them. (page 413)

23. It should seldom take longer than thirty minutes. A safe rule is: the shorter the better. (page 414)

24. The toast should be short, witty, and should have a definite application to the moment or occasion. (page 414)

25. It enables you to hear your

speech just as others will hear it. (page 415)

26. You can get a feeling of reality as you rehearse by delivering your talk to small groups of friends. (page 415)

27. Articulation is sometimes synonymous with pronunciation, but it refers more exactly to the position of the tongue in making sounds. (page 416)

28. Enunciation consists in giving fullness and clearness to every sound in pronunciation or articulation. (page 417)

29. Inflection should be varied to suit the sense of the statements you are making. (page 417)

30. It is excellent training in voice culture. (page 417)

31. The important words, those that carry the meaning. (page 418)

32. Distinctly, but lightly. (page 418)

33. A change in the pitch or tone of the voice. (page 419)

34. It may be either rising or falling. (page 419)

35. By practice and by listening to good speakers. (page 419)

36. For emphasis, to lend expression and drama, to let a thought sink in, to arouse suspense and interest. (page 419)

37. Between 150 and 200 words a minute. (page 419)

38. The good standing posture of everyday life—upright, feet firmly on the floor, head up, shoulders back. (page 420)

39. A forceful downward gesture, pounding on the table with the fist, or pounding one fist into the other hand. (page 421)

40. Solemnity when required—a

pleasant smile at proper moments. (page 421)

41. It gives convincing weight to a speech. (page 421)

42. The actor may be called upon to give in to powerful emotions that prevent his speaking, but the speaker must never allow himself to become so worked up that he cannot speak. (page 422)

43. Positive feelings are those which are directed toward healthful, progressive, forward-looking action. (page 422)

44. Negative feelings include fear, grief, pain, mistrust, jealousy, envy, hate, melancholy, and disrespect. (page 422)

45. A well-developed voice, one that can give fullness and clearness to the language sounds, and one that does not fatigue easily. (page 422)

46. Good speaking requires deep breathing and wide opening of the mouth; wide enough to give a full round tone to the vowels. (page 423)

47. Because of an improper conception of the physiology of speaking. (page 423)

48. "Ladies and gentlemen" or "Fellow townspeople" or "Friends." (page 423)

49. It should end sharply with the climax. (page 424)

50. No. It is out of date. (page 424)

X. LITERATURE

1. *Beowulf.* (page 438)
2. In Wales. (page 439)
3. Geoffrey Chaucer. (page 440)
4. They were in manuscript form, copied largely by monks in the monasteries. (page 441)
5. Sir Thomas More. (page 441)
6. Miracle plays. (page 442)
7. William Shakespeare. (page 442)
8. Edmund Spenser. (page 443)
9. He was born in 1564 and died in 1616. (page 443)
10. In both prose and poetry. (page 444)
11. *Hamlet* is a tragedy. (page 444)
12. Ben Jonson. (page 444)
13. John Donne. (page 447)
14. *Paradise Lost.* (page 447)
15. John Bunyan. (page 448)
16. *Robinson Crusoe.* (page 449)
17. An imaginary country gentleman appearing in the *Spectator.* (page 449)
18. As satire. (page 449)
19. With his English Dictionary, and with the biography of him written by James Boswell. (page 450)
20. *The Vicar of Wakefield.* (page 450)
21. William Wordsworth. (page 452)
22. He wrote a pamphlet on atheism. (pages 452–453)
23. Mary Wollstonecraft Shelley, second wife of the poet Shelley. (page 453)
24. Charles Lamb. (page 453)
25. The death of his friend, Arthur Hallam. (page 454)
26. A poet, the wife of Robert Browning. (page 455)
27. *A Tale of Two Cities.* (page 456)
28. William Makepeace Thackeray. (page 456)
29. Charles L. Dodgson. (page 457)
30. W. S. Gilbert. (page 458)
31. India. (page 459)

32. The drama, especially comedy. (page 460)
33. John Galsworthy. (page 460)
34. A. E. Housman. (page 461)
35. James Joyce. (page 462)
36. Dylan Thomas. (page 463)
37. William Butler Yeats. (page 464)
38. Thomas Jefferson. (page 466)
39. Romantic and adventurous. (page 467)
40. Ralph Waldo Emerson, Henry David Thoreau, Nathaniel Hawthorne, Amos Bronson Alcott, Margaret Fuller. (page 468)
41. Oliver Wendell Holmes, to save the frigate *Constitution* from destruction. (page 469)
42. Their eerie scenes, their impressions of gloom, their somber tragedy. (page 469)
43. Nathaniel Hawthorne. (page 469)
44. *Tom Sawyer* and *Huckleberry Finn.* (page 471)
45. William James, a philosopher. (page 471)
46. An almost photographic study of life in a typical small town. (page 473)
47. Upton Sinclair, *The Jungle.* (page 474)
48. Ezra Pound. (page 474)
49. A Negro who reverts to savagery. (page 475)
50. E. E. Cummings. (pages 475–476)
51. William Faulkner. (page 476)
52. John Steinbeck. (page 476)
53. In the Orient. (page 478)
54. A Babylonian legendary account of the hero Gilgamesh. (page 478)
55. *The Rubaiyat of Omar Khayyam.* (page 478)
56. The Egyptian classic, which gives the instructions thought necessary to the soul on its last journey. (page 478)
57. *The Thousand and One Nights* or *Arabian Nights' Entertainment.* (pages 478–479)
58. The Koran. (page 478)
59. In Sanskrit. (page 479)
60. 551–478 B.C. (page 479)
61. Homer's epic of the Greek expedition against Troy, or Ilium. (page 480)
62. Mythical beautiful maidens described in the *Odyssey* as seeking to lure mariners on dangerous rocks. (pages 480–481)
63. The first of the lyric Greek poets. She lived about 600 B.C. (page 481)
64. Aeschylus. (page 481)
65. Euripides. (page 482)
66. Herodotus. (page 482)
67. Socrates. (page 483)
68. Plutarch. (page 483)
69. In Latin. (page 483)
70. As "the tenderest of Roman poets." (page 484)
71. By its plaintive tone and mournfulness. (page 485)
72. A Greek slave credited with the invention of many fables. (pages 485–486)
73. St. Thomas Aquinas. (page 486)
74. *The Divine Comedy.* (page 486)
75. A collection of 100 tales told by ten people to while away the time while they were isolated to escape the plague raging in Florence. (page 487)
76. Machiavelli's *The Prince.* (page 488)
77. Luigi Pirandello. (page 489)
78. "The best novel in the world beyond all comparison." (page 489)
79. Some 1800. (page 490)

80. They recapture the simplicity and force of classical tragedy. (pages 490–491)
81. A poet, vagabond, thief, and rogue. (page 492)
82. From *Gargantua*, by François Rabelais. (page 492)
83. Jean Racine. (page 492)
84. *Candide*. (page 493)
85. *Les Miserables, The Hunchback of Notre Dame, Toilers of the Sea, Ninety-Three*. (page 494)
86. Charles Baudelaire. (page 495)
87. The short story. (page 497)
88. *The Remembrance of Things Past*. (page 498)
89. Jean Paul Sartre. (page 499)
90. Belgian. (page 500)
91. A philosopher. (page 501)
92. A medieval doctor of magic, who sold his soul to the devil. (page 502)
93. The doctrine of a superman and the will-to-power as the salvation of the race. (page 503)
94. *The Trial, The Castle, The Penal Colony*. (page 504)
95. For his fairy tales. (page 506)
96. Feminism. (page 507)
97. His earlier plays deal with realistically sordid, oppressive themes; later he expressed himself in symbolic and often morbid fantasy. (pages 507–508)
98. Turgenev, Dostoevski, and Tolstoy. (page 509)
99. Leo Tolstoy. (page 509)
100. Chekhov or Gorki. (page 509)

XI. THE ARTS

1. The desire to ornament his dwellings and to record facts in a more or less permanent form. (page 518)
2. Egypt. (page 518)
3. The human figure. (page 519)
4. Pompeii. (page 520)
5. The fact that the political personalities became more important than religious subjects. (page 521)
6. Cimabue. (page 522)
7. Leonardo da Vinci. (page 523)
8. 1475–1564. (page 523)
9. Caravaggio. (page 524)
10. Shepherds in satin, immaculate sheep nibbling Arcadian foliage, and romancing court lovers. (page 525)
11. Courbet. (page 526)
12. Claude Monet's studies of the Rouen Cathedral. (page 527)
13. His lithograph posters, particularly those of the Moulin Rouge. (page 527)
14. Picasso and Georges Braque. (page 528)
15. A style of pure design—consisting of only lines and blocks of color. (page 530)
16. Spanish. (page 530)
17. Hubert van Eyck and Jan van Eyck. (page 531)
18. Rembrandt. (page 532)
19. Illuminated manuscripts and inferior wall paintings. (page 533)
20. The fashions and vices of his time. (page 534)
21. In England. (page 535)
22. Alexander Calder. (page 536)
23. The obelisk. (page 537)
24. The temples. (page 537)
25. 80,000. (page 539)
26. The tomb of an Indian ruler's favorite wife. (page 540)
27. The style of Christian architecture founded on the Roman. (page 541)
28. Gothic. (page 542)
29. In Italy. (page 543)

30. Baroque. (page 545)
31. Fontainebleau and Versailles. (page 545)
32. Neo-Roman. (page 545)
33. Huge size and indestructibility. (page 546)
34. Phidias. (page 547)
35. Because it could not be used to teach Bible stories without suggesting heathen idols. (page 549)
36. A Florentine craftsman who worked in metals and enamels. (page 551)
37. Rodin. (page 552)
38. The song. (page 553)
39. From the church. (page 554)
40. Many-toned. (page 554)
41. Piccolo. (page 554)
42. Wagner's. (page 555)
43. A dramatic poem in musical setting. (page 556)
44. Handel's *Messiah*. (page 556)
45. The harpsichord and the clavichord. (pages 556–557)
46. As program music. (page 562)
47. As classical. (page 561)
48. Beethoven. (page 561)
49. Four. (page 561)
50. Stravinsky. (page 562)

XII. FRENCH

1. Dans la cour à la maison.
2. Au mur de ma chambre au deuxième étage, au-delà de la fenêtre.
3. Au-dessus de la bibliothèque près de son lit.
4. Je suis fâché que vous avez peur.
5. Il a une chambre au delà du salon.
6. Ce monsieur est mon professeur et l'ami de mon père.
7. J'ai tant d'argent; je suis très content.
8. J'ai mangé de la viande.

9. Avant de manger un poulet, on le rôtit.
10. Vous rappelez-vous du peu d'espace dont nous disposions?
11. Bientôt les officiers du port viendront à bord, et demain nous nous trouverons dans la ville du Havre.
12. Nous avons quitté la maison dans le petit village où nous demeurions, il y a huit jours.
13. Il était évident que tout le monde nous a pris pour américains; autrement on n'aurait jamais osé nous demander un tel prix pour deux chambres.
14. Il y avait même un téléphone sur une petite table dans un coin.
15. Après avoir quitté le vaisseau, nous avons monté dans un taxi qui se trouvait près du quai.
16. Messieurs désirent?
17. Combien faut-il payer par semaine?
18. Malgré les trois cent francs par semaine, nous sommes bien contents de nos chambres.
19. Nous venons de nous asseoir, il y a deux minutes au plus.
20. Il faut nous tenir sur nos gardes; ils coûtent cher.
21. Mon ami m'épargne la peine de choisir, et j'en suis bien content.
22. Les ris de veau, les soufflés, et une infinité de mets rares et délicats nous attendent dans tous les restaurants de la France; mais à présent un dîner simple et bien préparé nous va mieux.
23. Il est inutile de vous souhaiter un bon appétit.
24. J'aurai des fraises avec de la crème, des petits gâteaux, et naturellement du café noir avec un petit verre de cognac.

25. A la vôtre (A votre santé)! Moi, je préfère en gouter d'avance.
26. We are glad; they are hungry.
27. I am glad that they are not in the street.
28. My room is on the ground floor.
29. I have something to say to you, Mr. Lebon.
30. My (lady) friends are all beautiful, and their children are all fine-looking.
31. You have sugar and cream.
32. I have so many peaches that I have no desire to eat.
33. Is your father a friend of my professor?
34. The mothers are all beautiful.
35. I am not your father, but I am your friend.
36. She has a beautiful rug on the wall, from the ceiling to the floor.
37. I have peaches and cream to eat today.
38. That very evening, we found ourselves late.
39. That's enough! I am dying of hunger.
40. In short, you are eating a better dinner than I.
41. Here we are, old fellow, and I am very glad.
42. They are waiting for us, and, myself, I don't know what to do.
43. It is a dessert which goes with this white wine.
44. Furthermore, they are expensive.
45. Finally I found the station and climbed into the coach just as the train was stopping.
46. He doesn't want to wait on board the vessel.
47. No, I do not wish to go up.
48. Perhaps she is ready to sit down at the table.
49. He followed me to my bedroom.
50. The waiter seized the tip and preceded us to Number 40.

XIII. Spanish

1. La mujer habla español; usted lo escribe.
2. Él escribe su lección; usted no hace nada.
3. Nosotros tenemos calor; ella tiene sed; la madre tiene un resfriado.
4. La madre tiene razón; el perro tiene ganas de dormir.
5. San Francisco es una ciudad lejos de aquí.
6. Por contra, nosotros trabajamos.
7. Si no me equivoco, está enfermo.
8. Tengo que comprar muchas cosas para la cocina.
9. Cerca de la plaza están una buena fonda y dos o tres pequeños restaurantes.
10. ¿Cuánto valen estas naranjas?
11. Está bien. No me gustan manzanas; yo tomaré una docena de naranjas y media docena de limones.
12. Necesito también doce huevos, una libra de café, cinco libras de azúcar, y dos panes.
13. ¡Tengo mucho gusto en conocerle, señor!
14. ¡Que duerma usted bien la noche!
15. Al almuerzo se come una sopa, fideos o arroz con tomate y carne, la ensalada y frutas.
16. El almuerzo se sirve a la una de la tarde.
17. ¿Y qué lleva la mujer cuando sale de la casa?
18. Cuando hay una lluvia fuerte y se moja el traje, hay que mudar la ropa.

19. Algunas veces lleva un par de guantes y un bastón.
20. Los trajes de mujer se pasan de moda con tan frecuencia que yo no me atrevo a describirlos.
21. Por lo común, hace calor.
22. Mi querido amigo, ¿que le va a usted?
23. Desearía una mesita para máquina de escribir, modelo número 8 (ocho).
24. Tenemos el gusto de enviarle todos los artículos citados en su carta.
25. Llame usted al mozo; desearía pagar la cuenta.
26. The dog eats, but he does not work.
27. He is not writing anything now.
28. You are sleepy, but I am ashamed.
29. John is ill; he has a terrible cold.
30. On the other hand, he is here with us.
31. Mother is right.
32. I have water; I am not thirsty.
33. She has a dog; he is not afraid.
34. You are hot; you have no cold (you have not a cold).
35. John is ashamed.
36. Yes, if they are sold in those stores, and they are not dear.
37. Have the goodness to say thank you!
38. Before going to bed, he goes for a walk in the park.
39. We do not wear overcoats in summer.
40. I do not like a man who carries gloves and a cane.
41. After bathing, I found that I had one sock.
42. When it is cold I wear a felt hat; in summer I wear a straw (panama) hat.

43. I do not dare to go for a walk in the park (through the park).
44. Dinner is on the table (ready), isn't it?
45. It isn't worth the trouble to stay in bed.
46. We have received your letter of the current month.
47. Is there anything you would like? Yes. Bring me the salad.
48. Look out! What's the matter? What's wrong with you?
49. Pardon me (excuse me)! I am very sorry!
50. Give a tip? I should say so!

XIV. Latin

1. Agricolae terram amant.
2. Nuntii Gallia litteras portantne?
3. Legati urbis sumus.
4. Amici puellae non sunt.
5. Viri muros altos aedificabant.
6. Agricolae in oppido multum frumentum celabunt.
7. Periculum nautae magnum erit.
8. Multi viri pilis pugnaverunt.
9. Multae provinciae in Gallia sunt.
10. Caesar in nomine populi Romani senatum convocavit.
11. Quis est dux militum Romanorum?
12. Rex circum hostem milites movit.
13. Equus niger tela militum timet.
14. Nunc Gallia pars Romae est.
15. Iulia equum pulchrumque parvum habet.
16. Secunda hora milites ex navibus in urbem libenter tela portaverunt.
17. Pulchrum animal parvum a malis pueris lapidibus vulnerabatur.
18. Novi vici a militibus defessis post proelium aedificati sunt.

19. In mente semper crescere poterisne?
20. Prima luce dux ab urbe trans pontem pedites eduxit.
21. Rex facto obses cohortum erat.
22. Carolus miserior est quam Iulia.
23. Equites Romani fortiter pugnaverunt sed Helvetios superare non poterant.
24. Prima aetate Caesar terras Germanorum vastare voluit.
25. Roma urbs aeterna saepe vocatur.
26. The girl sounds the trumpet.
27. Are you telling the girls' story to the farmer?
28. No, I'm not telling the girls' story to the farmer.
29. The man shows the farmer's fields to the boys.
30. We were building the little town's new walls.
31. The horse will carry the farmer's grain.
32. Will the ambassadors spend the winter in their beloved native land?
33. The danger of war in Gaul was great.
34. The messenger praised the beautiful girls to the stars.
35. The farmer gave his dear son, Charles, a basket full of apples, both good and bad.
36. Where, in Rome, have the messengers concealed the general's weapons?
37. Who wounded the merchant with the broad sword?
38. The Roman soldiers attacked the people of Gaul with javelins and swords.
39. The king and his soldiers laid waste that part of the city on the river embankment around the great gate.
40. At night, the Roman emperor sees the enemy's camp in the high mountains and warns his men to destroy it by fire.
41. With great shouts the little children showed the pretty little horse to their father.
42. Where is the city of the Roman people?
43. It is in Italy on the banks of a river.
44. Cincinnatus was summoned from the fields to Rome by messengers.
45. In time of danger, a great man can save his country.
46. The journey led across high mountains and through great swamps.
47. It is good to be able to write Latin.
48. At dawn, Caesar will lead the legions out of the camp.
49. After the death of Caesar, Mark Antony made a great speech to the Roman people in the name of the state.
50. After Julius Caesar, the Roman emperors always bore the name of Caesar in his honor.

XV. MATHEMATICS

Exercise 1 (page 729)

a. Fifty-five million, six hundred forty-six thousand, eight hundred eight.
b. Four million, nine hundred thousand, nine.
c. One hundred six million, four hundred fifty-six thousand, eight hundred thirty-seven.
d. Ten billion, four hundred fifty-eight thousand, nine hundred seventy-five.
e. Eight hundred eight million, nine thousand, six hundred six.

f. Seventy-seven billion, fifty million, seven hundred thirty-one thousand, three hundred ten.

g. Four hundred sixty-five million, six hundred seventy-two thousand, four hundred eight.

h. Eighty million, seven hundred sixty-three thousand, twenty-nine.

i. Five billion, six hundred seventy-nine million, five thousand, fifty.

Exercise 2 (page 730)

a. 80,763,029
b. 10,000,458,975
c. 4,900,009
d. 55,646,808

Exercise 3 (pages 730–731)

a. Fifty-five thousand, fifty-five, and five-tenths.

b. Six thousand, nine sixty-seven, and sixty-seven hundredths.

c. One hundred thousand, six, and six hundred seventy-six thousandths.

d. Fourteen thousand, five hundred eighty, and eight thousand eight fifty-six ten thousandths.

e. Seven hundred three thousand, seven hundred three, and seven hundred three thousandths.

f. One thousand, five hundred five, and sixty-nine thousandths.

g. Two thousand, nine hundred sixty, and eight ten thousandths.

h. Twenty-two thousand, twenty-two, and twenty-two ten thousandths.

i. Four thousand, six hundred seventy-eight, and nine thousandths.

j. Five thousand and five thousandths.

k. Nine thousand and nine, and nine thousandths.

l. Forty thousand and four, and four ten thousandths.

m. Seven hundred twenty-nine, and eighty-six ten thousandths.

n. Seven thousand seven, and seven hundred seven ten thousandths.

o. Three thousand thirty-three, and thirty-three thousandths.

Exercise 4 (page 731)

a. 600.06
b. 1212.012
c. 50,000.050
d. 1,600,054.054
e. 1404.1404

Exercise 7a (page 733)

Totals by goods:

Millinery	$ 34,788.32
Clothing	122,849.62
Shoes	28,401.78
Handbags	14,729.73

Totals by months:

Jan.	$ 15,163.09
Feb.	11,262.06
Mar.	21,412.04
April	22,328.70
May	14,582.60
June	16,263.09
July	11,299.39
Aug.	11,807.20
Sept.	22,258.07
Oct.	20,726.07
Nov.	18,119.72
Dec.	15,547.42
Grand total	200,769.45

Exercise 7b (page 734)

1. 67.91
2. 71.1
3. 32.88
4. 28.105
5. 66.504

Exercise 9 (page 735)

a. $ 530.74
b. 267.39
c. 894.98
d. 923.73
e. 796.67
f. 1,359.38

Exercise 10 (page 736)

a. $231.74
b. 92.39
c. 757.84
d. 948.54
e. 333.52
f. 558.12
g. 817.81
h. 170.27
i. 61.03
j. 126.42

Total invoice amount, $4,187.81
Total net amount, $4,097.68
Total discount, $90.13

Exercise 12a (page 737)

	$1777.50
	90.00
	610.50
	166.25
	85.80
	495.00
	462.00
	69.30
	368.50
	26.10
	101.25
Total	$4252.20

Exercise 12b (page 738)

	$ 45.75
	38.22
	36.75
	87.04
	60.84
	223.74
Total	$492.34

Exercise 12c (page 738)

	$ 29.60
	29.48
	17.16
	30.24
	20.16
	30.60
	18.85
	33.00
	23.60
	45.50
	33.06
Total	$311.25

Exercise 14 (page 740)

$728.75

Exercise 15 (pages 740–741)

a. 5/8	g. 1/4	m. 7/8
b. 1/4	h. 3/4	n. 1/6
c. 1/8	i. 2/3	o. 1/6
d. 3/4	j. 1/8	p. 5/6
e. 1/3	k. 2/3	q. 3/8
f. 5/8	l. 2/3	r. 5/8

Exercise 17 (page 742)

a. 155.   f. 463.
b. 45.   g. 470.22
c. 67.   h. 831.
d. 345.   i. 33.57
e. 27.   j. 53.

Exercise 30 (page 757)

1. 40%   6. 20%
2. 16⅔%   7. 20%
3. 12½%   8. 30%
4. 40%   9. 70%
5. 37½%   10. 50%

Exercise 19 (page 745)

a.   544.34
b.   136.59
c. 30,399.30
d.   .20152
e.   8.62424
f.   .153054
g.   3.7577
h.   450.
i. 4500.
j. 45,000.
k.   45.
l.   45.
m. 3600.
n.   150.

Exercise 31 (page 758)

1. $600.   6. 1,536.
2. 2,320.   7.   40.
3. 720.   8. 1800.
4. 840.   9. 12,000.
5. 256.   10.   30.

Exercise 21 (page 746)

a. $1247.50   f. 177.63
b. 172.86   g. 10.25
c.   78.20   h. 32.29
d.   7.56   i. 18.70
e. 112.50   j. 28.50

Exercise 32 (page 759)

1. 240   6.   40
2. 220   7. 480
3.   73.5   8. 1000
4. 7000   9. 700
5.   18   10. 300

Problems (page 754)

1. $.50   7. $1755
2. 4,005.00   8. (a) ⅓
3. ¾   (b) ½
4. $20.00   9. $93.75
5. 20 pages   10. C. owns
6. $15.00   ¼

Exercise 33 (page 759)

1. 12   6. 800
2. 100   7. 112
3. 180   8. 2000
4. 200   9. 800
5. 90   10.   64

Problems (pages 760–761)

1. $75
2. 5%
3. $1.75
4. $17,000
5. $364
6. $60
7. $6320
8. $28.636
9. 37½%
10. 60%
11. $451.13
12. $48,000
13. 3.14% profit
14. A's profit $750
    B's profit   900
    Difference   150
15. $223.50 profit

Exercise 34 (page 762)

a. $5.40   f. 2.74
b. 25.65   g. 13.09
c. 8.40   h. 29.07
d. 1.60   i. 4.74
e. 8.50   j. 9.00

Exercise 35 (page 763)

a. 32½%   f. 37.66%
b. 43%   g. 56.35%
c. 47½%   h. 27.325%
d. 33⅓%   i. 21.03%
e. 43.3%   j. 50%

Problems (pages 763–764)

1. $25.14
2. 134.66
3. 53.98
4. 80.00
5. 50.67
6.   4.50
7. 105.00
8.   .87⅓ (decrease)
9.   .95
10. 30.00

Exercise 36 (page 765)

	Gross Profit	% of Gross Profit on Sales
1.	$1.20	50%
2.	5.00	25%
3.	1.80	33⅓%
4.	2.50	25%
5.	.49	28%
6.	.30	40%
7.	.50	40%
8.	2.00	36 4/11%
9.	2.50	28 4/7%

Exercise 38 (page 766)

	Equivalent Rate on Cost	Profit	Selling Price
1.	25%	$1.00	$5.00
2.	66⅔%	.50	1.25
3.	14 2/7%	.30	2.40
4.	50%	2.50	7.50
5.	60%	.39	1.04
6.	100%	.85	1.70
7.	42 6/7%	3.00	10.00

Exercise 39 (page 767)

1. $30.00   4. 1.90
2. 3.00   5. 2.00
3. 1.50

Exercise 40 (page 768)

1. $3.00   4. 6.00
2. 7.50   5. 50.00
3. 28.00

Problems (page 768)

1. $2.75
2. 33⅓%
3. 25%
4. $2.00
5. $687.27
6. A sells it for 45¢ less
7. $4.22
8. $1.33⅓%

Exercise 41 (page 770)

1. $1144.22
2. 2980.83
3. 456.32
4. 2289.08
5. 1657.25
6. 3275.20
7. 518.29
8. 990.48
9. 759.54
10. 1379.41

Problems (page 770)

1. $4565.45
2. 26.95%
3. $ 900.00
4. 2095.05
5. 3873.55
6. 102.00

Exercise 42 (page 772)

	2%	3%	4%	6%
1.	$10.00	$15.00	$20.00	$30.00
2.	4.00	6.00	8.00	12.00
3.	2.00	3.00	4.00	6.00
4.	4.00	6.00	8.00	12.00
5.	1.00	1.50	2.00	3.00
6.	50.00	75.00	100.00	150.00

Exercise 44 (page 774)

	6%	5%	7%	4%	2%
1.	$9.00	$7.50	$10.50	$6.00	$3.00
2.	18.00	15.00	21.00	12.00	6.00
3.	48.00	40.00	56.00	32.00	16.00
4.	1.80	1.50	2.10	1.20	.60
5.	8.80	7.33	10.27	5.86	2.93
6.	9.00	7.50	10.50	6.00	3.00
7.	12.00	10.00	14.00	8.00	4.00
8.	30.00	25.00	35.00	20.00	10.00
9.	60.00	50.00	70.00	40.00	20.00
10.	120.00	100.00	140.00	80.00	40.00

Exercise 45 (page 776)

1. 59 days
2. 89 days
3. 30 days
4. 60 days
5. 46 days
6. 92 days

Exercise 46 (page 777)

1. March 6
2. May 11
3. April 9
4. June 1
5. August 23

Exercise 47 (page 779)

1. $1522.50
2. 4567.50
3. 505.00
4. 5050.00
5. 3618.00
6. 4422.00
7. 741.60
8. 816.00

Exercise 48 (page 779)

1. 50 days
2. 48 days
3. 20 days
4. 49 days
5. 33 days
6. 117 days

Exercise 49 (page 780)

	Discount	Net Proceeds
1.	$10.10	$999.90
2.	6.19	602.81
3.	14.98	1233.47
4.	6.97	902.03
5.	3.83	761.98
6.	20.30	2009.70

Exercise 50 (page 781)

	Rate per $1	Rate per $100	Rate per $1000
1.	$.015	$1.50	$15.00
2.	.05	5.00	50.00
3.	.0175	1.75	7.50
4.	.0125	1.25	12.50
5.	.03	3.00	30.00

Exercise 51 (page 782)

	Rate per $100	Rate per $1000
1.	$3.50	$35.00
2.	3.50	35.00
3.	2.00	20.00
4.	2.75	27.50
5.	2.75	27.50
6.	1.864	18.64
7.	8.225	82.25
8.	7.50	75.00
9.	7.50	75.00
10.	1.864	18.64

Exercise 52 (page 782)

1.	$178.75	4.	365.00
2.	210.96	5.	204.96
3.	206.35	6.	215.20

Exercise 53 (page 783)

1.	.0175	4.	1.25 mills
2.	$32,000	5.	$850,000
3.	$2353.13		

Exercise 54 (page 787)

1. 825 yds.
2. 9600 acres
3. 160 pts.
4. 240 drachms
5. 200 pwt.
6. 384 qts.
7. 160 drams
8. 900 lbs.
9. 990 lbs.
10. 9.504 gr.
11. 364 pts.
12. 2239 gr.
13. 221,184 cu. in.
14. 20,434 sq. in.
15. 34,130 ft.
16. 391 days

Exercise 55 (page 788)

1. 25 rds. 5 yds. 2 ft. 8 in.
2. 1 sq. rd. 14 sq. yds. 4 sq. ft.
3. 22 A. 80 sq. rds.
4. 58 gals. 1 pt.
5. 10 bu.
6. 1 oz. 3 pwt. 8 gr.
7. 3 gal. 2 pts. 9 oz.
8. 11 cu. yds. 3 cu. ft.
9. 2 mi. 135 rds.
10. 7 T. 16 cwt. 25 lbs.

Exercise 56 (pages 789–790)

1. 100 yds. 1 ft. 2 in.
2. 39 cwt. 24 lbs.
3. 85 gals. 2 qts.
4. 151 A. 135 sq. rds.
5. 116 bu. 2 pks. 5 qts. 1 pt.
6. 10 yds. 2 ft. 1 in.
7. 3 cwt. 67 lbs. 13 oz.
8. 12 gals. 2 qts. 1 pt.
9. 4 A. 130 sq. rds.
10. 25 bu. 1 pk. 1 pt.

Problems (page 792)

1. $66.00
2. 8 rolls
3. 2648.37 ft.
4. 231 ft. 8 in.
5. 9424.8 ft.

Problems (page 796)

1. 88 sq. yds., 4 sq. ft.
2. 38 bundles
3. $15.71
4. $70.00
5. $15.71
6. $81.67

Exercise 57 (page 800)

1.	1 ft. 3.65 in.	7.	5625
2.	32.01 ft.	8.	15,625
3.	13.41 ft.	9.	2.62
4.	14.42 ft.	10.	19.38
5.	1764	11.	6.5
6.	11,025	12.	3.22

Exercise 58 (page 803)

1. 1914.88 gals.
2. 1436.16 gals.
3. 244.34 gals.
4. 3007.89 gals.
5. 4699.83 gals.
6. 187.99 gals.
7. 2537.91 gals.
8. 37.7 cu. in.
9. 41.89 cu. ft.
10. 37.7 cu. ft.
11. 615.75 cu. ft.
12. 2½ cds.
13. 6 cds.
14. 2¼ cds.
15. 80 bd. ft.
16. 277⅓ bd. ft.
17. 384 bd. ft.
18. 48 bd. ft.

XVI. ALGEBRA

Exercise I (page 811)

1. $\dfrac{bc}{a}$

2. $de + \sqrt[3]{a}$

3. $\dfrac{4bc}{b^2}$

4. $\dfrac{a + 3h - b^3}{10}$

5. $\dfrac{-b + \sqrt{b^2}}{2a}$

6. $\sqrt[3]{abc}$

7. 100

8. 72
9. 16
10. 58
11. 86.485
12. 5

Exercise II (page 812)

1.	10	4.	6	7.	10
2.	25	5.	10	8.	2
3.	5	6.	12		

Exercise III (page 813)

1.	-3	3.	$+5$	5.	$+1$
2.	-14	4.	$+5$	6.	-23

Exercise IV (page 815)

1.	$+12$	16.	-64
2.	-15	17.	4
3.	-14	18.	6
4.	-25	19.	-24
5.	$+4$	20.	-72
6.	$+9$	21.	27
7.	-8	22.	-8
8.	-6	23.	-1
9.	$+121$	24.	-48
10.	-6	25.	-15
11.	62	26.	-54
12.	36	27.	-120
13.	-18	28.	-750
14.	1	29.	-6
15.	10	30.	6

Exercise V (page 817)

1. $+15a$
2. $+5b$
3. $+8bc$
4. $5a-3b$
5. $2b+3c$
6. $a+3b-c$

Exercise VI (page 818)

1. $18x+14y-7z$ 3. $7x-y+6z$
2. $8d^2+12d-3$ 4. $10x-3y-6z$

Exercise VII (page 820)

1. $x+5y-12$ 4. $x-y-z$
2. $x^2+11x-9$ 5. $-10x^2-21y^2+5z$
3. $-a+5c+6$

Exercise VIII (page 821)

1. $x=3$ 3. $x=25$ 5. $x=10$
2. $x=4$ 4. $y=16$ 6. $y=-1$

Exercise IX (page 822)

1. $x=5$ 3. $x=9$ 5. $x=11$
2. $x=12$ 4. $x=9$ 6. $x=3$

Exercise X (page 822)

1. $x=17$ 3. $x=\frac{2}{3}$ 5. $x=-5$
2. $x=\frac{5}{8}$ 4. $x=-5$ 6. $x=6$

Exercise XI (page 823)

1. $x=42$ 3. $x=238$ 5. $x=310$
2. $x=60$ 4. $x=300$ 6. $x=36$

Exercise XII (page 825)

1. $x=4$ 3. $x=8$ 5. $x=1$
2. $x=-9$ 4. $x=8$ 6. $x=4$

Exercise XIII (page 825)

1. $3x-25=2x-15$
   $x=10$
2. $2x+10=14$
   $x=2$
3. $2x+30=90-3x$
   $x=12$

Exercise XIV (page 827)

1. Uncle = 24 yrs. old
   Nephew = 12 yrs. old
2. 3, 6
3. Son = 9
   Mother = 27
   Father = 28

Exercise XV (page 828)

1. 10 4. $3x+3y-z$
2. 2 5. $x-2a+b-3c+d$
3. 8 6. $x+2a-2$

Exercise XVI (page 830)

1. b^{12} 3. x^6 5. a^5b^4
2. a^{10} 4. a^5b^3 6. b^4d^5

Exercise XVII (page 831)

1. $12b^6$ 6. $30a^3b^3c^5$
2. $30a^6$ 7. $-24a^5b^2$
3. $28a^3b$ 8. $12a^3d^4$
4. $24b^4c^6$ 9. $-50x^8y^3$
5. $24x^6y^5z^7$ 10. x^9y^3

Exercise XVIII (page 832)

1. $2bx+4b^2-2bcd$
2. $2xy+6xy^2+4y^2$
3. $4x^4-5x^3+2x^2$
4. $40a^3bc+12a^2b^2c-16a^3bc^2$
5. $12a^3b^2-18ab^2c+9abc$
6. $8ab^4+4a^2b^3+4a^4b^2$

Exercise XIX (page 833)

1. 30 4. 48 7. 45
2. 77 5. 30 8. 26
3. 15 6. 52 9. -13

Exercise XX (page 833)

1. $x^2 - xy$
2. $2x^2 + 6xy$
3. $3a^3 + 9a^2b^2$
4. $4a^5 + 12a^3b + 4a^3c$
5. $a^3b + 2a^2b^2$
6. $2a^5 + 4a^6$
7. $5a^2b^4 - 15a^3b^5$
8. $10a^4b^5 - 40a^5b^4$

Exercise XXI (page 835)

1. $2x^4 - 4x^3 - 16x^2$
2. $a^5 + 3a^4b + 2a^3b + 6a^2b^2$
3. $4x^3 - 14x^2 - 4x + 32$
4. $6m^4 - 13m^3 + 20m^2 - 21m$
5. $9x^4 + 9x^3 - 16x^2 + 4x$
6. $x^4 - 2x^3 - 7x^2 - 4x$

Exercise XXII (page 839)

1. 196
2. 484
3. 2304
4. $x^2 + 2xy + y^2$
5. $4x^2 - 12xy + 9y^2$
6. $25 - 20y + 4y^2$
7. $9a^2 - 6ay + y^2$

Exercise XXIII (page 840)

1. $(18+3)(18-3) = 324 - 9 = 315$
2. $(22+5)(22-5) = 484 - 25 = 459$
3. $(25+5)(25-5) = 625 - 25 = 600$
4. $a^2 - 4b^2$
5. $9x^2 - 4y^2$

Exercise XXIV (page 841)

1. $2x^2$
2. $3a$
3. $2a^2bc^2$
4. $3a^3b^3$

Exercise XXV (page 842)

1. $2p - 4np^2$
2. $2a^2b^2 - 3a^3b^3 - 4a^4b^4$
3. $7 - 9xy^2 + y$

4. $3a - a^2x + 6a^3x^2$

Exercise XXVI (page 844)

1. $a - 2$
2. $2p - n$
3. $n^2 - 4n + 3$
4. $3a(1 + 2a)$

Exercise XXVII (page 845)

1. $3ax(1 - 5a)$
2. $4by(3b^2 + 2by - 1)$
3. $a(y - bc - by)$
4. $3c(c - 4 - 6c^3)$
5. $5ad(1 + 2ad - 3a^2)$

Exercise XXVIII (page 846)

1. $(4+a)(x+2y)$
2. $(a+b)(x^2+2)$
3. $(a+b)(x+y)$
4. $11(ax+by)$

Exercise XXIX (page 848)

1. $(x+2)^2$
2. $(a+3)^2$
3. $(y-5)^2$
4. $(b-7)^2$

XVII. PLANE GEOMETRY

Exercise II (page 891)

1. $x = 10$
2. $x = 21$
3. $x = 4$
4. $x = 2$
5. $x = 24$
6. $x = 12$
7. $x = 3$
8. $x = 1$
9. $x = 10$

Exercise III (page 893)

1. 6
2. 10.8
3. $10\frac{2}{7}$
4. 12
5. 20

Exercise IV (pages 900–901)

1. 10"
2. 7'
3. 5"
4. 29 yds.
5. 7.211"

6. 13′
7. 11.62″
8. 9.899″

Exercise V (page 913)

1. 120°
2. 360° (see Prop. XXII, cor. 1)
3. 18°
4. 9
5. 200 in.
6. 196π sq. ft.

Exercise VI (page 920)

1. 50°   2. 40°   3. 45°

XVIII. SOLID GEOMETRY

Exercise I (page 934)

1. 27 cu. ft.   3. 160 sq. ft.
2. 4 yds.   4. 72π sq. ft.

Exercise II (page 936)

1. 120 sq. ft.   4. 125 cu. yds.
2. 40π sq. in.   5. 108π cu. ft.
3. 120 cu. ft.

XIX. TRIGONOMETRY

Exercise I (page 943)

1. 1.0000   5. .7265
2. .5774   6. 20°
3. .5095   7. 35°
4. 3.0777   8. 53°

Exercise II (page 945)

1. 808 ft.   3. 110.1 ft.
2. 376.2 ft.   4. 37°

Exercise III (page 947)

1. $\dfrac{5}{13}, \dfrac{12}{13}, \dfrac{5}{12}, \dfrac{12}{5}, \dfrac{13}{12}, \dfrac{13}{5}$

$\dfrac{12}{13}, \dfrac{5}{13}, \dfrac{12}{5}, \dfrac{5}{12}, \dfrac{13}{5}, \dfrac{13}{12}$

2. $\dfrac{2}{\sqrt{29}}, \dfrac{5}{\sqrt{29}}, \dfrac{2}{5}, \dfrac{5}{2}, \dfrac{\sqrt{29}}{5}, \dfrac{\sqrt{29}}{2}$

$\dfrac{5}{\sqrt{29}}, \dfrac{2}{\sqrt{29}}, \dfrac{5}{2}, \dfrac{2}{5}, \dfrac{\sqrt{29}}{2}, \dfrac{\sqrt{29}}{5}$

3. $\dfrac{5}{13}, \dfrac{12}{13}, \dfrac{5}{12}, \dfrac{12}{5}, \dfrac{13}{12}, \dfrac{13}{5}$

Exercise IV (pages 948–949)

1. a. $\dfrac{3}{7}$
   b. $\dfrac{3}{11}$
   c. $\dfrac{8}{3}$
   d. $\dfrac{2}{3}$

2. a. cos
   b. cot
   c. sec
   d. sin
   e. tan
   f. csc

3. a. cos 20°
   b. cot 35°
   c. csc 18°

4. a. $\dfrac{3}{2}$
   b. $\dfrac{4}{3}$
   c. $\dfrac{8}{3}$

Exercise V (page 951)

1. 1
2. 0
3. 6$\sqrt{3}$
4. 6
5. 48$\sqrt{3}$
6. 8$\sqrt{3}$+3
7. 7
8. $\dfrac{\sqrt{3}+\sqrt{2}}{2}$
9. $\dfrac{3+8\sqrt{3}}{6}$
10. $\dfrac{1}{2}$

Exercise VI (page 953)

1. a. .9397
   b. 5.6713
   c. .3584
   d. 1.6243
   e. 1.3456
   f. .8693

2. a. 65°
   b. 80°
   c. 52°
   d. 76°
   e. 51°
   f. 77°

Exercise VII (page 956)

1. a. .5324
   b. .3773
   c. .8158
   d. .7674

2. a. 26°22′
   b. 15°7′
   c. 38°44′
   d. 19°40′

Exercise VIII (page 961)

1. 268 ft.
2. 659 ft.
3. 13 ft.
4. 82 ft.
5. 23°35′
6. 137 ft.
7. 423 ft.
8. 36°52′
9. 64 ft.
10. 13 ft.
11. 619 ft.

XX. GENERAL SCIENCE

1. Experimentation, observation, and measurement form the basis of scientific inquiry. (page 968)
2. Scientific principles are often called theories. (page 969)
3. Lavoisier discovered that substances gain weight when they are burned. (pages 968–969)
4. Halley's comet comes into view once every 75 to 77 years. (page 969)
5. A hypothesis. (page 969)
6. The two basic types are the analogue computer and the digital computer. (pages 970–971)
7. The slide rule is a type of analogue computer. (page 971)
8. The atmospheric conditions of temperature, pressure, and humidity. (page 972)
9. The dew point is the temperature at which condensation of water begins. (page 974)
10. Such a mixture is called sleet. (page 975)
11. They are different names for the same type of storm; "hurricane" is used for such storms in the Atlantic, "typhoon" for such storms in the Pacific. (page 976)
12. Humidity can be determined by a hygrometer, a sling psychrometer, or a recording hydrograph. (pages 976–977)
13. The correct name is a "wind vane." (page 977)
14. Isobars are lines connecting points of equal barometric pressure on a weather map. (page 978)

15. Liquid fuels vaporize easily and have a low kindling point, thus producing an explosion. (page 979)

16. The two main types of engines are the internal combustion engine and the external combustion engine. (page 978)

17. The body of an airplane is called the "fuselage." (page 983)

18. Most modern communication devices depend on electrical energy. (pages 983–984)

19. The telegraph was invented before the telephone. (page 984)

20. Albert Einstein devised the formula $E = mc^2$. (page 985)

21. A cyclotron is used to study the properties of highly radioactive uranium. (page 986)

22. The first man-made satellite was fired into space in 1957. (page 990)

23. Photosynthesis is the process in which, in the presence of sunlight, carbon dioxide and water combine to produce sugar and oxygen. (pages 991–992)

24. Dr. Alexander Fleming discovered the germ-killing powers of penicillin. (page 993)

25. Louis Pasteur developed the process of vaccination to protect against disease. (page 996)

XXI. ASTRONOMY

1. The science of the heavenly bodies—the sun, the planets, the moons, the comets, the meteors, the stars. (page 999)

2. Astrology, not now regarded as a science. (page 999)

3. 25 trillion miles. (page 999)

4. The distance traveled by light in one year. (page 1000)

5. Once. (page 1001)

6. Approximately 365¼ days. (page 1001)

7. In the west after sunset, or in the east before sunrise. (page 1002)

8. About 93 million miles. (page 1002)

9. About eight minutes. (page 1002)

10. About eight minutes. (page 1002)

11. Mercury, Venus, Earth, Mars, Jupiter, Saturn, Uranus, Neptune, and Pluto. (page 1004)

12. Saturn. (page 1004)

13. An ellipse. (page 1006)

14. 332,000 times as much. (pages 1006–1007)

15. About 11,000 degrees. (page 1008)

16. One part in 120 million. (page 1008)

17. 28 days. (page 1009)

18. An oblate spheroid. (page 1011)

19. 8,000 miles. (page 1011)

20. 23 hours, 56 minutes, and 4.095 seconds. (page 1012)

21. Polaris; Vega. (page 1012)

22. The force of gravity. (page 1014)

23. Its period of rotation so nearly coincides with its period of revolution around the earth. (page 1015)

24. The sun. (page 1018)
25. Mercury's is about 1/17 that of Earth. (page 1018)
26. Venus. (page 1019)
27. That there is very little chance of life anything like ours. (page 1019)
28. To an observer on earth, Mars appears a reddish hue, while Venus appears almost white. (page 1020)
29. Ceres; 500 miles in diameter. (page 1021)
30. Eros, which comes within 14,-000,000 miles of the earth. (page 1021)
31. The first four discovered satellites of Jupiter. (page 1022)
32. Almost thirty years. (page 1023)
33. Sir William Herschel. (page 1024)
34. About seventeen times as large. (page 1024)
35. About 75 years. (page 1025)
36. As many as 120,000. (page 1027)
37. Sometimes parts of comets' tails, but more often just isolated tiny bodies roaming through space. (page 1028)
38. Chiefly iron and nickel. (page 1029)
39. That all the starry universe is essentially of the same chemical composition. (page 1029)
40. About 6,000. (page 1030)
41. About six trillion miles. (page 1029)
42. Betelgeuse. (page 1031)
43. Nearly 100 times as great. (page 1032)
44. Stars which do not emit the same amount of light steadily. (page 1032)
45. The spectroscope. (page 1033)

46. About one and one-half billion years. (page 1034)
47. About as one to eighty. (page 1034)
48. Independent aggregates of stars. (page 1035)
49. The ecliptic. (page 1036)
50. Seven. (page 1037)

XXII. GEOLOGY

1. Geology is the study of the earth in all its aspects. (page 1043)
2. The lithosphere. (page 1044)
3. The earth's interior. (page 1044)
4. Igneous rocks which have been brought to the surface and which are exposed while hardening. (page 1047)
5. It is composed almost entirely of calcium carbonate derived from shells and other animal products. (page 1048)
6. Climate determines the rate of weathering. (page 1049)
7. Streams and rivers, ocean waves, glaciers, and wind. (page 1050)
8. Debris which accumulates at the base of a cliff or in a valley. (page 1050)
9. Sediment deposited by a stream, forming new land along the side of the stream opposite a bend. (page 1051)
10. Ordinarily tributaries meet the main stream at its own level. (page 1051)
11. Some falls result from a variation in rock levels which existed before the stream made its way. (page 1051)
12. Sediment deposited by a river at its mouth. (page 1051)
13. By blasting through impervious rock to water. (page 1053)

14. Saratoga, Carlsbad, Vichy. (page 1053)
15. Water brings soluble matter in the rocks into solution, then carries away the solution, leaving a chamber. (page 1053)
16. Sometimes a stream which flows into a lake deposits sediment which may form a delta, thus reducing area of lake. (page 1054)
17. Peat is composed of decomposed carbonaceous material. (page 1055)
18. A moving mass of ice. (page 1055)
19. A great glacier which blankets a large area with ice. (page 1055)
20. The level of the oceans would be raised 150 feet, thus submerging large areas now above sea level. (page 1057)
21. Meteorology is the science of the atmosphere. (page 1058)
22. Sand and other sharp rock particles blown by the wind against rocky surfaces aid in disintegrating the softer surfaces and in polishing the harder stones. (page 1061)
23. Loess consists of finely grained particles which are carried by the wind and deposited in compact masses. (page 1061)
24. There is twice as much sea area as land area. (page 1061)
25. 600 feet. (page 1061)
26. The coast of Maine is a shoreline of submergence. (page 1062)
27. An atoll is a circle of reef which remains after a coral island has disappeared. (page 1063)
28. Ocean tides are due to the gravitational pull on the earth by the sun and the moon. (page 1063)
29. A stratum of rock bent into rather regular curves. (page 1064)
30. The Giant's Causeway in northern Ireland. (page 1065)
31. Disturbances within the earth's interior. (page 1066)
32. Molten material in a volcano is called magma. (page 1067)
33. The lithosphere is probably 30 or 40 miles thick. (page 1071)
34. A seismograph measures earthquake shocks. (page 1071)
35. Oil and natural gas are formed in rock sufficiently porous to make a reservoir for them. (page 1072)
36. An ore is a mineral which contains metal. (page 1072)
37. Common salt is usually part of the residue accumulated when the sea receded from an inland area, and so has the same source as sea salt. (page 1073)
38. Laplace was a French astronomer who developed the Nebular Hypothesis. (page 1074)
39. Chamberlin and Moulton developed the Planetesimal Hypothesis. (page 1074)
40. A fossil is animal or plant matter that has been preserved through the ages or which forms an outline in a rock. (page 1076)
41. The Dust Cloud Theory. (page 1075)
42. In shallow sea water. (page 1076)
43. By studying rock formations and rock strata in all parts of the world. (page 1076)
44. The Archeozoic Era. (page 1078)
45. The abundant fossils belonging to this era indicate a variety of plant and animal life. (page 1079)
46. The Paleozoic Era ended in a great glacial period. (page 1081)

47. In the Mesozoic Era. (page 1081)
48. Mammals became the most important form of animal life in the Cenozoic Era. (page 1083)
49. To the Pliocene Period. (page 1084)
50. The Psychozoic Era. (page 1084)

XXIII. PHYSICS

1. Physics is the science which deals with energy and matter and with physical changes in matter. (page 1087)
2. The metric system. (page 1088)
3. The lever, the pulley, and the inclined plane. (page 1090)
4. "Give me a lever large enough, and I can move the Earth." (page 1091)
5. The lever of the second class. (page 1092)
6. A fixed pulley is one with an immovable axis. (page 1095)
7. The number of chains or ropes which it contains. (page 1096)
8. By dividing the length of the plane by the vertical height. (page 1096)
9. A pair of inclined planes back to back. (page 1097)
10. It means that if you start an object moving, it will keep on moving forever in a straight line until some force stops it. (page 1098)
11. It means that a body keeps on increasing in velocity under the influence of a constant force. (page 1098)
12. Thirty-two feet per second per second. (page 1098)
13. Both balls will hit the ground at the same instant. (page 1099)
14. In a vacuum, all bodies fall with exactly the same speed. (page 1099)
15. That every square foot of that floor is capable of meeting 150 pounds downward force with 150 pounds upward force. (page 1099)
16. For every force pulling one way on a body in equilibrium, there must be an equal and opposite force pulling in the opposite direction. (page 1100)
17. Stable, unstable, and neutral. (page 1100)
18. The longer the pendulum, the slower it will swing, and vice versa. (page 1101)
19. Potential and kinetic. (page 1101)
20. The height and the density of the fluid. (page 1103)
21. That any external force exerted on a unit of area in a confined liquid is transmitted undiminished to every unit of area of the interior of the containing vessel. (page 1103)
22. A body immersed in a fluid is buoyed up by a force equal to the weight of the liquid it displaces. (page 1104)
23. The ratio of the weight of a given volume of that substance to the weight of the same volume of water at 4° C. (page 1105)
24. Capillary action. (page 1106)
25. It is increased proportionately. (page 1106)
26. At sea level, about 15 pounds to the square inch. (page 1107)
27. Primarily a form of energy, due to extra-rapid motion of molecules. (page 1110)
28. No. (page 1110)
29. Because glass does not conduct heat rapidly, and the inside of the

vessel expands while the outside does not. (page 1111)

30. Zero. (pages 1111–1112)

31. 273° below zero Centigrade; because at this temperature all molecular motion would cease. (page 1112)

32. 15° C. (page 1112)

33. Silver and copper. (page 1113)

34. 186,000 miles per second. (page 1114)

35. The turbo-jet. (page 1116)

36. By vibrating matter. (page 1116)

37. 256 per second. (page 1117)

38. At zero Centigrade, approximately 1090 feet per second, increasing two feet per second for every degree rise in temperature. (page 1118)

39. The echo. (page 1118)

40. Refraction. (page 1123)

41. Red color. (page 1126)

42. Static electricity and current electricity. (page 1130)

43. Electric motors, electric dynamos, telegraph, electric bells, telephone. (page 1133)

44. Radio waves, infrared, visible light, ultraviolet, X rays, and gamma rays. (page 1139)

45. Whenever electrons surge rapidly back and forth in a wire. (page 1139)

46. By timing the interval between the sending and the return of radio waves, the distance to any object which reflects them back to the sender may be determined. (page 1145)

47. The emission of helium nuclei or electrons by heavy atoms and the resulting radiation. (page 1147)

48. By bombarding elements with neutrons in an atomic pile or with charged particles from a cyclotron. (page 1148)

49. Uranium. (page 1148)

50. $E = mc^2$. (page 1149)

XXIV. CHEMISTRY

1. Iron rusts, fruit decays, wood rots. (page 1152)

2. Oxygen and hydrogen. (page 1153)

3. An element is a substance which cannot be separated into other substances. (page 1153)

4. Oxides. (page 1153)

5. To inconceivably minute particles of a substance (usually carbon) heated to incandescence. (page 1154)

6. As a rule, the more intimately the substance is in contact with oxygen, the lower is its kindling temperature. (page 1154)

7. Oxygen. (page 1155)

8. About 78% nitrogen, 21% oxygen, and 1% a mixture of other gases. (page 1155)

9. By heating potassium chlorate and manganese dioxide in a test tube. (page 1155)

10. The diamond. (page 1156)

11. One-ninth. (page 1158)

12. Red. (page 1158)

13. When an acid and a metal interact chemically. (page 1158)

14. Hydrogen and chlorine in the proportion of one atom of hydrogen to one atom of chlorine. (page 1158)

15. A solution that will dissolve no more of a dissolved substance. (page 1161)

16. Atoms. (page 1162)

17. That a molecule of starch contains six atoms of carbon and ten atoms of hydrogen to five atoms of oxygen. (page 1162)

18. Gold, nickel, phosphorus, potassium, radium, sodium, tin, and tungsten. (pages 1163–1165)
19. Helium. (page 1165)
20. Yes. Only about twenty of the naturally occurring elements are nonmetals. (page 1165)
21. Protons, electrons, and neutrons. (page 1166)
22. Five electrons, because the total number of protons in an atom is the same as the total number of electrons. (page 1166)
23. The number and arrangement of the electrons. (page 1168)
24. When there is the same number of each kind of atom on each side of the equation—that is, before and after the chemical reaction. (pages 1169–1170)
25. Chlorine gas. (page 1170)
26. It eventually bursts into flame. (page 1172)
27. In sulphuric acid, fertilizers, explosives, kerosene, storage batteries, drugs, dyes. (page 1172)
28. Oxygen. (page 1173)
29. Whereas it reacts with a great many metals to form nitrates, hydrogen is not liberated. (page 1174)
30. By uniting nitrogen with hydrogen. (page 1175)
31. Bromine, chlorine, fluorine, astatine, and iodine. (page 1177)
32. From seaweed. (page 1178)
33. Because it dissolves glass. (page 1178)
34. Hydrogen. (page 1179)
35. Slaked lime. (page 1181)
36. Mercury. (page 1183)
37. Steel is cast iron with a great percentage of the carbon eliminated. (page 1184)
38. Eggs contain hydrogen sulphide,

a compound of sulphur, which blackens silver. (page 1185)
39. Gelatine and silver bromide. (page 1185)
40. It has 14 parts of pure gold and 10 parts of other metals. (page 1187)
41. Platinum. (page 1187)
42. Lead. (page 1188)
43. No. It is a can of sheet iron dipped in molten tin to prevent rust. (page 1188)
44. Carbon. (page 1189)
45. Because of the ability of carbon atoms to join other carbon atoms in numerous combustions. (page 1189)
46. Methane. (page 1190)
47. The process by which heavy hydrocarbons are broken down under great heat to form the simpler gasolines. (page 1190)
48. Asbestos and glass. (page 1192)
49. A fibrous material made from cellulose. (page 1192)
50. Carbohydrates. (page 1193)

XXV. BIOLOGY

1. The science of life, or of organisms. (page 1196)
2. Organic. (page 1196)
3. Botany, zoology, the science of microorganisms, physiology, and anatomy. (page 1196)
4. Protoplasm. (page 1196)
5. Granular. (page 1197)
6. Cavities within the cytoplasm are called vacuoles. (page 1198)
7. The single plant cell grows in size and splits into two new organisms; the nucleus also divides, one part going to each of the two cells formed by the division of the original cell. (page 1199)

8. The simplest unicellular animal. (page 1198)
9. The so-called flagellates. (page 1200)
10. Bacteria. (page 1201)
11. Cilia. (page 1201)
12. The xylem tissue. (page 1202)
13. The muscles under the control of the will. (page 1203)
14. Some 250,000. (page 1203)
15. The spermatophytes. (page 1204)
16. Annuals live for a year, biennials for two years, and perennials year after year. (page 1205)
17. Carbon, hydrogen, oxygen, nitrogen, sulphur, phosphorus, potassium, calcium, magnesium, and iron. (pages 1207–1208)
18. Osmosis. (page 1208)
19. Glucose. (page 1209)
20. Because plant protoplasm is stimulated by light. (page 1210)
21. The parent cell divides unequally and at first the baby cell or bud remains attached to the parent cell. (page 1211)
22. The stamens. (page 1211)
23. The passing of the pollen from stamen to pistil. (page 1212)
24. The fruit. (page 1213)
25. Something like 600,000. (page 1213)
26. The arthropods. (page 1214)
27. Amphibians live both in water and on land. (page 1215)
28. As mammals. (page 1216)
29. Herbivorous. (page 1216)
30. Ptyalin. (page 1217)
31. Through gills, utilizing the oxygen dissolved in the water. (page 1218)
32. By the union of the male and the female. (page 1219)
33. Ova (eggs). (page 1220)
34. No more than 1/125 of an inch in diameter. (page 1220)
35. Those which lay eggs. (page 1222)
36. Only in human beings and in the apes. (page 1222)
37. By the umbilical cord. (page 1222)
38. The mammary glands. (page 1223)
39. The branch of biology which deals with the phenomena of heredity. (page 1224)
40. A pink flower. (page 1225)
41. By watching and observing the laws of heredity. (page 1227)
42. Hybridization or cross-breeding. (page 1227)
43. With scientific human breeding. (page 1228)
44. Ecology. (page 1228)
45. The proboscis. (page 1229)
46. Bacteria and other organisms act upon dead organic matter, causing decomposition. (page 1230)
47. Organisms which live on other organisms, taking their nourishment from them. (page 1230)
48. Only by the Anopheles mosquito. (page 1231)
49. The process of development of higher organisms from lower. (page 1232)
50. Anatomical, physiological, and psychological evidence. (page 1238)

XXVI. PHYSIOLOGY

1. Anatomy is the study of the structure of the body, of its parts and how they grow; while physiology is the study of the functions of the organs and parts of the body

and how they work. (page 1241)

2. The end toward the head is referred to as anterior (or cephalic); the end toward the "tail" as posterior (or caudal). (page 1241)

3. The epidermis, or outer layer, and the dermis beneath. (page 1242)

4. The brain. (page 1243)

5. Carbon, hydrogen, oxygen, nitrogen, sulphur, phosphorus, chlorine, fluorine, iodine, silicon, sodium, lithium, calcium, potassium, magnesium, manganese, iron, zinc, and copper. (page 1243)

6. More than two-thirds. (page 1244)

7. The blood is a great transportation system for bringing nourishment to all parts of the body and for carrying waste products from all parts to a central department for the elimination of that waste. (page 1245)

8. Because in the adult some multiple bones grow together. (page 1246)

9. The breastbone. (page 1246)

10. The cervical vertebrae. (page 1246)

11. The lower jaw. (page 1248)

12. Because they are not attached on the ventral ends. (page 1248)

13. The humerus. (page 1248)

14. The joinings of the bones. (page 1248)

15. The skeletal muscles are controlled by voluntary impulses from the brain, while the visceral muscles operate automatically. (page 1249)

16. The heart. (page 1249)

17. The nervous system. (page 1252)

18. Almost cylindrical, and about three-quarters of an inch in diameter and about 17 inches long. (page 1253)

19. A trifle over three pounds in the male and a trifle under three pounds in the female. (page 1253)

20. The sense of smell. (page 1254)

21. Masses of nerve tissue forming nerve centers. (page 1254)

22. From 200 to 300 feet per second. (page 1254)

23. In the cortex, the superficial gray matter of the cerebrum. (page 1255)

24. A hormone is a substance which is secreted by one organ (as a gland) and carried in the circulation of the blood to some other organ or organs which it stimulates. (page 1257)

25. The thyroid gland. (page 1257)

26. Temperature (heat and cold), pain, hunger, thirst, balance or equilibrium, and the muscle sense. (page 1259)

27. From 60 to 4,000 vibrations per second. (page 1260)

28. The Eustachian tubes. (page 1261)

29. To a difference in the distance between the angles of the eyelids from end to end of the visible portion of the eyeball. (page 1262)

30. That which produces tears. (page 1263)

31. Red and green. (page 1265)

32. 75 billion. (page 1267)

33. About 70 times each minute. (page 1268)

34. The various valves. (page 1268)

35. The contraction is called the sys-

tole, and the relaxation the diastole. (page 1270)

36. Oxidation in the respiratory system. (page 1271)
37. Proteins, carbohydrates, and fats. (page 1273)
38. Eight incisors, four canines, eight bicuspids, and twelve molars. (page 1274)
39. The first foot of the length of the small intestine. (page 1276)
40. It has no apparent purpose. (page 1276)
41. The liver. (page 1276)
42. Two-tenths of one per cent. (page 1277)
43. Deglutition. (page 1278)
44. Carbon dioxide. (page 1279)
45. About 2,500,000. (page 1279)
46. Around 98.6 degrees Fahrenheit. (page 1280)
47. The male sexual cells. (page 1282)
48. In the uterus. (page 1283)
49. Parturition. (page 1283)

XXVII. PSYCHOLOGY

1. Such aspects of behavior as the basis of mental activity, habits and learning, intelligence and personality. (page 1288)
2. Biology, physiology, and philosophy. (page 1288)
3. Because the brain cells are of the same fundamental structure as other cells of the body. (page 1288)
4. Irritability. (page 1289)
5. Introspection. (page 1290)
6. How to control ourselves, how to guide children in their best interests, how to find out what vocation we are best fitted for, and how to control or eradicate crime. (page 1290)
7. A reflex. (page 1291)
8. A simple reaction. (page 1291)
9. The olfactory center. (page 1292)
10. No. (page 1292)
11. Yes, unless the higher brain centers inhibit it. (page 1293)
12. A glandular response. (page 1293)
13. Fear, rage, and love. (page 1294)
14. Native. (page 1294)
15. Vocal sounds are native, but speech is acquired. (page 1294)
16. A drive with some inherited basis but whose expression is determined by environmental factors. (page 1295)
17. No. (page 1296)
18. When it is satisfied in some learned or acquired way. (page 1296)
19. No. (page 1296)
20. The sense of well-being, or just "feeling good." (page 1296)
21. It is the desire to be with one's kind, based on the need for security, sympathy, and understanding. (page 1297)
22. Hate, fear, anger, and love. (page 1298)
23. They are conditions of the individual as a whole, and not of any one organ or part. (page 1298)
24. Just after eating a hearty meal. (page 1299)
25. Adrenalin, which acts as a tonic throughout the body. (page 1299)
26. Displeasure, disgust, or some similar feeling. (page 1299)
27. The fact that he is not afraid in the emotional sense. (page 1300)

28. The mating drive, accompanied by love. (page 1299)
29. Approach-approach, approach-avoidance, and avoidance-avoidance. (page 1300)
30. A response to a stimulus, made by the sense organ stimulated, and recognized or interpreted in the associated brain centers. (page 1301)
31. By an almost instinctive caution. (pages 1296–1297)
32. The determination to surpass one's fellows, or to overcome the thing itself. (page 1297)
33. Taste, smell, sight, hearing, and touch. (page 1301)
34. Sweet, sour, bitter, and salty. (page 1302)
35. Spicy, fragrant, fruity, flowery, foul, resinous, and scorched. (page 1302)
36. If you stare at an electric light, and suddenly shut it off, you will continue to see it for a moment afterward. (page 1302)
37. Usually by setting up, through practice, a counter-habit, or substitute response to the stimulus which brought on the habitual reaction. (page 1306)
38. That it saves time and effort to go over it twice each day for twelve days rather than to go over it twenty-four times in one day or six times daily for four days. (page 1307)
39. Fear, anxiety, doubt, embarrassment, surprise, or some distraction. (page 1308)
40. The smell of the lemon is associated with the taste that has been experienced. (page 1309)
41. An error in perception. (pages 1309–1310)
42. It is an auditory illusion, due to

preoccupation with a specific idea. (page 1311)
43. Abstract, mechanical, and social. (page 1312)
44. The exact relationship of intelligence to the size of the brain is as yet unknown. Some men with rather small brains have been highly intelligent. (page 1312)
45. Logic. (page 1313)
46. A form of self-justification, which is not reasoning. (page 1313)
47. Imaginative self-projection. (page 1313)
48. It is the fundamental energy in a person, basically a sex urge, or, more broadly, a love urge. (page 1315)
49. The will to power. (page 1318)
50. The discovery of a relationship between mental disturbance and blood composition. (page 1319)

XXVIII. Sociology

1. Sociology is concerned with man's behavior in groups; psychology is concerned with the behavior of the individual. Sociology is concerned with the effect of institutions upon human beings; psychology does not concern itself with institutions. (pages 1322–1323)
2. Primitive cultures are much simpler than our own. (page 1324)
3. Until European culture occupied the greater part of the world, diffusion was the principal factor in its development. (pages 1324–1325)
4. Caucasian, Mongoloid, Negroid, and Australoid. (page 1326)
5. Human races differ in the struc-

ture of the hair, the color of the skin, and in other physical traits. (page 1326)

6. Marriage is actually the relatively permanent association of a man with a woman. Marriage is ideally a life partnership of a man and a woman based on mutual love and admiration. (page 1328)

7. Monogamy. (page 1329)

8. Polyandry is the association in marriage of one woman with several men. (page 1329)

9. Polyandry usually exists where there is a considerable surplus of men over women, produced by the practice of infanticide where male children are preferred to female. It is usually associated with unfavorable climatic conditions. (page 1329)

10. Polygyny, the condition where a man has more than one wife, may be produced by the existence of an excess of females, due to infanticide, war, or the difficulties of economic existence. It may also be produced by inequalities of wealth and power among men. (page 1329)

11. Group marriage is the marriage of several men to several women, usually where the men travel about and visit the women. (page 1330)

12. Yes. Inbreeding stabilizes the type and prevents the rapid progress of evolution. But this objection only holds if the practice is made common. Otherwise there is a fairly even balance between the advantages and disadvantages. (page 1330)

13. The tribe, caste, or class, and sometimes the local group, tend

to be endogamous. (page 1331)

14. The family, sib, marriage class, moiety, and sometimes the local group, tend to be exogamous. (pages 1330–1331)

15. Cross-cousins are the children of brother and sister. (page 1331)

16. If the group is patrilinear, the child of the brother will belong to the same group as the brother and sister, while the child of the sister will belong to the group of the sister's husband, necessarily a different group. If the group is matrilinear, the sister's child will belong to her group and her brother's child to a different one. (page 1331)

17. When a man marries the eldest of a group of unmarried sisters, and then may take the younger sisters as subordinate wives, the practice is known as sororate. (page 1331)

18. Marriage by purchase, the commonest form, is significant of the interfamily or intergroup nature of marriage, rather than the purely personal significance to the husband and wife. (page 1332)

19. Marriage by arrangement is the type of marriage where the families decide upon the choice of mate, largely from social, economic, or political motives. (page 1333)

20. Yes. (page 1333)

21. This depends upon two factors. First, whether divorce should occur depends upon whether any children by the marriage would be harmed or benefited thereby. Second, even in the absence of children, divorce should only take place if there is a genuine

incompatibility between the marital partners. When selfishness leads to divorce, there is no reason to suppose that any other marriage would be more successful. (page 1334)

22. Because we count the relatives of both father and mother equally (father's brother and mother's brother are both uncles). (page 1335)

23. A gens is a patrilinear sib. (page 1335)

24. Patrilinear means descent in the male line, children belonging to their fathers' groups. Patrilocal means residence of the wife with or near the husband's family. Patriarchal means the authority of the man, usually the oldest man of the group. (page 1335)

25. A tabu is the prohibition of an act or a thing. (page 1335)

26. Tabus are frequently found between a person and his or her parents-in-law; also between brother and sister. (page 1335)

27. The mother-in-law–husband tabu is the commonest, undoubtedly to prevent a conflict of authority and subsequent ill-will. (page 1335)

28. The caste system of India was the division of the populace into classes according to their occupation, each person assuming the occupation of his parents, and normally remaining in that caste forever. Each caste had its own customs and social status, and the castes were endogamous. (pages 1336–1337)

29. Differences in individual ability inevitably lead to greater recognition, authority, and higher social standing. (page 1337)

30. No. Rigid distinctions are neither necessary nor desirable. (page 1337)

31. The commonest form of secret society is the association of adult men. (page 1337)

32. The primitive society is not exclusive. (page 1337)

33. It exercises the functions of government and religion, and has often an important educational function at the time of the initiation of boys into membership. (pages 1337–1338)

34. The moiety functions in games and social activities. (page 1338)

35. Friendships develop understanding, sympathy, and co-operation. (page 1339)

36. It might be theoretically possible, but it could never be practicable, because work is not merely a means to live but also a manner of living, which man could not do without. (page 1339)

37. No. It is found among all primitives. (pages 1340–1341)

38. The state had no specific beginning, but grew gradually out of the control which one man or a group of men had over the community generally. (page 1345)

39. Such intervention is necessary at times, and obviously should occur when it is. (pages 1346–1347)

40. Confined criminals should be permitted to work and study, to enable them to be re-educated to the point where they can adapt themselves to society. (page 1348)

41. Informal education is education derived from work and play and from the experiences of everyday living. (page 1350)

42. Education should enable a person to work and to accept his other responsibilities toward society. In addition, education should broaden a person's outlook and enable him to have a fuller, a more meaningful, existence. (page 1351)

43. Language and handicrafts, the origins of which go back to the very beginnings of human life. (page 1353)

44. The earliest form of writing was by the use of pictures. (page 1353)

45. The most common primitive religious belief is in the existence of nature deities, or personal spirits that control the sun and moon and other natural phenomena. (page 1354)

46. Fetishism is the belief that certain objects have mysterious and magical powers, such as a horseshoe to bring luck. (page 1354)

47. Yes. (page 1356)

48. A mob consists of individuals in such an emotional state that their inhibitions are released and their reasoning powers suspended. (page 1357)

49. Social forces are those elements within society that bring about social change. (pages 1357–1358)

50. The fundamental doctrine of Marx was the doctrine of economic determination, that economic factors were the basic ones to produce changes, that social forces were at bottom economic. (page 1359)

Index

Abbey Theatre, 465
Abdomen, 1275
Abdominal cavity, 1242
Abélard, Peter, 78
Aberdeen, Lord, 127
Ablative, Latin, 677, 678, 688, 689
Abolitionists, 192, 194–195
Abraham, 7
Abstract numbers, 736, 783–784
Acceleration, 988, 1098–1099
Accent, Spanish, 621
Accents, French, 566
Account purchase, 771
Account sale, 769
Accueillir, conjugation of, 592
Accusative, Latin, 677, 678
Acetic acid, 1159
Acetylene, 1158
Achaean League, 24
Achaeans, 10, 12
Acids, 1158–1160, 1169–1171, 1174, 1177–1178, 1179
Acoustics, 1118
Acquired characters, 1224
Acre, 787
Acropolis, 19, 537
Act of 1824, 118
Act of 1832, 118
Act of 1867, 119
Act of 1884, 119
Act of Supremacy, 90
Actium, battle of, 36
Active voice, 369–370
Acute accent, 566
Adam's apple, 1278, 1280
Adams, John, 177, 181, 182
Adams, John Quincy, 186, 188
Adams, Samuel, 176
Adaptation, natural, 1228–1232
Addison, Joseph, 449
Addition, 731–735
    Algebraic, 816–818
    Denominate numbers, 788–789
    Fractions, 750
    Polynomials, 817–818
    Proofs for, 732
Aden, 269, 293
Adenauer, Konrad, 158
Adipose tissue, 1249, 1284
Adjectives, 349, 375, 378–379, 381
    French, 570, 575, 577
    Latin, 684–686, 690, 702, 703, 704
    Spanish, 626, 635
Adrenaline, 1257

Adrianople, Turkish conquest of, 75
Adriatic, Queen of, 77
Adverbs, 349, 375–376, 378–379
"AE," 464
Aegean Islands, 9–10
Aegean New Stone Age, 9
Aeneid, 27, 484
Aeschylus, 20, 481
Aesop, 485–486
Aetius, 42
Afghanistan, 294
Africa
    Animals of, 255
    Countries of, 299–306
    Map of, 300
    Plants of, 255–256
    Tribes of, 1326
After-image, 1302
Agana, 268
Age of Mammals, 1236
Age of Man, 1085
Age of Reptiles, 1236
Agradecer, conjugation of, 648
Agricola, 38
Agricultural Adjustment Administration, 209
Agricultural Revolution, 116–117
Agriculture, 202, 208
    Colonial, 173
    Department of, 241
    in the U.S., 261–268
Aguinaldo, Emilio, 205
Air, 1106–1109, 1155–1157, 1175
Airplane, 982–983
Air pressure, 1106–1109
Aix-la-Chapelle, 52
Alabama, 195, 261, 264
Alabama River, 259
Aladdin, 506
Alamo, battle of, 190
Alarcón, Don Pedro Antonio de, 490
Alaric, 41
Alaska, 201, 220, 259, 261, 262, 267
Albania, 75, 288
Albedo, 1018
Albee, Edward, 478
Albigenses, 88
Albumen, 1220
Alchemy, 79
Alcibiades, 21
Alcott, Louisa May, 470
Aldebaran, 1030, 1038
Alemanni, 49, 52
Alexander I, 109–110
Alexander II, 128

Alexander III, 128
Alexander III, Pope, 64
Alexander the Great, 5, 6, 22–24
Alexandria, 23, 24, 301
Alfieri, Count Vittorio, 488
Alfred the Great, 59, 439
Algae, 1200
Algebra, 807–848
Algebraic products, special, 835–840
Algebraic signs, 810–811
Algeria, 163, 299
Algiers, 182, 299
Algol, 1032, 1038
Algomian Revolution, 1079
Algonquian, 1326
Alhambra, 57, 540
Alice in Wonderland, 457
Alien and Sedition Acts, 182
Alimentary canal, 1273–1276
Aliquot parts, 739–740
Alkalies, 1158, 1159
Allegro, 559
Allemagne, 49
Aller, conjugation of, 591–592
Alliance for Progress, 222
Alligators, 1216
All-India Federation, 136
Alliteration, 432–433
Almqvist, Ludvig, 507
Alphabet, Phoenician, 9
Alpine-Cascadian Revolution, 1084
Alpines, 1326
Alps, 30, 32, 51, 67, 254, 284, 286
Alsace, 51, 95, 124
Alsace-Lorraine, 125
Altimeter, 1108
Altitude, 792, 857, 861, 1108
Aluminium, 1179, 1187–1188
Alva, Duke of, 94
Alveoli, 1271
Amalgamation process, 1186–1187
Amalgams, 1183
Amalia, 510
Amare, declension of, 688–689
Amazon River, 278
Ambassadors, U.S., 240
Amboina, 130
Amending process, 229, 246
Amendments to U.S. Constitution, 246
    Eighteenth, 209, 246
    Eleventh, 243, 246
    Fifteenth, 199
    Fourteenth, 199, 200
    Nineteenth, 139, 246

Amendments (*cont'd*)
  Seventeenth, 206, 246
  Sixteenth, 206, 246
  Thirteenth, 199
  Twelfth, 246
  Twentieth, 209, 246
  Twenty-first, 209, 246
  Twenty-second, 246
  Twenty-third, 246
America, discovery of, 83–84, 167–168
American Expeditionary Forces, 207
"American Scholar, The," 468
American Tragedy, An, 473
Amiens Cathedral, 78, 543, 550
Amiens, peace of, 109
Amino acids, 1198
Ammonia, 1159, 1174, 1175, 1176
Ammonium hydroxide, 1174, 1175
Amoeba, 1198–1199, 1200
Amoy, 132
Amperes, 1132, 1133
Amphibians, 1080, 1081, 1215–1216, 1223
Amphitheaters, Roman, 539
Amsterdam, 84, 283
Amylopsin, 1217
Anabasis, 21, 482
Añadir, conjugation of, 642–643
Anagni, 87
Anapestic foot, 431, 432
Anatomy, 1241
Ancient history, 1–45
Andante, 559
Andersen, Hans Christian, 506
Anderson, Maxwell, 477
Anderson, Sherwood, 473
Andes Mountains, 275, 276, 280
Andesite, 1047
Andorra, 285
Andreyev, Leonid, 509
Andromeda, 1030, 1035, 1037, 1039
Anesthetics, 191
Anger, 1299–1300
Angiosperms, 1204
Angles (people), 41, 48, 52, 53
Angles
  Acute, 852
  Adjacent, 858
  Alternate exterior, 875
  Alternate interior, 875
  Bisecting, 854–856
  Complementary, 858, 947–948
  Corresponding, 875
  Cosine of, 952
  Exterior, 875
  Interior, 875
  Measuring, 852
  Obtuse, 852
  Perpendicular, 859
  Right, 852
  Sine of, 952
  Straight, 852
  Supplementary, 858

Tangent of, 952
  Vertical, 859
Anglia, East, 53
Anglican Church, 99, 169
Anglo-American Committee, 138
Anglo-Iranian Oil Company, 162
Anglo-Saxon Chronicle, 439
Anglo-Saxons, 53, 60, 69
Angola, 305
Animal kingdom, 1213–1224
Animal processes, 1216–1224
Animals, 254–257
  Growth of, 1216–1218
  Intelligence of, 1289
  Oviparous, 1222
  Parasitic, 1230–1232
  Viviparous, 1222
Anjou, 71
Anna Christie, 475
Anna Karenina, 509
Annam, 131, 160
Annapolis Convention, 180
Anne of Austria, 99
Anne of Bohemia, 88
Annelids, 1214
Annuals, 1205
Anopheles, 995, 1231
Antarctic Circle, 252
Antecedents of pronouns, 358
Antennae, 1214
Anterior, 1241
Anthony, Susan B., 139
Anthropoid apes, 1238
Anthropology, 1328
Antibiotics, 993–994
Antibodies, 1267
Anticline, 1064
Antietam, battle of, 198
Antigone, 482
Anti-inflation act, 211
Antilles, 275
Antioch, 24, 25, 56
Anti-Trust Act, Sherman, 203
Antoninus, Marcus Aurelius, 38, 485
Antonius, Marcus, 36
Antony, Mark, 36
Ants, 1231–1232
Antwerp, 77, 84, 149, 283
Anus, 1276
Anxiety, 1314
Aorta, 1268, 1269, 1270
Ape Man of Java, 1238
Apelles, 520
Apes, 1232, 1238
Aphids, 1221, 1231–1232
Aphrodite, 27
Apogee, 1014
Apollo, 13
Apollo Belvedere, 25
Apollodorus, 520
Apothecaries' fluid measure, 785
  Weight, 786
Appalachian-Hercynian revolution, 1081
Appalachian Mountains, 258, 261, 264, 1070
Appeasement, 147
Appendicitis, 1232, 1276

Appendix, vermiform, 1232, 1276
Appian Way, 28
Appius Claudius, 28
Appomattox Court House, 199
Aptitude tests, 1319
Apuleius, 485
Aqua regia, 1187
Aqueduct, Roman, 28
Aqueous humor, 1125, 1264
Aquinas, Thomas, 78
Arabesques, 58
Arabia, 7, 16, 54, 56, 143, 293
Arabian architecture, 57–58
Arabian manufacturing, 57
Arabian Nights' Entertainments, The, 57, 478
Arabian sciences, 57
Arabians, Moslem, 55
Arabic numerals, 7
Arabic number system, 729–730
Arab League, 137
Arabs, 23, 56, 82, 83, 137, 138, 162
Arachnids, 1214
Arachnoid, 1242
Aragon, 71
Aragon, Louis, 499
Arbela, 23
Arch of Constantine, 539
Archean rocks, 1078–1079
Archeozoic Era, 1078–1079
Archimedes, 25, 1091
Archimedes' Principle, 1104
Architecture, 536–546
  Arabian, 57–58
  Athenian, 19–20
  Byzantine, 56, 540
  Christian, early, 540
  Colonial, 545
  Egyptian, 536–537
  Georgian, 545
  Gothic, 78, 542–543
  Greek, 537–539
  Modern, 545–546
  Moorish, 540
  Norman, 541–542, 543
  Ostrogothic, 48
  Primitive, 536
  Renaissance, 543–545
  Rhenish, 541
  Roman, 38, 539–540
  Romanesque, 78, 541
  Tudor, 543
Arctic Circle, 252, 259, 288
Arcturus, 1031, 1032
Ardennes forest, 149
Areas, measuring, 792–796
Argentina, 155, 280
Argonne, 141
Argos, 21
Argumentation, 411–414
Aries, 1030, 1036, 1039
Ariosto, 435
Aristarchus, 25
Aristides, 17, 18
Aristophanes, 20, 429
Aristotle, 20, 25, 445
Arizona, 191, 262, 266
Arkansas, 189, 195, 264

Arkansas River, 259
Armenia, 36, 74, 143, 290
Armistice, 142, 207
Arms, 1248
Arnim, Bettina von, 503
Arno River, 26
Arnold, Matthew, 455
Arouet, François Marie, 493
Arrowsmith, 474
Art
    Appreciation of, 1314–1315
    Athenian, 15, 20
    Forms of, 514
    Nature of, 514–516
    Use of, 514–516
Arteries, 1266, 1267, 1268–1270
Artesian wells, 1053
Arthropods, 1214
Arthur, Chester A., 202
Arthur, King, 78, 439, 440
Articles, in Grammar, 350
    French, agreement of, 570
    Spanish, agreement of, 626
Articles of Confederation, 179, 180, 181
Articulations, 1249
Arts, 514–564
Artsibashev, Mikhail, 509
Aruba, 275
Aryans, 1326
As, comparisons with, 379–380
Ascending reduction, 790–791
Asia, 42–44, 73–74, 130–138, 142, 250
    Animals of, 254–255
    Countries of, 291, 293–299
    Map of, 292
    Plants of, 255
Asoka, 42
Aspern, 110
Asphyxia, 1271
Assembly
    Legislative, 107
    National, 106, 107
        French, 125
        German, 123
Assessed valuation, 780
Associations
    Controlled, 1309
    Social, 1327, 1336–1339
Associations Act, 125
Assonance, 432, 433
Assurbanipal, 6
Assyria, 5, 6, 8, 16
Astatine, 1177, 1178
Asteroids, 1005
Astrology, 79, 999
Astronomy, 999–1042
    Greek, 25
Asunción, 279
Asymmetrical arrangement, 514
Atacama Desert, 276
Athena, statue of, 548
Athene, 19

Athenian
    Architecture, 19–20
    Art, 15, 20
    League, 18
    Literature, 15, 20
    Oratory, 20
    Philosophy, 16, 20
    Sculpture, 19–20
Athens, 13–16, 17, 18–21, 24, 25, 28, 288, 537
Atlantic Charter, 150, 151, 212
Atlantic Conference, 212, 213
Atmosphere, 249, 1044, 1045, 1057–1060, 1155
Atmospheric pressure, 988, 1058, 1106–1109
Atmospheric temperature, 1058
Atoll, 1063
Atomic Age, 154
Atomic bomb, 140, 155, 156–157, 214, 216, 986
Atomic energy (*See* Nuclear energy)
Atomic numbers, 1165
Atomic theory, 968
Atomic weights, 1162–1164
Atoms, 1161–1168
    Helium, 1167
    Hydrogen, 1166–1167
    Size of, 1166–1168
Attention, 1303–1304
Attic school, 548
Attica, 13, 14, 15, 16, 17, 19
Attila, 41, 42
Attlee, Clement, 154, 161, 215, 216
Attorney-General, 240, 241, 243
Attraction, sex, 1295–1296
Auden, Wystan Hugh, 429
Audience
    Sense, 401
    Speaking to, 422
Augsburg, 77
    Diet of, 89
    Peace of, 89
Augusta, 150
Augustan Age, 37
Augustine, St., 53, 428, 439, 486
Augustulus, Romulus, 42, 46, 48
Augustus, 37, 520
Aurelius, Marcus, 38, 40
Auricle, 1268
Austen, Jane, 453
Austerlitz, 109
Australia, 139, 250, 254, 256, 269, 306–307
    Animals of, 256
    Map of, 308
    Plants of, 256
Australoids, 1326
Austria, 53, 64, 72, 94, 95, 99, 100, 102, 103, 107, 108, 109, 110, 112, 121–122, 123, 124, 141, 142, 143, 147, 156, 158, 172, 286
Austria-Hungary, 124, 126, 127, 140, 142, 143

Austrian Succession, War of, 172
Autobiography, 427
Autocrat of the Breakfast Table, The, 469
Automobile engine, 979–980
Automobile industry, 206, 265
Autonomic nervous system, 1256, 1271
Avar tribes, 41, 43, 51, 52
Avignon, 87
Avoir, conjugation of, 590
Avoirdupois weight, 786
Avunculate, 1335.
Axioms, geometric, 859–860
Axis Powers, 147
Axle, 1093–1094
Azerbaijan, 143, 290
Azoic Era, 1077
Azores, 285
Aztec Indians, 168

Babbitt, 473
Baber, 74
Babies, reactions of, 1293, 1294
Babylon, 6, 23, 24
Babylonia, 8, 16, 38, 42
Babylonian Captivity, 87
Babylonian Empire, 6, 10
Bacchae, 482
Bacchanalia, 703
Bach, Johann Sebastian, 556, 557, 558, 560
Bachelor of Arts degree, 78
Bacillus, 1201
Back to Methuselah, 460
Bacon, Francis, 428, 445, 1285
Bacon, Roger, 79
Bacteria, 992–993, 1201, 1217, 1230, 1231, 1232, 1236, 1277
Baghdad, 73, 293
Bahama Islands, 84, 269, 275
Bahrain, 269, 293
Baily's Beads, 1011
Bakewell, Robert, 117
Balance, sense of, 1262
Balboa, Vasco Nuñez de, 168
Balder, 58
Balearic Islands, 285
Balfour Declaration, 137
Balkans, 56, 126–127, 140, 143, 289
Ballad, 430
Ballad stanza, 434
Ball games, medieval, 79
Ballistic missiles, 221
Ballot
    Australian, 204
    Secret, 204
Baltic Sea, 48, 73, 95
Baltimore, 184, 263
Baltimore, Lord, 170
Baltimore and Ohio Railway, 191
Balzac, Honoré de, 495
Bamberg Cathedral, 550
Bancroft, George, 189
Bank discount, 778–782
Banim, John, 464
Banim, Michael, 464

Bank
First national, 182
of France, 111
of England, 161
Second National, 188
U.S., 188
Bannockburn, 69
Barbados, 269, 274
Barbarossa, Frederick, 64, 66, 72
Barbusse, Henri, 498
Barcelona, 285
Barchester Towers, 457
Barometer, 977
Baroque Period, 544, 545
Barrack Emperors, 40
Barrie, Sir James Matthew, 460
Barrier reefs, 1063
Bartók Béla, 563
Basalt, 1047
Base, in mathematics, 756, 792, 861, 901
Bases, chemical, 1158-1160
Basilicas, 540
Basques, 52
Bastille, 105
Basutoland, 305
Bat, 1230
Bataan, 211, 214
Batavia, 130
Batteries, 1132, 1141
Battle of the Nations, 111
Batu Khan, 74
Baudelaire, Charles, 495-496
Bauhaus, 546
Bavaria, 72, 114, 550
Bavarians, 52
Beaconsfield, Lord, 127
Bear, polar, 1229
Beaumarchais, 493
Beccaria, 104
Bechuanaland, 305
Becquerel, Henri, 985
Bede, the Venerable, 439
Bedrock, 1049
Bees, 1221, 1229
Beethoven, Ludwig van, 557, 558-559, 561, 562
Behavior, 1288
Motivated, 1295
Native, 1294
Observation of, 1289-1291
Belgian literature, 500
Belgium, 50, 51, 77, 94, 112, 121, 140, 141, 148, 156, 163, 164, 214, 283
Belisarius, 55
Bell, electric, 1134-1135
Bell, John, 194
Bellatrix, 1037
Bellini, Giovanni, 523
Benavente, Jacinto, 490
Benefit of clergy, 62
Benenato, 541
Benét, Stephen Vincent, 476
Bennett, Arnold, 460
Benton, Thomas, 535
Beowulf, 430, 438-439
Berber tribes, 30, 57
Berg, Alban, 562
Bergen, 77, 287

Berlin, 149, 164, 286
Congress of, 126
Berlin and Milan Decrees, 110
Berlioz, Hector, 562
Bermuda, 269, 274
Bernadotte, 110
Bernini, Lorenzo, 544-545
Bertha, 54
Betelgeuse, 1030, 1032, 1037
Bevin, Ernest, 215
Bible, 440, 441, 444, 445, 466, 501
Gutenberg, 86
King James Version, 96, 441, 444-445
Mosaic Code, 6
Old Testament, 7-8
Biceps muscle, 1249-1250, 1252
Bicuspids, 1274
Biennials, 1205
Bierce, Ambrose, 472
Bilateral, 1335
Bilbao, 285
Bile, 1217, 1276
Bill of exchange, 325
Bill of Rights, 99, 182, 236, 244, 245-246
Bills, Congressional, 234-235
Bimetallic standard, 318
Binary numbers, 971
Binomial, 817
Biography, 427, 428
Biology, 1196-1240
Birds, 1216, 1236
Birds, The, 482
Birmingham, 118, 264
Birth, 1222, 1223
Bisecting
an angle, 855-856
a line, 853-854
Bismarck, Otto von, 124, 126
Bison, American, 191
Bi-symmetrical arrangement, 514, 515
Bizet, Georges, 556
Björnson, Björnstjerne, 507
Black Death, 85, 440
Black Hole of Calcutta, 102
Black magic, 79
Black markets, 211
Blackmore, Richard Doddridge, 457
Black Prince, 70
Blake, William, 429, 451, 534
Bland-Allison Act, 203
Blank verse, 433
Blasco Ibáñez, Vicente, 490
Blastula, 1221, 1222
Bleaching powder, 1182
Blends, psychological, 1302
Blight, potato, 1231
Blind spot, 1264
Bloch, Ernest, 563
Blood, 1265-1268
Blood capillaries, 1226, 1250-1251, 1268-1269, 1278
Blood, Council of, 94
Blood pressure, 1270
Bloody Mary, 91, 92
Blowpipe, oxyhydrogen, 1156
Blue Bird, The, 500
Blueprints, 1184

Boards, government, 242
Boccaccio, Giovanni, 85, 487
Böcklin, Arnold, 533
Body of Civil Law, 49
Body, human, 1241-1287
Boeotia, 16, 17, 18
Bohemia, 72, 88, 94, 122, 124, 143
Bohemians, 52
Boire, conjugation of, 597
Bojer, Johan, 507
Bokhara, 73
Boleyn, Anne, 90, 92
Bolivar, Simon, 169
Bolivia, 279
Bologna, University of, 78
Bolshevists, 120, 122, 128-129
Bombs, volcanic, 1067
Bonaparte, Jerome, 110
Bonaparte, Joseph, 110
Bonaparte, Louis, 110
Bonaparte, Napoleon, 108-112, 114, 115, 121, 123, 182, 183
Bones, 1203, 1243, 1246-1249
Boniface VIII, Pope, 87
Book of Common Prayer, 90
Book of the Dead, The, 478
Boone, Daniel, 182
Boötes, 1030, 1039
Booth, John Wilkes, 200
Booth, William, 139
Bordeaux, 84
Bordeaux mixture, 1185
Boris Godunov, 508, 556
Borneo, North, 269, 296
Bosch, Hieronymus, 531
Bosnia, 87, 127, 143
Bosporus, 55, 291
Boston, 176, 177, 178, 201, 262, 263
Massacre, 176
Tea Party, 176
Boswell, James, 428, 450
Botanical classification, 1235
Botswana, 163, 269, 305
Botticelli, Sandro, 523
Boucher, François, 525
Boulanger, General, 125
Bourbons, 99, 100, 111, 114, 115, 125
Bourgeoisie, 76, 106, 120
Boxer Rebellion, 133, 239
Boyne, battle of, 98-99
Brachial plexus, 1254
Braddock, Edward, 172
Bradford, William, 170
Brahman cattle, 995
Brahmans, 1336
Brahmins, 136
Brahms, Johannes, 554, 557, 559, 561-562
Brain, 1253, 1254-1256, 1289, 1291-1293, 1312
Brains, electronic, 970
Brancusi, Constantin, 552
Brand, 507
Brandenburg, 52, 73, 101
Braque, Georges, 528
Brasidas, 21
Brass-wind instruments, 560
Brave New World, 462

Brazil, 83, 142, 168, 276, 278–279, 341
Breastbone, 1248
Breathing, 1271–1272
Breccia, 1067
Breckinridge, John, 194
Breeding, 994–995, 1227–1228
Bremer, Fredrika, 507
Brentano, Clemens, 503
Bretton Woods, 152, 213
Breughel, Pieter, 531
Bricker, John, 212
Bridal Veil Falls, 1056
Bridge, George Washington, 1111
Brieux, Eugène, 498
Britain, 38, 41, 164
  Roman Conquest of, 35, 38
British Commonwealth of Nations, 128, 136, 144, 163, 269–270, 280, 294
British East India Company, 102, 135
British East Indies, 149, 211
British Empire, 114, 122, 127–129, 360
British Guiana, 278
British Honduras, 269, 275
British Isles, 48, 52, 53–54, 69, 110, 114, 251, 269, 280–282, 438
British Railways, 161
British Solomon Islands, 307
Britons, 48, 54, 69
Brittany, 48, 71
Broker, 769
Brokerage and commission, 768–770
Bromide, silver, 1185–1186
Bromides, 1177, 1178
Bromine, 1165, 1177, 1178, 1179
Bronchi, 1271
Brontë, Charlotte, 457
Brontë, Emily, 457
Brontosaurus, 1236
Bronze Age, 10
Brook Farm, 189
Brown, John, 194–195
Brown University, 174
Browne, Sir Thomas, 445, 448
Browning, Elizabeth Barrett, 455
Browning, Robert, 454–455
Bruce, Robert, 69
Bruges, 77, 283
Brunei, 296
Brunelleschi, Filippo, 544, 550
Brunswick, Duke of, 107
Brussels, 94, 140, 283
Brutus, 36
Bryan, William Jennings, 204
Bryant, William Cullen, 189, 467
Bryophytes, 1204
Bubonic plague, 85
Buccal cavity, 1274
Buchanan, James, 193, 195
Budapest, 158, 289
Buddenbrooks, 504

Buddha, 42, 479
Buddhism, 42, 43, 479
Budget, 783
Buds, 1221
Bueckelaer, 531
Buena Vista, battle of, 190
Buenos Aires, 280
Buffalo, 191
Bulganin, Nikolai, 157
Bulgaria, 75, 87, 127, 142, 148, 154, 157, 217, 288
Bulge, battle of, 149
Bull Run, battle of, 196
Bulwer-Lytton, Edward, 457
Bumpo, Natty, 467
Bundesrat, 124
Bunker Hill, battle of, 177
Bunyan, John, 448
Burbank, Luther, 995, 1227
Burchfield, Charles, 535
Buren, Martin Van, 189, 190
Burgesses, House of, 172
Burghley, Lord, 92
Burgoyne, John, 178
Burgundians, 49, 52
Burgundy, 51, 71, 500
Burke, Edmund, 451, 464
Burma, 130, 131, 144, 148, 154, 161, 211, 270, 295
Burne-Jones, Edward, 457, 534
Burning, 1154
Burns, Robert, 429, 450
Buoyancy, 981
Burr, Aaron, 182
Burton, Sir Richard, 478
Burundi, 163, 305
Bushel, 785, 786
Bushmen, 1238–1239, 1326
Business cycle, 332–335
Butler, Samuel, 459
Butterfly, 1229
Buttocks, 1276
Byrnes, James, 215
Byron, Lord, 435, 452
Byzantine
  Architecture, 56, 540
  Empire, 50, 55–56
  Scholars, 56
Byzantium, 40, 55, 56

Caballero, Fernan, 490
Cabell, James Branch, 474
Caber, conjugation of, 654
Cabinet, President's, 240
Cable, first Atlantic, 139, 191
Cabot, John, 84, 169
Cacti, 1229
Cadenza, 559
Cadiz, 84
Calcium, 1179, 1181
  Carbonate, 1178, 1179, 1181
  Hydroxide, 1159, 1160, 1179, 1181

Oxide, 1160, 1179, 1181
  Phosphate, 1182
  Sulphate, 1182
Calcutta, Black Hole of, 102
Calder, Alexander, 536
Calderón, 490
Calendar, Latin, 702–703
Calhoun, John Caldwell, 183
California, 191, 192–193, 259, 266, 267
Caligula, 37
Caliphs, Arabian, 66
Callisto, 1021, 1036
Calomel, 1183
Calvin, John, 89
Calyx, 1211
Cambio, Arnolfo di, 543
Cambium, 1205
Cambodia, 131, 160, 296
Cambridge, 76, 77, 78
Cambyses, 16
Camera, 1125, 1126
"Camerata," 554
Cameroun, 163, 270, 303
Camoëns, Luis de, 491
Canaan, 7, 8
Canada, 114, 138, 166, 169, 172, 177, 178, 184, 192, 218, 269, 270, 450
Canal Zone, 205, 268, 273
Canary Islands, 306
Candidates, presidential, 236–237
Candide, 104, 493
Canines, 1274
Cannae, battle of, 32
Canopus, 1032
Cantatas, 556
Canterbury, 54, 79, 90
  Cathedral, 542, 543
Canterbury Tales, 79, 430, 440, 441
Canton, 132, 133, 297
Canute the Dane, 59
Canzoniere, 487
Capet, Hugh, 59, 69–70
Capillaries, 1250–1251, 1266, 1268–1269, 1271, 1278
Capillary action, in physics, 1105–1106
Capital, 313–317, 1341
Capitalist, 315
Capitalization, 380–381
Capital punishment, 1348
Capitol, 184, 545
Capitoline, 27
Capote, Truman, 477
Capua, 32
Carat, 788, 1187
Carbides, 1178
Carbohydrates, 1193, 1197–1198, 1209, 1273
Carbon, 1009, 1154–1155, 1156, 1157, 1162, 1178, 1182, 1189–1190
  Dioxide, 1155, 1156, 1170, 1175, 1209, 1251, 1279
  Monoxide, 1156
Carbonates, 1178
Carboniferous Age, 1080
Cardiac muscle, 1249, 1250, 1251

Cardiac plexus, 1254
Cards, playing, 79
Carducci, Giosuè, 488
Carew, Thomas, 446
Carey Act, 266
Caribbean Sea, exploration of, 84
Carleton, William, 464
Carlyle, Thomas, 428, 455, 468, 502, 503
Carmen, 495, 556
Carnegie, Andrew, 139
Carnegie Hall, 1118–1119
Carnivorous animals, 1216
Carolina, North, 171, 180, 195
Carolina, South, 171, 174, 188, 194, 195
Caroline Islands, 146, 269
Carolingian dynasty, 50, 52, 59
Caro, Miguel Antonio, 510
Caron, Pierre Augustin, 493
Carpals, 1248
Carpet-baggers, 200–201, 202
Carroll, Lewis, 457
Carthage, 16, 23, 26, 27, 29, 30–33
    Map of, in 218 B.C., 31
Cartier, Jacques, 168
Cartilages, 1203, 1246
Cartwright, Edmund, 103
Casablanca, 150
    Conference, 150, 213
Casanova de Seingalt, 488
Case of nouns, 356–357
    Latin, 677–678
Case of pronouns, 360–362
Caspian Sea, 16, 51, 66, 251
Cassiopeia, 1037
Cassius, 36
Cast iron, 1157, 1183
Caste system, 1336–1337
Castile, 71
Castilian School, 530
Castle Church, 88
Castles, 61, 80
Castor, 1032, 1037
Castro, Fidel, 164, 220
Catesby, Robert, 96
Cathedrals, Gothic, 542–543
Cather, Willa, 476
Catherine of Aragon, 90, 92
Catherine the Great, 102, 104, 128, 450
Catholic Church, Roman, 54, 67, 88, 89, 91, 93, 94, 96, 104, 109, 125
Catholics, 92, 93, 96, 118, 169, 170, 172
Catiline, 35, 485
Cato, 35, 36
Cato the Elder, 33
Cats, 1234
Cattle, selective breeding of, 117
Catullus, 38, 484
Caucasians, 1326
Caucus, 189, 233, 234
Caudal, 1241
Caustic potash, 1159
Caustic soda, 1159
Cavalier poets, 446

Cavaliers, 97, 171
Caverns, 1053–1054
Cavour, Count di, 49, 122
Caxton, William, 86, 440–441
CCC, 209
Cebidae, 1236
Cedilla, 566
Celestial sphere, 1001, 1036
Cell, 1196–1198, 1200, 1203, 1243, 1266, 1288–1289
    Membrane, 1197
    Sap, 1197
    Somatic, 1219
    Voltaic, 1132
Cellini, Benvenuto, 428, 488, 551
Cellular reproduction, 1199–1201
Cellulose, 1217, 1277
Celtic natives, 53
Celtic revival, 464
Cenozoic
    Era, 1077, 1082–1084
    Mammals, 1083
    Time, 1236
Centigrade, 1111–1112
Centimeter, 1166
Central African Republic, 163, 304
Central America, 84, 186, 205, 222, 272–275
Central Powers, 141, 142, 144, 207
Centrifugal force, 989
Centrosphere, 1044
Cephalic, 1241
Cercopithecidae, 1238
Cerebellum, 1251, 1253, 1255
Cerebral hemispheres, 1253
Cerebrum, 1238, 1253, 1255
Ceres, 1021
Cervantes Saavedra, Miguel de, 489
Cervical plexus, 1254
Cervical vertebrae, 1246
Ceylon, 114, 130, 161, 269, 295
Cézanne, Paul, 528
Chad, 163, 301
Chagall, Marc, 529–530
Chain reaction, 986
Chalcidice, 22
Chaldean reliefs, 547
Chaldeans, 5
Châlons, battle of, 42
Chamber music, 559
Chamber of Deputies, French, 125
Chamberlain, Neville, 147
Chamberlin, Thomas C., 1074
Chamisso, Adelbert von, 503
Champlain, Lake, 184, 262
Champollion, 3
Chandragupta, 42
Channel Islands, 282
Chanson de Roland, 491
Characters, in biology, 1225–1227
Chardin, Jean Baptiste Siméon, 525
Charlemagne, 49, 50–52, 53,

58, 59, 60, 63, 78, 487–488
Charles I, 96–97, 169–170, 171, 446
Charles II, 97, 98, 448
Charles IV, 110
Charles V, 89, 90, 94
Charles VIII, 71
Charles X, 115, 120
Charles XII, 101
Charles the Hammer, 50
Charleston, 199, 264
Chartists, 118–119
Chartres Cathedral, 78, 542, 550
Chase, William Merritt, 535
Château-Thierry, battle of, 142
Châteaubriand, François René de, 494
Chaucer, Geoffrey, 79, 430, 434–435, 437, 440
Chavannes, Puvis de, 526
Chekhov, Anton, 428, 509
Chemistry, 1152–1195
Cheops, 4, 10
Cherbourg, 84
Chesapeake, 184
Chesapeake Bay, 179, 180, 184, 258, 263
Chess, 61
Chest, 1242, 1271
Chesterfield, Lord, 450, 451
Chiang Kai-shek, 147, 150, 155, 158–159, 213, 218
Chicago, 201, 204, 263, 265
Chickamauga, battle of, 198
Child labor, 119, 340
Children, instincts of, 1296–1297
Children of the Lord's Supper, 507
Children's Crusade, 67
Chile, 141, 276
Chimborazo, 276
China, 42, 43, 50, 57, 73, 82, 85, 126, 130, 132–133, 134, 142, 144, 146–147, 148, 150, 151, 153, 154, 156, 158, 160, 164, 213, 218, 219, 239, 297
Chirico, Giorgio de, 529
Chlorides, 1171, 1177, 1178, 1179
Chlorine, 1169–1171, 1177, 1178, 1179
Chlorophyl, 991, 992, 1197, 1200, 1203, 1206, 1209
Chloroplasts, 1197, 1202, 1206, 1209
Chopin, Frédéric, 557, 559
Chordates, 1214, 1215
Choruses, polyphonic, 554
Chosroes II, 55
Chou dynasty, 43
Chou En-lai, 159
Christ, 3, 40, 66
Christian IV, 94
Christianity, 41, 43, 48, 50, 54, 55, 58, 59, 66, 133, 439

Christians, 37, 38, 40, 41, 66, 67, 75, 126
Chromosomes, 1196, 1225–1226
Chromosphere, 1007
Chronicles, 443
Chrysalis, 1223
Chungking, 147
Church, 1355–1356
Anglican, 91, 99, 169
Castle, 88
Episcopal, 89, 92
Greek, 54, 59
Holy Orthodox, 54
Lutheran, 89
of the Apostles, 541
Presbyterian, 89
Roman Catholic, 54, 62, 86, 88, 89, 91, 93, 94, 96, 109, 125
Churchill, Winston, 129, 148, 150, 151, 152, 153, 212, 213
Chyme, 1278
Cicero, Marcus Tullius, 30, 38, 485, 727
Cid, Le, 71
Cid, The, 489, 492
Cilia, 1200
Cimabue, 522
Cimon, 18
Cincinnatus, 707
Cinders, volcanic, 1067
Cinnabar, 1182
C.I.O., 210, 212
Circle, 791–792, 794, 913–920
Circuit courts of appeal, 243
Circuit of the World, 505
Circular measurements, 797–798
Circulatory system, 1265–1270
Circumcision, 1282
Circumflex accent, 566
Cirque, 1056
Cisalpine Gaul, 30
Cistercian order, 63
Citizenship, U.S., 167, 224–225
Citrate of magnesia, 1182
Citric acid, 1159
Civics, 224–248
Civil Law, Body of, 49
Civil Rights, 200, 221
Civil Service Commission, 202, 242
Civil War, 119, 185, 191, 192–200, 226, 246
Civilian Conservation Corps, 209–210
Civilized peoples, 1323–1324
Clan, in sociology, 1335
Classes, social, 1327, 1336–1339
Claudius, 37
Clause, 353–355
Clavichord, 557
Clavicles, 1248
Clay, Henry, 183, 186, 193
Clayton Anti-Trust Act, 206
Clemenceau, Georges, 142
Clemens, Samuel Langhorne, 471

Clement VII, Pope, 87
Cleon, 21
Cleopatra, 5, 36
Clergy, benefit of, 62
Clermont, 191, 979
Cleveland, Grover, 203, 204
Climate, 253–254, 972, 1049
Clisthenes, 15
Clitoris, 1284
Clive, Robert, 102, 135
Cloak, The, 509
Cloisters, Romanesque, 541
Clothing, selecting, 516
Clouds, 974, 1059
Clouds, The, 482
Clovis, 49–50
Clubs, social, 1337–1338
Cluny order, 63
Cnossos, 9
Coagulation, 1267–1268
Coal, 115–116, 161, 191, 263, 1072, 1102
Coalition, Third, 109
Coccus, 1201
Coccyx, 1233, 1246, 1254
Cochin-China, 131, 160
Coefficient, 829–831, 840–841
Coefficient of expansion, 1110
Table of, 1111
Coelenterates, 1213, 1215
Coelenteron, 1213
Coelom, 1214
Cogwheel, 1094
Coins, first, 9
Colbert, Jean Baptiste, 100
Cold war, 129, 156–157
Cole, Thomas, 535
Coleridge, Samuel Taylor, 429, 432, 452
Coligny, Admiral, 93
Collective bargaining, 118
Colleges, 174, 192
Collins, Wilkie, 429, 430, 456
Colloid, 1244
Cologne, 52, 77, 286, 533, 541
Cathedral, 543
Colombia, 205, 275
Colon, intestinal, 1276, 1278
Colon, punctuation, 384
Colonial life, American, 173–175
Colonial Period, American, 169–175
Color-blindness, 1227, 1265
Colorado, 191, 203, 241, 266
Colorado River, 259, 266
Colors, 514, 516, 1126–1129
Colosseum, 37, 38, 539
Colum, Padraic, 465
Columbia River, 259, 266, 986, 1068
Columbia University, 174
Columbus, Christopher, 58, 72, 83–84, 167, 168
Combined Chiefs of Staff, 213
Combined Production and Resources Board, 213
Combined Raw Materials Board, 213
Combustion, 1154, 1155
Comedies, 429

Comer, conjugation of, 641–642
Comets, 969, 1025–1028, 1029
Comma, 382–384
Commerce, Department of, 241
Commission and brokerage, 768–770
Committee for Industrial Organization, 210
Committees, standing, 234, 235
Commodius, 40
Common Market, 164
Common Sense, 177
Commons, House of, 69, 446
Commonwealth, 97, 98, 171
Commune, 107, 124
Communication, modern, 983–985
Communism, 122, 129, 164, 217, 290, 296, 337–338
Communist International, 120
Communist Manifesto, 120
Communists, Chinese, 147, 155, 158–159
Communities, planning of, 515
Comparative degree, 380
Comparisons, 378–380
Compass, 83, 1130
Compasses, geometrical, 853
Complement, per cent, 767
Complementary angles, 858, 947–949
Compound interest, 774–775
Compound numbers, 783
Compounds, metallic, 1181–1188
Computers, 970–972, 990
Concave, 1122, 1124
Concerto, 559
Concord, 176, 177
Concordat, 109, 111, 125
Concordat of Worms, 63
Concrete numbers, 736, 783–784
Condé, Prince de, 93
Conductors
Electrical, 1131
of Heat, 1113–1114
Cone, 800, 934
Confederate Congress, 199
Confederates, 195–199
Confederate States of America, 195
Confederation, Articles of, 179, 180, 181
Confessio Amantis, 440
Conflict, 1299–1300
Confucius, 43, 479
Congo, Democratic Republic of, 163, 304
Congo (Brazzaville), 163, 304
Congress, First Continental, 176
Congress of Berlin, 126
Congress of Industrial Organizations, 210
Congress of Vienna, 112–114, 123, 130

Congress, Second Continental, 177, 178, 179
Congress, U.S., 226, 227, 228, 229–236, 243–247, 266
Congressional districts, 230
Congressional Record, 235
Congreve, William, 448
Congruent triangles, 862–863, 864
Conjugation
  French, 585–600
  Latin, 680, 696, 697, 715
  Spanish, 638–656
Conjunctions, 349, 354, 379
Conjunctiva, 1262
Connaître, conjugation of, 597
Connecticut, 170, 171, 268
Connecticut River, 172, 258, 262
Connecticut Valley, 261, 262
Conrad, Joseph, 460
Conservation, 994
Consignee, 769
Consignor, 769
Consonant sounds, 1280
Constable, John, 534
Constance, Council of, 87, 88
Constantine, 40, 41, 42, 53, 54, 55, 539, 540
Constantinople, 40, 42, 46, 48, 55, 56, 59, 71, 75, 77, 86, 87, 127, 167, 440, 540
Constellations, 1035–1039
Constitution, 184
Constitution, U.S., 99, 104, 180–181, 183, 225–229, 245–247
    Amendments to, see Amendments to U.S. Constitution
Constitutional Convention, 180
Constitutional Unionist party, 194
Consul, First, 109
Consulates, 240
Consuls, Roman, 28
Consuls, U.S., 240
Consumer's credit, 322
Consumers' goods, 311
Contar, conjugation of, 650–651
Continental shelves, 1061
Continents, 250
Contractile tissue, 1250
Contractions, 376–377
Contrat Social, Le, 494
Convection, 1113
Convention of 1888, 162
Convention system, 189
Converses, geometry, 884
Convex, 1122, 1124–1125
Convolutions, brain, 1253, 1254
Coolidge, Calvin, 208
Cooper, James Fenimore, 467
Copernicus, Nicolaus, 510
Copper, 1153, 1173, 1179, 1184–1185
  Oxide, 1153, 1179
  Sulphate, 1173, 1179, 1185
  Sulphide, 1172

Copulative verb, 363–364
Coral reefs, 1062
Coral Sea, 214
  Battle of, 149, 214
Corday, Charlotte, 108
Cord of wood, 800, 802
Cordova, 57
Cordovan, 57
Corinth, 21, 22, 33
Corinthian order, 538
Corium, 1243
Cork tissue of plants, 1202
Corn Laws, 119
Cornea, 1125, 1263
Corneille, Pierre, 492
Cornelia, 711–712
Cornwallis, Charles, 179
Corolla, 1211
Corollary, 859, 869
Corona, 1009, 1011
Corpuscles, 1266–1267
Corot, Jean Baptiste Camille, 526
Correggio, Antonio Allegri da, 524
Corregidor, 214
Corsica, 26, 30, 108, 283
Cortex, 1204–1205, 1208, 1253, 1255, 1291–1292, 1312
Cortez, Hernando, 168
Cosecant, 945
Cosine, 945, 962, 963
Cosmic Era, 1077
Cosmic rays, 985
Cossacks, 129
Cost, 327–328, 764–768
Costa Rica, 273
Cotangent, 945
Cotton, 262, 264, 270, 279, 1191
Cotton gin, 191
Cotyledons, 1212
Coughing, 1272
Council of Blood, 94
Council of Constance, 87, 88
Council of Five Hundred, 109
Council of Ministers, Big Five, 154
Council of Nobles, Great, 68–69
Counter-Reformation, 91–92
Counterfeiters, The, 499
Countries, 258–259
Couplet, heroic, 434
Courbet, Gustave, 526
Courir, conjugation of, 600
Court
  Circuit, 243
  Customs, 243
  District, 243
  Federal, 233, 243–244
  of Claims, 243, 244
  of Customs and Patent Appeals, 243, 244
  of Justice, English, 68
  of Justice, International, 215
  Supreme, U.S., 210, 243, 244
  World, 153
Courtship, 1296
Coverley, Sir Roger de, 449
Cowper, William, 451

Craindre, conjugation of, 597–598
Cranach, Lucas, the Elder, 533
Crane, Stephen, 472
Cranium, 1246
Cranmer, Thomas, 90, 91, 92
Crassus, 35
Crécy, 70
Credit, 321–325
Cretaceous, 1082
Crete, 9, 10
Crime, 1347–1348
Crime and Punishment, 509
Crime of Reconstruction, 200
Crimean War, 127
Cripps, Sir Stafford, 136
Critique of Pure Reason, 501
Crockett, David, 190
Crocodiles, 1216
Croesus, 9, 16
Cro-Magnon Man, 1238
Cromwell, Oliver, 97, 109, 171, 446, 448
Cromwell, Thomas, 90
Crop rotation, 116, 994
Cross-breeding, 1228
Cross-cousin relationship, 1331
Cross-pollination, 927
"Crossing the Bar," 454
Crowds, 1357
Crusades, 55, 66–67, 75, 77, 82, 440
Crustaceans, 1214
Crystalloid, 1244
Cuba, 164, 169, 204, 220, 273
Cubic measure, 785
Cubists, French, 528–529
Cuchulain, 463
Culture, 138–140, 1327, 1352–1353
  Mass, 1227
  Medieval, 77–80
  Modern, 1353
  Primitive, 1353
Cumberland River, 259
Cummings, E. E., 475
Cuneiform, 5, 9, 478
Curaçao, 275
Curius, 29
Currency, managed, 325–327
Current electricity, 1130, 1131–1133, 1138
Currents, ocean, 1063
Curzon line, 151
Custer, George Armstrong, 202
Customs duties, 231
Cuticle, leaf, 1207
Cuttings, plant, 1211
Cyanide
  Potassium, 1184, 1185
  Salts, 1184
  Silver, 1185
Cyclones, 976, 1058
Cyclotron, 986, 1147–1148
Cylinder, 932
  Area of, 794–795
  Vascular, 1204–1205
  Volume of, 800–801
Cynewulf, 439

Cyprus, 4, 24, 269, 291
Cyrus, 6, 16
Cyrus the Younger, 21
Cytoplasm, 1197, 1198, 1208
Czechoslovakia, 143, 147, 157, 217, 289
Czolgosz, Leon, 205

Dactylic foot, 431
Da Gama, Vasco, 83
Dahomey, 163, 303
Dairying, U.S., 262, 263
Daladier, Edouard, 147
Dali, Salvador, 529–530
Damascus, 56, 57, 291
Damask, 57
Damaskinos, Archbishop, 152
Dana, Richard Henry, 470
Danes, 52, 59, 438, 439
Danish Literature, 506
Danish national anthem, 506
Dante, 79, 85, 437, 486–487
Danton, George Jacques, 107, 108
Danube River, 38, 72
Danzig, 147
Dar, conjugation of, 652
Darío, Rubén, 510
Darius I, 17
Darius III, 23
Dark Ages, 46, 56
D'Artagnan, 495
Dartmouth College, 174
Darwin, Charles, 1232
Dasht-i-Kavir Desert, 294
Das Kapital, 120
Dative, Latin, 677, 678
Daubigny, Charles François, 526
Daudet, Alphonse, 497
David, 7, 8
"David," 551
David, Jacques Louis, 526
Da Vinci, Leonardo, 86, 523, 525
Davis, Jefferson, 195
Dawes, Charles Gates, 176
Day, Clarence, 476
Daydreaming, 1314
Day of Doom, The, 466
DDT, 995
Dead Souls, 509
Death, 1285
Death Valley, 259
Debating, 411, 413
Debussy, Claude, 556, 558, 559
Decameron, 487
Decay, 1230
Decimals, 730–731, 743, 744
Decir, conjugation of, 652
Declaration of Independence, 177–178, 225, 226, 466
Declensions, Latin, 678, 679, 682–683, 692–693, 698–699, 712–715, 722–725
Decomposition, rock, 1049
Decoration, home, 515–516
Decouvrir, conjugation of, 592–593
Defense Department, 241
Deflation, 326–327
Defoe, Daniel, 427, 449

De Gaulle, Charles, 150, 163
Degas, Edgar, 527
Deglutition, 1278
Degree in Grammar, 378–380
Degrees, university, 78
Deimos, 1020
Dejar, conjugation of, 639–641
De Kalb, Baron Johann, 178
Delacroix, Eugène, 526
Delaware, 171, 180, 195, 198, 261, 263, 341
Delaware River, 258
Delhi, 74
Della Quercia, 551
Della Robbia, 551
Delphi, 13
Deltas, 1051
Demagogues, 12
Demand, 327–328, 329–330
Democracy, 118–119, 225
Democratic party, 182, 188, 200, 208, 233
Democrats, 185, 189, 190, 193, 194, 202, 203, 204, 206, 220, 233, 247
Democritus, 16
Demosthenes, 22, 482–483
Denmark, 52, 58, 89, 94, 114, 142, 148, 156, 287, 288
  Literature of, 506
Denominate numbers, 783–790
Denominator, 742, 748–750
Density, chemical, 1166
Denver, 241, 267
Departments, U.S. Government, 240–242
Depression, 209–210, 333–335
De Profundis, 459
Depth, testing ocean, 1118
De Quincey, Thomas, 428, 453
Derain, André, 528
Derby, Lord, 127
Der Messias, 501
Dermis, 1242
Descending reduction, 789–790
Deserted Village, The, 450
Deserts, 1061
De Soto, Hernando, 168
Design, 514, 516
Determination, 1297
Developer, photographic, 1186
Devoir, conjugation of, 594–595
Dew, 974, 1060
Dewey, Commodore George, 205
Dewey, Thomas E., 212, 217
Dialogues, 483
Diameter, 791, 792
Diamond, 1156, 1160
Diaphragm, 1241, 1242, 1270, 1275
  in Telephone, 1135–1136
Diarrhea, 1277
Diastole, 1270
Diastrophism, 1063–1064
Diaz, Rodrigo, 71, 526
Dickens, Charles, 456
Dickinson, Emily, 473
Diderot, Denis, 104, 494

Dienbienphu, 160
Dieresis, 568
Dies Irae, 78
Diesel engine, 980, 1115
Diet of Augsburg, 89
Diet of Spires, 89
Diet of Worms, 89
Diffused reflection, 1121
Diffusion, 1208, 1217, 1266, 1325
Digestion, 1210, 1277–1279
Digestive system, 1272–1280
Dihedral angle, 921
Dikes, 94
Dilute solution, 1161
Dimeter, 431–432
Diminishing returns, 343–344
Dinesen, Isak, 462–463, 506
Dinosaurs, 1083, 1236
Diocletian, 40
Diorite, 1047
Diphthongs, French, 568
Dipper, Big, 1036
Dipper, Little, 1037
Dire, conjugation of, 598
Directory, French, 108, 109
"Discobolus," 547
Discount, 761–764, 775–780
Disintegration, rock, 1049
Disraeli, Benjamin, 127
Dissenters, 169
Distillation, water, 1160–1161
District Courts, 243
Districts, Congressional, 230
Dividend, 742
Divine Comedy, The, 79, 437, 486–487
Division, 741, 744
  Algebraic, 840–844
  of Negative numbers, 816
  of Positive numbers, 816
Divisor, 742
Divorce, 1333–1334
Dix, Dorothea, 189
DNA, 1225
Dr. Faustus, 443
Dr. Jekyll and Mr. Hyde, 458
Dodgson, Charles L., 457
Doge's Palace, 77, 544
Dollar, content of half, 1185
Doll's House, A, 507
Dolomite, 1053
Dominance in art, 514, 515
Dominant characters, 1226
Dominic, St., 63
Dominican Republic, 273
Domitian, 37–38
Don Carlos, 502
Don Juan, 452
Don Quixote, 489–490
Donatello, 551
Donation of Pepin, 50
Donne, John, 447
Dorian tribes, 9, 10, 14
Doric order, 538
Dormir, conjugation of, 652
Dorsal cavity, 1241
"Doryphorus," 548
Dos Passos, John, 476
Dossi, Dosso, 524
Dostoevski, Fëdor, 509
Doughty, Thomas, 535

Douglas, Stephen A., 193, 194
Dowry, 1332
Doyle, Sir Arthur Conan, 461
Draco, 15, 28
Draft, bank, 325
Drake, Sir Francis, 93, 169, 442
Drama, 428–429, 442, 481–482
Dravidian peoples, 42
Dreamer's Tales, A, 465
Dreams, 1313–1315
Dreiser, Theodore, 473
Dreyfus Affair, 125
Drift, glacial, 1056
Drives, 1295–1298
Dry measure, 785
Dryden, John, 434, 448, 449
Duccio, 522
Dufy, Raoul, 528
Duma, 129
Dumas, Alexandre, 495
Dumbarton Oaks Conference, 151, 152, 213
Dumouriez, Charles François, 107
Dunant, Jean Henri, 139
Dunes, 1061
Dunsany, Lord, 465
Duodenum, 1276
Dupin, Lucile Aurore, 495
Dupleix, Joseph, 102
Duquesne, Fort, 172
Dürer, Albrecht, 533
Durham Cathedral, 541
Dust Cloud Theory, 1075
Dutch East Indies, 149, 156, 211, 299
Dutch literature, 505
Dutch philosophy, 505
Dutch Republic, formation of, 94
Dutch West India Company, 170
Duties, customs, 231
Dvořák, Antonin, 559
Dying Gaul, 25
Dynamics, 1098–1102
Dynasts, The, 458

Ear, 1260–1262
Eardrum, 1260, 1261
Earth, 249, 250, 1001–1005, 1011–1014, 1071–1085
Earthquakes, 1063–1064, 1066–1067
Earth's biological past, 1235–1239
Earthworms, 1218
East Germany, 158, 164, 217, 286
East Indies, 57, 83, 84, 102, 130, 131–132, 154, 155, 211
East Mark, 53
Easter, 54
Eastern question, 126
Ebert, Friedrich, 143
Ecbatana, 23
Echegaray, José, 490
Echidna, 1222
Echinoderms, 1214, 1215
Echo, 1118

Eclipse, 1009–1010, 1016–1018
Ecliptic, 1036, 1039
Ecology, 1228
Economic and Social Council, United Nations, 153, 215
Economic Conference of 1933, 209
Economic wealth, 311
Economics, 311–346, 1328
Economy, planned, 343
Ecrire, conjugation of, 598
Ecuador, 276
Eddas, 430, 505
Edgeworth, Maria, 464
Edict of Nantes, 93, 100
Education, 1327, 1350–1351
U.S., 191–192, 261
Edward I, 69
Edward II, 69
Edward III, 70
Edward VI, 90, 91, 92
Edward VII, 128
Edward VIII, 128
Edward the Confessor, 59
Edwards, Jonathan, 466
Effigies, 96
Effort, in physics, 1090–1094
Egbert, King, 53
Egbert of Wessex, 59
Egg, 1220–1223, 1282–1283
Egmont, 503
Egypt, 2–5, 7, 10, 16, 23, 36, 38, 56, 57, 66, 83, 109, 138, 156, 162, 213, 222, 301, 518–519
Eighteenth Amendment, 209, 246
Einstein, Albert, 970, 985, 1009
Eire, 282
Eisenhower, Dwight D., 149, 156, 211, 213–214, 218, 219, 220
E.L.A.S., 152
Elba, 111, 284
Elector, Great, 101
Electoral college, 237
Electoral Commission, 202
Electors, 237
Electric bell, 1134–1135
Electricity, 1088, 1130–1138
Electrolysis, 1161
Electromagnet, 1088, 1135–1137
Electromagnetic waves, 1128, 1129
Electromotive force, 1136–1137
Electron theory, 1166–1168
Electronics, 1141–1145
Electrons, 1144, 1166–1168
Elegy, 429
Elegy Written in a Country Churchyard, 429, 450–451
Elements, 1044, 1153–1155, 1169–1175, 1243–1244
Table of, 1163–1165
Eleventh Amendment, 243, 246
Elgin Marbles, 20
Elia, 453
Eliot, George, 433, 456
Eliot, T. S., 437, 475

Elixir of life, 79
Elizabeth, Queen, 90, 91, 92, 93, 95, 170, 442
Age of, 92, 442–445, 446
Elizabeth II, Queen, 128
Elmer Gantry, 474
Elopement, 1332
Elsie Venner, 469
Embassies, 240
Embryo, 1212, 1213, 1220–1223, 1233–1234, 1283
Emergence, shore line of, 1062
Emerson, Ralph Waldo, 189, 428, 468
Emotions, 1298–1299
Empathy, 1313
Empedocles, 16
Emperor, Holy Roman, 52, 55, 63, 64, 72, 89, 90, 95
Emperor Jones, 475
Emperors, 62–64
Barrack, 40
Empire State Building, 545, 1101
Encender, conjugation of, 647–648
Enclosure movement, 117
Encyclopedia, French, 494
Encyclopedias, Byzantine, 56
Endocardium, 1268
Endocrine glands, 1258
Endogamous groups, 1331
Endosperm, 1212, 1213
Energy, 1009, 1101–1102
Nuclear, 985–987, 1102
Engels, Friedrich, 120
England, 48, 54, 58, 59–60, 67–69, 77, 85, 92–93, 100, 102, 103, 104, 110, 126, 130, 135, 148, 151, 168, 169, 172, 174, 175, 178, 179, 183, 184, 212, 221, 269, 280–282, 438, 439
Medieval cities of, 77
Norman conquest of, 59–60, 67
Seventeenth-Century, 95–99
England's rise to power, 92–93
English, good, 347–398
English grammar, 348–371
English literature, 438–463
Ennius, 708
Enoch Arden, 454
Ensemble, musical, 559
Entablature, 538
Entelodont, 1083
Entente, Triple, 140
Enteron, 1214, 1221
"Entombment of Antwerp, The," 531
Enzymes, 1217, 1225
Epaminondas, 21
Ephors, 14
Epic of Gilgamesh, 478
Epics, 78, 430
Epictetus, 38, 483
Epicurus, 25, 483
Epidermis, 1202, 1242, 1266
Epiglottis, 1242, 1274, 1278
Epirus, 26, 27

Episcopal Church, English, 89, 92
Epithelium, 1202, 1243, 1244
Equations, 820–828
Equator, 82, 83, 251, 252, 253
Equiangular triangle, 862
Equilateral triangle, 861, 869, 885
Equilibrium, 1100, 1262
Equinox, 1013, 1036, 1039
Eras, geologic, 1077–1085
Erasmus, Desiderius, 86, 505
Eratosthenes, 25
Erechtheum, 538
Erepsin, 1217
Erg, 1101
Ericson, Leif, 58, 84
Erie, Lake, 184, 185, 258, 263
Erie Canal, 185
Eritrea, 156, 301
Eroica Symphony, 561
Eros, 1021
Erosion, 1050, 1060–1061
Eskimos, 1326, 1329
Esophagus, 1274–1275
Essay, 427, 428
Essen, 286
Estar, conjugation of, 646–647
Estates-General, 69, 105, 106
Estates, three, 105
Estimating results in mathematics, 751–752
Estonia, 143, 290
Ethan Frome, 427, 473
Ethelbert, 54
Ethics, 1352
Ethiopia, 144, 301
Ethmoid, 1248
Etre, conjugation of, 590–591
Etruscans, 26–28
Euclid, 25
Eugenics, 1228
Euphoria, 1296
Euphrates River, 2, 5, 6, 16, 38, 293
Euphues, 443
Euripides, 20, 429, 482
Europe
  Animals of, 256
  Countries of, 280–291
  Eastern, 54–60
  in 218 B.C., map of, 31
  in 476 A.D., map of, 47
  in 1815, map of, 113
  in 1919–1920, map of, 145
  Map of, 281
  Modern, beginnings of, 51
  Plants of, 256
  Western, 48–54, 83
European Economic Community, 164
European nations, rise of, 67–73
European Recovery Program, 156, 218
Eustachian tubes, 1261, 1274
Evald, Johannes, 506
Evangeline, 432
Evil eye, 79
Evolution, 1, 1232–1239
  of Society, 1324–1325

Organic, 968, 1076, 1196
  Social, 1357–1359
Evolutionary evidence, 1232–1235
Exchange, bill of, 325
Excise taxes, 231
Exclamation point, 382
Excrement, 1277
Excretion, 1279–1280
Executive branch, U.S., 226, 229, 236–242
Exercise, 1304–1305
Exogamous groups, 1330–1331
Expansion
  Coefficients of, table, 1111
  of Liquids, 1109
  of Metals, 1110–1111
Expatriation, right of, 224
Expenses, 766
Exploration, medieval, 82–83
Exponent, 829–831, 840–841
Exposition, musical, 558
Ex post facto law, 245
Expressionists, 530
External combustion engine, 978
Extraterritoriality, 132
Extremes in geometry, 890–891
Eyck, Hubert van, 531
Eyck, Jan van, 531
Eye, 1125–1126, 1262–1265
  Contact, 416

Faber, Cecilia Böhl von, 490
Fabian tactics, 32
Fabliau, 491
Factories, early, 77
Factoring in algebra, 844–848
Factors, flower, 1225–1226
Factors, multiplication, 736
Factory system, 115–117
Faculae, 1007, 1008
Faerie Queene, The, 443
Fahrenheit, 1111–1112
Fair Deal, 216, 219
Faire, conjugation of, 599
Fair Oaks, battle of, 196
Fairs, medieval, 76
Falkland Islands, 269, 280
  Battle of, 141
Falloir, conjugation of, 595
Fallopian tubes, 1222, 1283
Fallout, radioactive, 986
Falls, 1051
Falmouth, 177
Family, 1327, 1328–1336
Farewell to Arms, A, 476
Farm relief, 209
Farmers, 203
Farming, 116–117
  in U.S., 262–268
Faroe Islands, 287
Farragut, Commodore David G., 196
Farrell, James T., 477
Fascism, 155, 338
Fascists, 146, 147, 529
Fathers and Sons, 509
Fatigue, 1254, 1299, 1303
Fats, 1193
Fauces, 1274

Faulkner, William, 476–477
Faults, geologic, 1065, 1070
Fauna, 254
Faust, 502–503, 556
Fawkes, Guy, 96
Fear, 1294
Feces, 1277
Federal Bureau of Investigation, 232, 241
Federal Communications Commission, 231, 242
Federal Government, 225–246
Federal Reserve Board, 242
Federal Reserve System, 189, 206, 241, 242
Federal Trade Commission, 206, 232, 242
Federalist party, 182, 188, 190
Feelings, 1300–1301
Feet, 1248–1249
Feminist movement, 139
Femur, 1248
Fenian cycle, 463–464
Ferdinand I, 89
Ferdinand II, 94
Ferdinand, King, of Aragon, 71, 72, 90
Fermi, Enrico, 986
Ferrero, Guglielmo, 489
Ferric cyanides, 1184
Ferric oxide, 1183, 1184
Ferricyanide, 1184
Ferrous cyanides, 1184
Ferrous ferricyanide, 1184
Fertilization, 1220–1222
Fertilizers, 992, 1209
Festivals, medieval, 79
Fetus, 1283
Feudal system, 60–62, 67, 75, 105, 1341
Fiat money, 318
Fibula, 1248
Fiction, 426–428
Fief, 60, 63–64
Field, Eugene, 472
Fielding, Henry, 451
Fifteenth Amendment, 199, 246
Fighting, 1299
Fiji Islands, 270, 307
Fillmore, Millard, 193
Finland, 59, 89, 114, 143, 156, 157, 288
Finns, 41, 52, 508
Firdausi, 478
Firebird, The, 562
First International, 120
Fisher Maiden, The, 507
Fishermen, The, 506
Fishes, 1215
Fishing in U.S., 262, 263, 267
Fission, 986, 1199, 1210
  of Cells, 1199, 1200, 1210, 1219, 1222
Fissures, 1065, 1068
Fitch, Clyde, 473
FitzGerald, Edward, 457, 478, 490
Fitzgerald, F. Scott, 476
Flagellum, 1200
Flanders, 77, 141, 532
Flatworms, 1213, 1215

Flaubert, Gustave, 496–497
Flavius Vespasianus (Vespasian), 37
Fleas, 1231
Fleming, Alexander, 993–994
Fleming, Ambrose, 1141
Flemings, 77
Floodplain, 1051
Flora, 254
Florence, 77, 522, 554
  Cathedral, 543, 551
Florentine vernacular, 79
Florentine school, 522
Florida, 84, 168, 169, 171, 179, 184, 185, 190, 195, 264
Flower, parts of, 1204–1207
Fluid measure, 785
Fluorine, 1177, 1178, 1179
Fog, 974, 1059
Fold, semilunar, 1232–1233
Folds, geologic, 1064, 1070
Folkways, 1358
Follicles, hair, 1279
Fontaine, Jean de la, 493
Fontainebleau, 111, 545
Foochow, 132
Food, production of, 338
Food supply
  maintaining, 991
  safeguarding, 997
Foods, 1193, 1272–1273
Foot, in poetry, 431
Foot of lumber, 800
Foot-pound, 1101
For Whom the Bell Tolls, 476
Foramen magnum, 1248, 1253
Force, 1101
Ford, Henry, 979
Foreskin, 1282
Forgetting, 1307–1308
Formosa, 130, 134, 158, 218, 300
Fort McHenry, 184
Fort Sumter, 195
Fort Ticonderoga, 177
Fortress Europa, 214
Forty-niners, 192
Forum, 28
Forum, Roman, 717
Fossils, 1076, 1235–1236
Four Hundred, 21
Four Power Treaty, 146
Fourier, Charles, 120
Fourteenth Amendment, 199, 200, 201, 246
Fractions, 742–752
  Addition of, 749
  Changing, 743, 746–747
  Common, 743, 746
  Decimal, 743
  Multiplication of, 750–753
  Subtraction of, 749
  Writing, 743
Fractures, geologic, 1065
Fragonard, Jean, 525
France, 26, 50, 51, 55, 58, 59, 60, 64, 69–71, 77, 78, 85, 89, 92, 93, 95, 99–100, 102–115, 123, 124, 125, 127, 130, 132, 135, 140, 146, 147, 148, 153, 156, 160, 162, 163, 168, 172,

173, 178, 180, 181, 182, 183, 214, 217, 218, 219, 270, 282, 286, 309, 439
France, Anatole, 125, 498
Francesca, Piero della, 522
Franchise, 331
Francis Ferdinand, Archduke, 140
Francis I, 93, 525
Francis, St., 550
Francis, St., of Assisi, 63
Franck, César, 556, 557, 559, 561
Franco, General Francisco, 146
Franco-Prussian War, 123, 124, 142
Frankenstein, 453
Frankfort, 123
  Treaty of, 125
Franklin, Benjamin, 177, 180, 428, 466
Franks, 41, 48, 49–52
Franz, Robert, 553
Fraternities, Greek letter, 1338
Frau Sorge, 504
Frederick I, 64, 101
Frederick II, 64
Frederick III, 126
  Statue of, 552
Frederick the Great, 101, 102, 103, 104, 450, 501
Frederick William, 101, 102
Frederick William IV, 122, 124
Free will, 1316
Freedmen's Bureau Act, 200
Free verse, 437–438
Freezing, 1109
French, 565–618
  Accents, 566, 568
  Conjugations, 585–600
  Consonants, 568–570
  Diphthongs, 568
  Nasal sounds, 567–568
  Phonetic spelling, 570–576
  Pronunciation, 566–577
  Vocabulary, 606–617
French and Indian War, 103, 172
French Community, 282
French East India Company, 102
French Guiana, 278
French Literature, 491–500
French Morocco, 163
French Republic
  First, 107
  Second, 121
  Third, 124–125
French Revolution, 103–108, 112, 114–115
French, Romanic, 52
Freneau, Philip, 466
Frescoes, Babylonian, 519
Freud, Sigmund, 1315, 1317
Freudian school, 1295, 1317
Friars, 63
Friction, 1098
Friedland, 109
Friendly Islands, 307
Friends, circle of, 1339

Frobisher, Sir Martin, 93
Frogs, 1216, 1218, 1223
Frogs, The, 482
Fronde, War of the, 100
Frontal bone, 1246
Frost, 974
Frost, Robert, 475
Fruit, 1213, 1227
Frustum, 934
Fuels, 979, 1190
Fugitive Slave Act, 192
Fulcrum, 1090–1094
Fulton, Robert, 115, 191, 467, 979
Fumaroles, 1069
Fundamental Orders, 172
Fungi, 1203, 1204, 1231
Furniture, selecting, 516
Fusion, atomic, 986
Futurists, 528

Gabbro, 1047
Gabon, 163, 304
Gabriel, Jacques de, 545
Gadsden Purchase, Map of, 187
Gage, General, 176, 177, 178
Gainsborough, Thomas, 534
Galaxy, 1000, 1001, 1030, 1034
Galileo, 970, 1022, 1040, 1101
Gall, 1276
Gall bladder, 1217, 1275, 1276
Gallic invasion, 25
Gallipoli, 75
Gallstones, 1276
Galsworthy, John, 460
Galveston, 264
Gama, José Basílio da, 510
Gama, Vasco da, 83
Gambia, 163, 269, 302
Gametes, 1211, 1220, 1224
Gamma rays, 1140, 1147
Gandhi, Mahatma, 135, 136
Gandhi, Mohandas, 135, 136
Ganges, valley of, 42
Ganglia, 1254, 1289
Garfield, James A., 202
Gargantua, 492
Gargoyles, 542
Garibaldi, Giuseppe, 49, 122
Gas
  Manufactured, 191
  Measuring temperature of, 1112
  Mechanics of, 1106
  Nascent, 1170–1171
  Natural, 1073
Gasoline, 1190–1191
Gastric juice, 1217
Gastrula, 1221, 1222
"Gates of Paradise," 551
Gateway, Lion, 537
Gaucho poetry, 510
Gauguin, Paul, 528
Gaul, 35, 36, 38, 41, 57
Gauls, 24, 26, 28, 51
Gautama, 42
Gautier, Théophile, 494–495
Gearshift, 980–981
Gear wheel, 1094
Gegenschein, 1031

Geiger counter, 987, 1148, 1194
Gemini, 1036, 1037
Gems, 1073
Gender of nouns, 355
Gender of pronouns, 359
General Assembly, 153, 162, 215
General science, 967–998
Generation, spontaneous, 1198
Genes, 1225
Genetics, 1224–1227
Geneva, 89, 284
Genghis Khan, 73–75
Genitive, Latin, 677–678
Genoa, 77
Gens, 1335
Geoffrey, Count of Anjou, 68
Geography, 249–310
Medieval, 82
Geologic time, periods of, 1077–1085
Geology, 1043–1086
Geometry, plane, 849–920
Greek, 25
Geometry, solid, 921–941
George, David Lloyd, 119, 142
George I, 103
George II, 103, 152
George III, 118, 175, 176, 450
George V, 128
George VI, 128, 136
Georgia, republic of, 143, 290
Georgia, 171, 176, 188, 192, 195, 261, 264
Geosyncline, 1070, 1082
Géricault, Jean, 526
German
Confederation, 112, 123
Crown Prince, 142
Empire, 124
Literature, 500–505
Philosophy, 501, 503
Republic, 143
Revolution, 123, 142
States, 52–53
Tribes, 46, 48, 49, 54
Germania, 485
Germany, 51, 52–53, 55, 58, 60, 64, 72–73, 78, 86, 93, 94, 95, 100, 111, 112, 122, 123–124, 126, 132, 140–143, 144, 147, 148, 149, 151, 154, 155, 156, 158, 164, 207, 211, 213, 215, 286, 338
Germinal, 497
Germination, 1210
Germs, 1267
Gershwin, George, 556, 563
Gerund, 365
Gestures, 405, 415, 420–421
Gettysburg, battle of, 198
Geyser tube, 1069
Geysers, 1069
Ghana, 163, 269, 303
Ghent, 77, 531
Ghiberti, Lorenzo, 550–551
Ghosts, 507
Giacometti, Alberto, 552
Giant's Causeway, 1065

Gibal al Tarik, 57
Gibbon, Edward, 451
Gibraltar, 57, 100, 269, 291
Gide André, 499
Gil Blas, 493
Gilbert, Sir Humphrey, 169
Gilbert, W. S., 458
Gilgamesh, 478
Gillmore, Quincy Adams, 199
Giorgione, 524
Giotto, 522, 543, 550
Giraud, Henri Honoré, 150
Girondists, 107–108
Girth, 800
Gissing, George, 459
Glacial
Age, 1084–1085
Climates, 1057
Period, Great, 1084–1085
Glaciation, 1055–1056
Glaciers, 1055–1057
Gladiatorial games, Roman, 34
Gladstone, William, 127
Gland, prostate, 1282
Gland, thyroid, 1257, 1258
Glands
Endocrine, 1258
Lachrymal, 1263
Mammary, 1223
Salivary, 1277
Sebaceous, 1280
Sweat, 1279
Glans, 1282
"Gleaners, The," 526
Gluck, Christoph, 555
Glucose, 1209
Gneiss, 1049
Gobi Desert, 44, 298
Godwin, Mary, 453
Godwin, William, 453
Goethals, George W., 205
Goethe, Johann Wolfgang von, 502–503
Gogol, Nikolai, 509
Gold, 192, 202, 203, 318, 322, 1179, 1186–1187
Coinage of, 203
in California, 192
Leaf, 530, 1187
Mining of, 202
Golden Age of American literature, 189
Golden Ass, The, 485
Golden Horde, 74
Goldoni, Carlo, 488
Goldsmith, Oliver, 450
Gomara, Francisco López de, 510
Gomulka, Wladyslaw, 158
Gorgas, William C., 205
Gorki, Maxim, 509–510
Gothic architecture, 78, 542–543
Gothic cathedrals, 78, 542–543
Goths, 41
East, 48
West, 48
Goujon, Jean, 551
Gounod, Charles, 556

Government, U.S., 224–248
Federal, 225–246
Forms of, 1346
Primitive, 1344–1345
State, 247
Government of India Act, 135, 136, 144
Gower, John, 440
Goya y Lucientes, Francisco José de, 531
Gram, 1089, 1166
Granada, 57, 71, 540
Grand Canyon, 259, 1044, 1070, 1078
Grandfather's Chair, 470
Granite, 1047
Grant, Ulysses S., 191, 198, 199, 201, 202
Grave accent, 566
Grave in Perrho, The, 507
Gravitation, 1013, 1027
Gravities, table of specific, 1105
Gravity, 988–989, 1016, 1099
Gravity, specific, 1105
Discovery of, 25
Gray matter, 1254
Gray, Thomas, 429, 450
Great Britain, 74, 102, 109, 118–119, 132, 137, 140, 141, 146, 147, 148, 150, 151, 152, 153, 154, 156, 157, 161–163, 178, 183, 184, 186, 194, 207, 212, 213, 218, 219, 221, 225
Great Council of Nobles, English, 68–69
Great Elector, 101, 552
Great Gatsby, The, 476
Great Lakes, 181, 184, 258
Great Plains, 261, 262
Great Schism, 87
Great Wall of China, 43, 73
Greco, El, 530
Greece, 9–25, 26, 27, 36, 38, 75, 83, 87, 114, 126, 127, 148, 152, 156, 157, 218, 288
Greek
Architecture, 537–539
Church, 54, 59
Literature, 25, 85, 479–483
Religion, 13
Sculpture, 25, 547–548
Greek Anthology, 483
Greenback party, 203
Greenland, 58, 250, 252, 287, 1055, 1082, 1084
Gregory, Lady, 465
Gregory the Great, Pope, 53
Gresham's Law, 319
Grey, Lady Jane, 92
Grieg, Edvard, 553, 559
Grimm, Jacob Ludwig Karl, 503
Grimm, Wilhelm Karl, 503
Grimm's Fairy Tales, 503
Gris, Juan, 529
Gristles, 1246
Gross profit, 764–768
Grotius, Hugo, 95

Groups, mathematical, 805–806
Growth, human, 1245
Growth, plant, 1207–1210
Guadalcanal, 214, 307
Guadalupe-Hidalgo, treaty of, 191
Guadeloupe, 275
Guam, 205, 214, 268
Guatemala, 272
"Guernica," 529
Guiana, British, 278
Guilds, 76
Guillotine, 107, 108
Guinea, 163, 302
Guiscard, Robert, 60
Guise, Duke de, 93
Guiteau, Charles J., 202
Gulf Stream, 251, 253, 259
Gullet, 1274–1275
Gulliver's Travels, 449–450
Gunpowder, 80, 1175, 1179
Gunpowder Plot, 96
Gustavus Adolphus, 94–95
Gutenberg, Johann, 86
Gutturals, 1280–1281
Guy Fawkes Day, 96
Guyana, 269, 278
Guys (effigies), 96
Gymnosperms, 1204, 1211

Habeas corpus, 244
Habeus Corpus Act, 98
Haber, conjugation of, 644–645
Habits, social, 1358
Habits and learning, 1304–1306
Hacer, conjugation of, 655
Hadrian, 38, 548
Hague Conferences, 144
Haile Selassie, Emporer, 144
Hailstones, 975, 1059
Hair follicles, 1279
Haiti, 274
Hale, Edward Everett, 470
Halley's comet, 969, 1027
Hallucinations, 1311
Halogens, 1177–1178
Hals, Frans, 532
Halsey, Admiral, 149, 214
Hamburg, 77, 286
Hamilcar, 30
Hamilton, Alexander, 180, 181, 182
Hammarskjold, Dag, 153
Hammer, ear, 1260, 1261
Hammurabi, 6, 42
Hamsun, Knut, 507
Han dynasty, 43
Hancock, John, 176
Handel, George Frederick, 556, 557, 560
Hands, 1248
Hannibal, 30, 32, 34
Hanover, 124
    House of, 103
Hanseatic League, 77
Hapsburg dynasty, 64, 72, 94, 95, 99, 121
Hard water, 1161
Harding, Warren G., 208

Hardy, Thomas, 458
Hare-Hawes-Cutting Act, 144
Hargreaves, James, 103
Harold, King, 59
Harp, 1119
Harpers Ferry, 194
Harpsichord, 86, 556–557, 560
Harris, Joel Chandler, 472
Harris, Townsend, 134
Harrison, Benjamin, 203
Harrison, William Henry, 190
Harte, Francis Bret, 472
Hartford, 170
Harvard, 174
Hasdrubal, 32
Hastings, battle of, 59
Hauptmann, Gerhart, 504
Havana, 204, 273
Hawaii, 220, 224, 259, 261, 262, 267–268, 1068
Hawkins, Sir John, 169
Hawthorne, Nathaniel, 189, 428, 467, 468, 469–470
Hay, John, 132
Haydn, Franz Joseph, 556, 559, 560–561
Hayes, Rutherford B., 202
Health, 996, 1285, 1351–1352
Hearing, defects of, 1261
Heart, 1217, 1242, 1266, 1268–1270
Heat, 1110–1116, 1271, 1280
Heater, electric, 1114
Hebbel, Christian Friedrich, 503
Hebrews, 7–8
Hedjaz, 143
Hegel, Wilhelm, 503
Heidelberg Man, 1238
Heidenstam, Verner von, 507
Heimskringla, 505
Heine, Heinrich, 503
Helium, 1008, 1009, 1046, 1157, 1165
    Atom, 1167
Hellas, 17
"Hellenistic," 548
Hellenistic Age, 23–25
Hellenistic culture, 24, 55
Hellespont, 23, 24
Hellman, Lillian, 477
Héloïse, 78
Helots, 13, 14
Helsinki, 287
Hemingway, Ernest, 428, 476
Hemispheres, 251
Hemispheres, cerebral, 1253
Hemoglobin, 1155, 1218, 1267
Henry I, 52
Henry II, 68
Henry III, 63, 68
Henry IV, 93, 99, 444
Henry VII, 72, 84, 90, 92–93
Henry VIII, 54, 90–91, 96, 533
Henry, O., 472
Henry of Navarre, 93
Henry, Patrick, 175
Henry the Fowler, 52, 73
Henry the Navigator, Prince, 83
Heptameron, 492

"Her Lover," 509–510
Heraclea, 26
Heraclitus, 16
Heraclius, 55
Hernandia, 510
Herat, 73
Herbaceous plants, 1205
Herbivorous animals, 1216
Herculaneum, 37, 1068
Hercules, 1030, 1039
Hercynian, 1081
Herder, Johann Gottfried von, 501
Heredia, José María, 510
Heredity, 995, 1224, 1225–1226, 1347
Heretics, punishment of, 88, 91
Hermann und Dorothea, 503
Herod the Great, 37
Herodotus, 20, 482
Heroic couplet, 434
Herrick, Robert, 430, 446
Herschel, Sir William, 1005, 1024, 1040
Herzegovina, 127, 143
Hesiod, 16, 481, 1038
Hesperus, 1019
Hexameter, 432
Hexapoda, 1214
Hiawatha, 468
Hiccoughing, 1271–1272
Hidalgo, 1022
Hieroglyphics, 3, 478
Hildesheim columns, 550
Himalayas, 294, 295
Hindemith, Paul, 563
Hindenburg line, 141
Hindenburg, Paul von, 143
Hindus, 135–136, 1326
Hipparchus, 25
Hiroshima, 150, 154, 214
Hispania, 71
Hispaniola, 273, 274
Histology, 1241
Historians, Greek, 482–483
Historical present, 369
History
    Ancient, 1–45
    Medieval, 46–81
    Modern, 82–166
    of the Earth, 1074–1085
    United States, 167–223
Hitler, Adolf, 143, 144, 147, 148
Hittites, 5, 7
Hobbes, Thomas, 446
Hoffman, Ernst Theodor, 502
Hogarth, William, 534
Hohenlinden, battle of, 109
Hohenstaufen dynasty, 64
Hohenzollerns, 52, 101, 122
Holbein, Hans, the Younger, 533, 534
Holberg, Ludvig, 506
Holinshed, Raphael, 443
Holland, 50, 51, 77, 94, 95, 96, 102, 110, 112, 142, 144, 148, 170, 283, 286
Holmes, Oliver Wendell, 189, 469
Holmes, Sherlock, 461

Holy Alliance, 114
Holy Roman Emperor, 52, 55, 63, 64, 72, 89, 90, 95
Holy Roman Empire, 50, 53, 64, 87, 88, 94, 101, 109, 112, 123
Map of, 65
Homer, 12, 15, 430, 443, 479–481, 1038
Homer, Winslow, 535
Homeric epics, 479–481
Hominidae, 1238
Homo sapiens, 1238
Honduras, 272
Honduras, British, 275
Honegger, Arthur, 563
Hongkong, 269, 297
Hooch, Pieter de, 532
Hookworm, 1213
Hoover, Herbert, 209
Hoplites, 17
Hopper, Edward, 535
Horace, 38, 485
Horde, Golden, 74
Hormones, 1257–1259
Horn, geologic, 1056
Horsepower, 1101
Horses, 265
Hot springs, 152, 1069
Hot Springs, Conference at, 152
Houdon, Jean Antoine, 551–552
Hours, working, 339–340
House of Burgesses, 172
House of Commons, 69, 118, 119, 127, 269
House of Lords, 69, 118, 119
House of Mirth, The, 473
House of Representatives, 186, 201, 209, 229–231, 233–235, 237, 239
House of Seven Gables, The, 469–470
Housman, A. E., 461
Houston, Samuel, 190
Howard, Lord, 93
Howe, William, 178
Howells, William Dean, 471
Huckleberry Finn, 471
Hudson, Henry, 170
Hudson, W. H., 460
Hudson River, 185, 258, 261
Hughes, Charles Evans, 146
Hughes, Thomas, 457
Hugo, Victor, 494
Huguenots, 93, 94, 100, 171
Human
Beings, growth of, 1245
Groups, classification of, 1325–1326
Race, divisions of, 1326
Human Comedy, The, 495
Humanism, 85, 550
Humanists, 85, 487
Hume, David, 446
Humerus, 1248, 1250
Humidity, 253, 974, 976–977, 1059
Humor, aqueous, 1125, 1126, 1264
Humor, vitreous, 1126, 1264

Hunchback of Notre Dame, The, 494
Hundred Years' War, 70, 440
Hungary, 53, 72, 74, 87, 122, 124, 143, 148, 154, 156, 157, 158, 217, 289
Hunger, 1293, 1298, 1303
Huns, 41, 42, 43, 52, 53, 56, 73
Hunt, William Morris, 535
Hurricanes, 976, 1059
Huss, John, 88
Hussite wars, 88
Hutchinson, Anne, 170
Huxley, Aldous, 462
Huxley, Thomas, 428, 462
Hwang-ho River, 42, 297
Hyades, 1038–1039
Hybrids, 1225, 1228
Hydraulic press, 1104
Hydrobromic acid, 1177
Hydrocarbons, 1190
Hydrochloric acid, 1158, 1159, 1169, 1171, 1217
Hydrofluoric acid, 1178, 1179
Hydrogen, 1009, 1153, 1157–1160, 1169, 1179
Atom, 1167
Bomb, 157, 986, 1349
Chloride, 1169, 1170, 1171
Peroxide, 1170
Sulphide, 1172, 1179
Hydrolysis, 1277
Hydrosphere, 249, 251, 1044
Hydroxides, 1160, 1178, 1179, 1190
Hydroxyl radical, 1159, 1160
Hygiene, 1241, 1285, 1351–1352
Hyksos, 4
Hymen, 1284
Hymns, Latin, 78
Hyoid bone, 1248
Hyperbolus, 21
Hypo, 1186
Hypocotyl, 1212
Hypotenuse, 799–800, 861, 943
Hypothesis, geometry, 859
Hypothesis, scientific, 970

Iambic foot, 431
Ibáñez, Vicente Blasco, 490
Ibn Saud, 137
Ibsen, Henrik, 507
Iberians, 26, 30, 71
Ice, formation of, 1109
Ice, manufacture of, 1176
Icebergs, 1055
Iceland, 58, 156, 288
Ichthyosaurs, 1081
Iconoscope, 1143
Idaho, 203, 262, 266, 267
"Ides of March," 703
Idus, 703
Idylls of the King, 454
Ifni, 301
Igneous rocks, 1047, 1070, 1072
Ileocolic valve, 1278
Ileum, 1276
Iliad, 10, 12, 15, 430, 450, 479–480, 484
Illinois, 193, 265
Illusions, 1311

Images, mental, 1308–1309
Imagination, 1308, 1313–1315
Imago, 1223
Immigrants, 185
Immigration, 146, 204, 208, 227
Imperialists, 124
Importance of Being Earnest, The, 459
Impressionism, 526, 527, 536
Impulses, nervous, 1254
In God's Way, 507
In Memoriam, 429
Inbreeding, 995, 1228
Incas of Peru, 1331
Incestuous relations, 1330
Incisors, 1274
Inclined plane, 1096
Incus, 1260
Independence Day, 177
Index, establishment of, 91
India, 23, 42, 43, 50, 57, 74, 82, 83, 84, 102, 114, 130, 135–137, 144, 148, 160–161, 164, 168, 269, 294, 450
British, 296–297
Empress of, 135
Government of, Act, 135, 136, 144
Indian territory, 167, 189
Indiana, 185, 189
Indians, American, 84, 91, 167, 168, 170, 171, 172, 173, 174, 184, 189, 201, 1329
Creek, 184
Iroquois, 1335
Indies, East, 57, 83, 84, 102, 130, 131–132, 154, 155, 270
Indies, West, 84, 168, 173, 274, 275
Indo-China, 130, 131, 144, 148, 149, 154, 160
Indo-Europeans, 9
Indonesia, 144, 298
Inductive reasoning, 969–970
Indus River, 16, 23, 294
Industrial Revolution, 115–116, 131, 1343
Industrial Workers of the World, 120
Industries, U.S., 261–269
Inert elements, 1165
Inertia, 1101
Inertia of motion, 989
Infections, 1267
Inferior maxilla, 1248, 1251
Inferior turbinate bones, 1248
Infinitive, 364
Inflation, 320–327
Inflection, 419
Infra-red, 1127
Inge, William, 478
Ingersoll, Robert G., 473
Ingres, Jean, 526
Inheritance, 1294
Inherited characters, 1224
Injunction, 244
Inness, George, 535
Innocent III, Pope, 64, 88

Innocents Abroad, 471
Inquisition, Spanish, 91, 94
Insect poisons, 995
Insects, 994–995, 1214, 1218
Inspector-General, The, 509
Instinct, 1295
Institutions, social, 1326–1327
Instruments, orchestral, 560
Insulator, 1131
Insulin, 1259, 1277
Integers, 729, 730, 742
Intelligence, 1218, 1289, 1311–1312, 1319
Intensity, sound, 1120
Interbreeding, 1225–1227
Interest, 770–775
Interest-bearing notes, 777
Interior, Department of, 241
Interjection, 349–350
Interludes, 442
Internal combustion engine, 978
International
   Communist, 120
   First, 120
   Second, 120
   Third, 120
International Court of Justice, 215
Interregnum, 64
Interrogation point, 382
Interstate Commerce Commission, 231, 242
Intestinal juice, 1276
Intestine, large, 1217, 1242, 1273, 1275–1276, 1277–1278
Intestine, small, 1217, 1242, 1273, 1275–1276, 1277–1278
Introduction, speech, 402
Introductions, Spanish, 632–633
Introspection, 1290
Invar, 1110, 1111
Invertebrates, 1214, 1215
Investiture, 63
Involuntary actions, 1316
Iodides, 1177, 1179
Iodine, 1177, 1178, 1179, 1180
Ionians, 9, 10, 14
Ionic order, 538
Iowa, 190
Iphigenia, 482
I Promessi Sposi, 488
Ir, conjugation of, 654
Iran, 161–162, 213, 294
Iraq, 137, 138, 143, 156, 162, 293
Ireland, 48, 54, 58, 69, 97, 98, 119, 127–128, 270, 282, 438
   Northern, 128, 280, 282
Iris, 1126, 1263
Irish Free State, 128, 282
Irish literature, 463–465
Iron, 115–116, 161, 264, 1047, 1072–1073, 1183
Iron Curtain, 129, 157
Iron Heel, The, 472
Iroquois Indians, 1335

Irregular verbs, 370–374
Irrigation, 1, 262, 266, 994
Irritability, 1289
Irving, Washington, 467
Isaac, 7
Isabella, Queen, 71, 72, 83, 90
Islam, 50, 55, 56–57, 58, 75
Islands, 250, 1062
Isle of Man, 280–282
Isobars, 978
Isosceles trapezoid, 901
Isosceles triangle, 861, 869
Isostasy, 1071
Isotherms, 978
Isotopes, 987, 1146
Israel, 138, 162, 293, 530
Israel, Kingdom of, 8
Issus, battle of, 23
Istanbul, 87, 291
Isthmus, 205, 250
Italian literature, 486–489
Italy, 16, 23, 25–30, 32, 34, 38, 42, 48, 51, 52, 53, 55, 56, 60, 64, 78, 82, 85, 86, 88, 100, 108, 109, 114, 122–123, 126, 140, 141, 144, 147, 148, 150, 154, 156, 163, 164, 211, 217, 284, 338
   Protestantism in, 93
   Unification of, 122–123
Ivan the Great, 101
Ivan III, 74
Ives, St., 76
Ivory Coast, 163, 302
Iwo Jima, 214
I.W.W., 120
Ixtlilxochitl, Fernando de Alva, 510

Jacks, principle of, 1097
Jackson, Andrew, 184, 185, 186, 188–189, 201
Jackson, "Stonewall," 196, 198, 199
Jacob, 7–8
Jacobsen, Jens, 506
Jacobins, 106–107
Jamaica, 269, 274
James I, 69, 93, 95, 96, 170
James II, 98, 99, 172
James VI, 95
James, Henry, 471–472
Jamestown, 96, 170
Janizaries, 75
Japan, 128, 130, 131, 132, 133–134, 142, 144, 146, 147, 148–149, 154–155, 156, 159–160, 208, 211, 215, 298
Java, 299, 1068
Jean-Christophe, 498
Jefferson, Thomas, 177, 181–183, 188, 466
Jejunum, 1276
Jena, battle of, 109
Jenghiz Khan, 73–75
Jenner, Edward, 996
Jenny, spinning, 103
Jerusalem, 8, 37, 55, 56, 66
Jerusalem Delivered, 488
Jesuits, 91, 172

Jesus, 40, 41
   Society of, 91
Jet planes, 214, 967, 971, 983, 1129
Jet propulsion, 983
Jewels, 1073
Jewish nationalist, 137
Jews, 7–8, 37, 40, 118, 137, 138
Jinnah, Ali, 136
Joan of Arc, 70–71
John, King, of England, 64, 68
John, King, of France, 70
John XII, Pope, 52
Johnson, Andrew, 200–201, 240
Johnson, Lyndon B., 221
Johnson, Samuel, 449, 450
Joints, geologic, 1065
Joints, human, 1249
Joliet, 172
Joliet-Curie, Frédéric, 985–986
Jones, Inigo, 545
Jones, John Paul, 179
Jonson, Ben, 430, 444
Jordan, 291
Joseph, 504
Joseph II, 104, 105
Joshua, 8
Joyce, James, 462, 465
Judah, 8
Judas Maccabaeus, 8
Judea, 8, 37, 40, 41
Judges, state, 243
Judicial branch, U.S., 226, 228, 229, 242–244
Jugar, conjugation of, 649–650
Juice, gastric, 1217
Juice, pancreatic, 1217
Juif Errant, Le, 497
Julius Caesar, 33, 35, 36, 444
Juneau, 267
Jung, Carl, 1317–1318
Jungfrau, 1056
Jungfrau von Orleans, Die, 502
Jungle, The, 474
Juno, 1021
Jupiter, 28, 1004, 1005, 1006, 1021, 1022–1023, 1040
Jurgen, 474
Justice, Department of, 241
Justice, primitive, 1345
Justices, Chief, 243
Justinian, 48–49, 55, 56, 540
Jutes, 41, 48, 52, 53, 438
Jutland, battle of, 141
Juvenal, 485

Kafka, Franz, 504
Kaiser Wilhelm, 126, 142
Kalendae, 703
Kalevala, The, 508
Kalidasa, 479
Kandinsky, 530
Kangaroos, 256, 1235
Kansas, 130, 191, 219, 265, 266
Kansas-Nebraska Act, 193
Kant, Immanuel, 501
Kashmir, 136, 294
Keats, John, 429, 452

Keller, Gottfried, 505
Kennedy, John F., 164–165, 220–221, 222
Kensett, John Frederick, 535
Kentucky, 182, 195, 198, 261, 264
Kenya, 163, 269, 304
Kepler, Johannes, 989
Key, Francis Scott, 184
Khan, Genghis, 73–75
Khan, Kublai, 73
Khrushchev, Nikita, 157, 164, 165, 221
Kidneys, 1217, 1242, 1266, 1279
Kierkegaard, Sören, 506
Kiev, 74, 290
Kilauea, 1068
Killarneyan Revolution, 1079
Kim, 459–460
Kindling temperature, 979, 1154
Kinescope, 1143–1144
Kinetic energy, 1101–1102
King George's War, 172
King, Rufus, 180
King William's War, 100, 172
King's College, 174
Kingsley, Charles, 457
Kipchak Empire, 74
Kipling, Rudyard, 430, 459–460
Klee, Paul, 530, 534
Kleist, Heinrich von, 503
Klopstock, Friedrich Gottlieb, 501
Knickerbocker's History of New York, 467
Knights of the Round Table, 78
Knox, John, 89
Kobe, 301
Koch, Robert, 996
Koran, 478
Korea, 73, 130, 132, 134, 156, 159–160, 218–219, 298
Korean War, 159–160, 218–219
Krakatoa, 1068
Kreutzer Sonata, The, 509
Kropotkin, Prince, 509
Ku Klux Klan, 201, 202
Kublai Khan, 73
Kuniyoshi, Yasuo, 536
Kuomintang, 146–147, 158
Kuwait, 293

Labia majora, 1284
Labia minora, 1284
Labor, 1341–1344
  Child, 340
  Department of, 241–242
  Government, 161
  Movement, 117–118
  Organizations, 117–118, 1343
  Party, 119, 154
  Shortages, 211
  Strikes, 206, 210, 216
  Unions, 189, 1343
  Unrest, 1343
Labrador, 58, 84, 270
  Current, 253

Lachrymal bones, 1248
Lachrymal glands, 1263
Laconia, 13, 14
Lady Windemere's Fan, 459
Lafayette, 106, 178, 179
Lagerlöf, Selma, 508
Lake Champlain, 184, 261
Lake Erie, 184, 185, 258, 263
Lake Nicaragua, 273
Lakes, Great, 258
Lakes, in geology, 1054–1055
Lamb, Charles, 428, 453
Lamb, Mary, 453
Lame duck sessions, 209
Lament of Arianne, 554
Lancaster, house of, 90
Landon, Alfred M., 210
Landscape cycle, 1052
Landslide, 1050
Langland, William, 440
Languages, Romance, 49
Laocoön, 25
"Laocoön," 548
Laokoön, 501
Laos, 131, 160, 296
Lao-tse, 43, 479
Laplace, Marquis Pierre Simon de, 1074
Laplacian Theory, 1074
Laramide-Himalayan Revolution, 1082
Lardner, Ring, 428
Larva, 1223
Larynx, 1280
La Salle, Robert Cavalier, Sieurde, 172
Lassen Peak, 1044, 1068
Lasso, Orlando de, 554
Lateral surfaces, 795
Lateran Palace, 63
Latin, 676–728
  Conjugations, 696, 697
  Declensions, 678–679, 721–725
  Future Indicative Tense, 686, 687
  Hymns, 78
  Languages, 1326
  Nouns, 677–679
  Numerals, 701–702
  Passive Voice, 705–706
  Perfect Tense, 688–689
  Phrases, 717–720
  Tense, 686–690
  Value of, 676–677
  Verb forms, 680–681
Latins, 26
Latitude, 251–252, 253
Latitudes, horse, 1060
Latvia, 143, 290
Laughter, 1297
Laurentian Revolution, 1079
Lava, 1067–1068
Lavoisier, Antoine, 968
Law
  Civil, 49
  Common, 68
  English, 68–69
  Primitive, 1345
  Roman, 27–28, 46, 49
  Law of adequate returns, 328–330

Law of pressure, 1106
Law, Ohm's, 1133
Law, Pascal's, 1103–1104
Law, periodic, 1165
Lawrence, D. H., 462
Laws of motion, Newton's, 1098–1101
Lays of Ancient Rome, The, 26
Lazarillo de Tormes, 489
Lead, 1180, 1188
Lead carbonate, 1180, 1188
League of Nations, 137, 142, 143, 144, 146, 153, 207, 208, 1349
Learning, 1304–1306
Learning and habits, 1304–1306
Leaves, 1206–1207
Leaves of Grass, 470
Lebanon, 291
Lech River, battle on, 53
Le Corbusier, 546
Lee, Robert E., 191, 196, 198, 199, 200
Leeches, 1214
Leeds, 118
Leeward Islands, 269, 274
Legal tender, 318
Legations, 240
Léger, Fernand, 530
Legion of Honor, 112
Legislative Assembly, 107
Legislative branch, U.S., 226, 229–236
Legitimists, 125
Legnano, battle of, 64
Legs, 1248
Legumes, 1232
Leipzig, 111, 286
  University, 78
Leitmotifs, 555
Lend-lease, 211
Length, units of, 1089
Lenin, Nikolai, 102, 129, 130, 143
Leningrad, 102, 290
  Churches, 56
Lens, 1124–1126
Leo, Pope, 42
Leo III, Pope, 51
Leon, 71
León, Francisco Ruíz de, 510
León, Juan Ponce de, 168
Leonid showers, 1029
Leonidas, 17
Leopardi, Giacomo, 488
Leopold of Saxe-Coburg-Gotha, 121
Lepanto, battle of, 87
Lepidus, 36
Lesbos, island of, 15, 481
Les Misérables, 494
Lesotho, 163, 269, 305
Lessing, Gotthold, 501
Letts, 52
Leutze, Emanuel, 535
Lever, 25, 1090–1094
Lever, Charles, 464
Levirate, 1331
Lewis and Clark, 183
Lewis, Cecil Day, 463

Lewis, Matthew Gregory (Monk), 451
Lewis, Sinclair, 473–474
Lexington, 176, 177
Leyden, 94
Leyte, 214
Liberal construction, doctrine of, 183
Liberation, war of, 111, 112
Liberia, 303
Liberty Loans, 207
Liberty, Sons of, 175
Libraries, Constantinople, 56
Library, first, Ancient World, 6
Libya, 156, 301
Lice, plant, 1221, 1231–1232
Lichen, 1231
Lie, Jonas, 507
Lie, Trygve, 153
Liechtenstein, 287
Liége, 140, 149
Life
    Cycle, 1230, 1284–1285
    Evidences of Ancient, 1076–1077
    Expectancy, 996
    Origin of, 1076
    Theory, 1198
Light, 1121–1128
    Refraction of, 1122–1124
    Speed of, 1000, 1121, 1129
    Zodiacal, 1032
Lighthouse of Alexandria, 25
Lightning, 975, 1060, 1131
Likes and dislikes, 1301
Liliom, 505
Lime, 1181
Limelight, 1156
Limestone, 1048, 1182
Lincoln, Abraham, 194, 195, 196, 198, 199, 200, 226
Lindbergh, Charles A., 208
Lindbergh Law, 232
Line, bisecting a, 851
Linear measure, 784, 790
Lines, 850–851
    Parallel, 875–882, 892
    Perpendicular, 859
Link, missing, 1232
Lion Gateway, 537
Liquid measure, 785
Liquid pressure, 1102–1104
Liquids
    Expansion of, 1109
    Mechanics of, 1102–1106
Lisbon, 83, 84, 285
List price, finding, 767–768
Liszt, Franz, 557–558, 562
Liter, 1089
Literature, 426–513
    American, 189, 465–478
        Colonial, 465–466
        Nineteenth Century, 466–473
        Twentieth Century, 473–478
    Anglo-Saxon, 438–439
    Athenian, 15, 20
    Belgian, 500
    Danish, 506

Dutch, 505
English, 438–463
    Eighteenth Century, 448–451
    Romantic, 451–453
    Seventeenth Century, 446–448
    Transitional, 458–459
    Twentieth Century, 459–463
    Victorian, 453–458
Finnish, 508
French, 491–500
German, 500–505
Greek, 25, 85, 479–483
Hungarian, 505
Irish, 463–465
Italian, 85, 486–489
Norwegian, 506–507
Oriental, 478–479
Polish, 510
Portuguese, 491
Roman, 38, 40, 483–486
Russian, 508–510
Scandinavian, 505–508
South American, 510–511
Spanish, 489–491
Swedish, 507–508
Swiss, 505
Lithosphere, 249, 251, 1044, 1045, 1071
Lithuania, 143, 290
Litmus paper, 1158
Liver, 1242, 1258, 1275, 1276–1277, 1279
Lives of the Painters, 488
Living, standard of, 321
Livy, 38, 485
Lloyd George, David, 119, 142
Lobbying, 236
Locke, John, 104, 178, 446
Locomotive, 115
Locus, 921
Loess, 297, 1061
Logic, 1313
Logrolling, 236
Loire River, 48, 49, 70
Lollards, 88
Lombards, 41, 48, 49, 50, 51, 52, 55
Lombardy, 49, 51, 112
London, 77, 86, 154, 280
    Fire, 448
    Tower of, 68, 543
London, Jack, 472
Longfellow, Henry Wadsworth, 189, 432, 468
Longitude, 252
Loom, power, 103
López de Gomara, Francisco, 510
Lords, House of, 69
Lords Veto Act of 1911, 118
Lorenzetti brothers, 522
Lorrain, Claude, 525
Lorraine, 51, 124
Los Angeles, 267
Loss, net, 766
Lothair, 51
Loti, Pierre, 497
Louis XI, 71, 72
Louis XIII, 94, 99

Louis XIV, 99–100, 105, 172, 551
Louis XV, 105, 525
Louis XVI, 105, 107, 108, 111
Louis XVIII, 111, 114
Louis Napoleon, 121, 124
Louis Philippe, 120–121, 124, 557
Louis the Pious, 51
Louisburg, 172
Louisiana, 172, 183, 185, 195, 198, 264, 466
    Purchase, map of, 187
    Territory, 183, 186
Louvre, 545
Love, romantic, 1296
Lovelace, Richard, 446
Lover, Samuel, 464
Lowell, Amy, 437, 474
Lowell, James Russell, 189, 428, 468
Lower Depths, The, 509
Loyola, Ignatius, 91
Lübeck, 77
Lublin Committee, 151
Lucan, 38
Lucerne, Lake, 72
Lucretius, 38, 484
Luftwaffe, 212
Lumbar bones, 1246
Lumbar plexus, 1254
Lumber, foot of, 803
Lunar eclipse, 1018
Lungs, 1234, 1242, 1279
Lusiad, 491
Lusitania, 141
Luther, Martin, 88–89, 441, 501
Lutheran Church, 89
Luxembourg, 140, 156, 164, 214, 283
Lydia, 9, 16
Lyly, John, 443
Lymph, 1244–1245, 1266, 1278
Lymphatic fluid, 1245
Lynching, 1348
Lyons, 77, 282
Lyric poetry, 429, 481
Lysander, 21
Lysicrates, monument of, 538
Lysippus, 548

MacArthur, Douglas, 149, 154, 159, 160, 211, 215, 218, 219
Macaulay, Thomas Babington, 26, 455
MacDonald, James Ramsay, 119, 136
Macedonia, 22, 24, 33, 36, 48, 87
Machines, principles of, 1090
Macpherson, James, 464
Macropodidae, 1235
Macropus, 1235
Madame Bovary, 496
Madame Chrysanthème, 497
Machiavelli, Niccoló, 480
Machine, slot, 1093
Madagascar, 255, 306
Madeira Islands, 285
Mademoiselle de Maupin, 494

Madison, James, 183, 184
Madrid, 285
Maeterlinck, Maurice, 500
Magalhães, Domingo José
  Gonçalves de, 510
Magellan, Fernando, 84, 168, 205
Magic, black, 79
Magic Mountain, The, 504
Magma, 1067, 1068, 1071, 1072
Magna Carta, 68, 97, 99
Magnesia, citrate of, 1182
Magnesia, sulphate of, 1182
Magnesium, 1180, 1182
  Citrate, 1182
  Sulphate, 1160, 1180
Magnet, 1129–1130, 1134, 1136–1137
Magnetic poles, 1129–1130
Magnetism, 1088, 1129–1130
Magyars, 52, 53, 72, 73
Mahabharata, 479
Mahomet, 56
Maid of Orleans, The, 502
Mailer, Norman, 477
Main Street, 473
Maine, 170, 171, 177, 186, 210, 263, 1062
Maine, battleship, 204
Majorca, 285
Makin, 214
Malagasy Republic, 163, 306
Malaria, 26, 993, 994, 1231
Malars, 1248
Malawi, 163, 269, 305
Malay States, 130, 131
Malaya, 144, 148, 149, 154, 161
Malaysia, 269, 296
Maldive Islands, 270
Malenkov, Georgi, 157
Mali, 163, 301
Mallarmé, Stéphane, 496
Malleus, 1260
Malory, Sir Thomas, 440
Malta, 269, 291
Malthus, 338, 339
Mammalia, 1235, 1238
Mammals, 1083, 1216
  Age of, 1236
  Cenozoic, 1083
Mammary glands, 1223
Man
  Age of, 1085
  Ancestors of, 1238
  Races of, 1238
  Story of, 1238–1239
Manchester, 118, 263
Manchu government, 132–133
Manchuria, 134, 146, 147, 156, 215, 297
Mandamus, 244
Manet, Edouard, 526–527
Mangan, James Clarence, 464
Manila, 214, 299
Mann, Thomas, 504
Manon Lescaut, 493
Manor houses, medieval, 61, 75, 80
Mansur, Abul Kasim, 478
Mantegna, Andrea, 523
Mantle, geologic, 1049
Manufacturing, U.S., 262–268

Manutius, Aldus, 86
Manzoni, Alessandro, 488
Mao Tse-tung, 158–159, 164, 218
Marat, Jean Paul, 107, 108
Marathon, plain of, 17, 18
Marbury vs. Madison, 244
Marble, 284, 1049, 1181
Marcellus, 32
Marco Polo, 73, 82
Marcus Antonius, 36
Marcus Aurelius Antoninus, 38
Marengo, battle of, 109
Margaret, Queen of Navarre, 492
Marginal
  Cost, 327
  Productivity, 328
  Utility, 327, 328
Maria Theresa, 102, 105
Mariana Islands, 146, 269
Marie Antoinette, 105, 107
Marin, John, 536
Maritime Commission, 242
Marius, 34
Mark Antony, 36
Mark, East, 53
Marlowe, Christopher, 442–443
Mármol, José, 510
Marne River, battle of, 141
Marquette, Jacques, 91, 172
Marriage
  by Capture, 1332
  by Purchase, 1332
  Classes, 1338
  Customs, 1331–1332
  Group, 1330
  Modern, 1332–1333
  Primitive, 1328
  Restrictions, 1330–1331
Mars, 1004, 1005, 1019–1020, 1021
Marseillaise, 107
Marseilles, 77, 107
Marshall, George C., 218
Marshall, John, 244
Marshall Islands, 146, 214, 269
Marshall Plan, 156, 218
Marshes, tidal, 1062
Marston Moor, 97
Marsupialia, 1235
Martel, Charles, 50, 57
Martial, 38, 485
Martin V, Pope, 87
Martinique, 275, 1068
Marvell, Andrew, 448
Marx, Karl, 120, 1359
Mary, Bloody, 91, 92
Mary, Queen of Scots, 92–93, 95
Mary II, 98, 99
Maryland, 170, 171, 180, 182, 195, 198, 261, 263, 341
Masaccio, 522–523
Masefield, John, 461
Masolino da Panicale, 522
Mason and Dixon line, 186
Masque, 442
Mass culture, 1227
Massachusetts, 96, 170, 172, 176, 188, 189, 258, 264

Master of Arts Degree, origin of, 78
Masters, Edgar Lee, 437, 474
Matches, friction, 191
Mathematics, 729–966, 970
Mather, Cotton, 466
Matriarchate, 1335
Matrilinear, 1335
Matrilocal, 1335
Matsys, Quinten, 531
Matter, structure of, 1161–1166
Matterhorn, 1056
Maturity, date of, 776–777
Maturity value, 778–779
Maugham, W. Somerset, 462
Mauna Loa, 1067, 1068
Maupassant, Guy de, 428, 497
Mauritania, 163, 301
Mauritius, 269
Maxilla, inferior, 1248, 1251
Maxillae, superior, 1248
May Day, 79
Mayflower, 170
Mayflower Compact, 172
Mayors of the Palace, 50
Mazarin, Cardinal, 100
Mazzini, Giuseppe, 122, 488
McCarthy, Joseph R., 219
McClellan, George B., 191, 198
McCormick, Cyrus, 117, 467
McHenry, Fort, 184
McKinley, William, 204, 205
McTeague, 472
Meade, George Gordon, 198
Mean proportional, 890
Means, geometry, 890
Measure
  Cubic, 785
  Dry, 785
  Fluid, apothecaries', 785
  Linear, 784, 790
  Liquid, 785
  Square, 784
  Weight, 786
Measurement, 1088–1090
Measurements, 793–796
  Circular, 794–796
Measuring
  Angles, 852
  Areas, 792–796
  Distances, 790–791
  Stone work, 800
  Tank capacity, 801
  Volume, 800–803
Meat packing, 265
Mechanics
  of Gases, 1087, 1106–1109
  of Liquids, 1087, 1102–1106
  of Solids, 1087, 1090–1098
Medea, 482
Medes, 5, 6, 16
Media, 16, 36
Medici, Catherine de, 93
Medici, palaces of, 544
Medici, Tomb of, 551
Medicines, 1193
Medieval
  Cities, 75–77
  Culture, 77–80
  History, 46–81
  Philosophy, 78

Meditations, 38, 485
Medulla oblongata, 1254
Meetings, town, 172
Meissonier, Jean Louis Ernest, 526
Meistersingers, 501
Melanesians, 1326
Melody, poetic, 430, 432
Melville, Herman, 470
Membrane
  Cell, 1196–1197
  Mucous, 1243
  Nictitating, 1232, 1233
  Serous, 1242
Memling, Hans, 531
Memorabilia, 482
Memorizing, 1307
Memory, 1291, 1306–1308
  Aids to, 410–411
Memphis, 4
Men of Good Will, 499
Menander, 484
Mencken, H. L., 428
Mendel, Gregor, 995, 1225
Mendelism, 995, 1225–1226
Mendelssohn, Felix, 556, 561
Mental images, 1308
Mephistopheles, 502
Mercantilism, 174
Mercuric oxide, 1154
Mercuric sulphide, 1182
Mercurous chloride, 1183
Mercury, 1107–1108, 1180, 1182–1183
Mercury (planet), 1004, 1005, 1011, 1018, 1025, 1040
Meredith, George, 458
Meridian, 252
Mérimée, Prosper, 495
Merovingians, 50
Merrimac, 196
Mersen, Treaty of, 51
Merv, 73
Mesopotamia, 2, 5–7, 9, 16, 56, 73, 137
Mesozoic Era, 1077, 1081–1082, 1236, 1237
  Reptiles of, 1081
Messiah, The, 556
Metabolism, 1216–1218, 1219, 1257
  Plant, 1208
Metacarpals, 1248
Metalloids, 1113
Metals, 1113, 1165, 1181–1188
  Expansion of, 1110–1111
Metamorphic rocks, 1047, 1048–1049
Metamorphoses, 485
Metatarsals, 1248
Metaurus, 32
Metazoans, 1213
Meteoric showers, 1029
Meteorites, 1028
Meteoroids, 1031
Meteorology, 1058
Meteors, 1028–1029, 1072
Methyl orange, 1158
Metopes, 538
Metric system, 108, 1088–1090, 1166

Metternich, Prince, 112, 114, 115, 121–122, 123
Mettre, conjugation of, 599
Meuse-Argonne, 207
Mexican Cession, 192–193
Mexican War, 190–191, 192
Mexico, 168, 190, 191, 270–272
Mexico City, 191, 272
Meyer, Adolf, 1319
Michelangelo, 86, 487, 523–524, 544, 551
Michigan, 189
Microorganisms, 1196
Microphone, 1135
Middle Ages, 46, 51, 54, 57, 58, 60, 62, 63, 75–80, 82, 83, 85, 86, 88, 92, 168
Middle Atlantic region, 263
Middle East, 161–162
Middle Kingdom, 10
Middle West, 172, 202, 265
Midway, 214
  Battle of, 149, 214
Midway Islands, 268
Milan, 77, 284, 543
Milky Way, 1029–1030, 1031
Mill, John Stuart, 139, 428
Millay, Edna St. Vincent, 435–436
Miller, Arthur, 477
Millet, Jean François, 526, 535
Miltiades, 17, 18
Milton, John, 429, 432, 433, 435, 436, 442, 447–448
Mind, 1288–1289
Mineral resources, 1072–1074
Mineral springs, 1053
Mines, deepest, 1071
Mining, 202
Ministers, Conference of, 154
Ministers, U.S., 240
Minnesota, 194, 259
Minuend, 734
Minuet form, symphonic, 560
Minute men, 176
Mirabeau, Count de, 105, 106
Miracle plays, 79, 442
Mirrors, 1121–1122, 1125, 1185
Missing link, 1232
Missionaries, 54
Mississippi, 185, 195, 264
Mississippi delta, 1051
Mississippi River, 168, 172, 179, 181, 183, 189, 196, 258, 259, 262, 264, 267
Missouri, 186, 195, 198, 212
Missouri Compromise of 1820, 186, 194
Missouri River, 259
Mist, 1059
Mistletoe, 1231
Mistral, Gabriela, 511
Mithridates, 34, 35
Mitosis, 1245
Mobs, 1348, 1357
Moby Dick, 470
Modernism, German, 501–502
Modifiers, English, 354–355, 375–376
Mogul Empire, 74
Mohammed, 55, 56, 58
Mohammed II, 75

Mohammedans, 50, 51, 56, 66, 89
Moieties, 1338
Moisture, sensation of, 1301
Molars, 1274
Moldavia, 87, 289
Molecules, 1161–1162
Molière, 429, 492–493
Mollusks, 1214, 1215
Molnár, Ferenc, 505
Molotov, V. M., 157, 215
Moltke, Count von, 124
Monaco, 283
Monadnocks, 1052
Monasteries, Catholic, 90
Monasteries of Northumbria, 439
Monasticism, 62–63
Monet, Claude, 527
Money, 317–319
Mongol Empire, 74
Mongolia, 297, 298
Mongoloid Race, 937
Mongoloids, 1326
Mongols, 73–74, 82
Monitor, 196
Monks, 54, 62–63, 441
Monogamy, 1329
Monometer, 431
Monomial, 817, 831
Monopoly, 330–332
Monroe Doctrine, 186, 467
Monroe, James, 185
Mons, 140
Montagu-Chelmsford reforms, 144
Montaigne, Michel de, 492
Montana, 203, 262, 266, 267
Monte Carlo, 283
Montenegro, 75, 127, 143
Montesquieu, Baron de, 104, 493–494
Monteverdi, Claudio, 554
Montgomery, Sir Bernard L., 214
Months, in Latin, 702–703
Montpellier, 78
Montreal, 172, 270
Monument of Lysicrates, 538
Moods of English verbs, 367–368
Moody, William Vaughn, 473
Moon, 1001–1002, 1005, 1009–1011, 1014–1018, 1034
Moonstone, The, 456
Moore, George, 459, 465
Moore, Thomas, 464
Moors, 56, 57, 71, 82, 83, 86, 540
Moraines, 1057
Moralities, 79
Morality plays, 79, 442
Moravians, 52
More, Sir Thomas, 441
Moreau, Jean Victor, 109
Mores, 1358
Morley, Christopher, 428
Mormons, 266
Morocco, 126, 163, 182, 299
Morris dance, 79
Morris, Gouverneur, 180
Morse, Samuel F. B., 984

Mortar, 1181–1182
Mosaic Code, Bible, 6
Mosaic work, Babylonian, 519
Mosaics, Italian, 521
Moscow, 56, 74, 110, 129, 151, 154, 157, 158, 159, 213, 215, 218, 290
Moscow Conference, 150, 213
Moscow Pact, 150, 151
Moses, 8
Moslems, 48, 55, 56, 60, 66, 67, 78, 135, 136, 163
Mosques, 56
Mosquito, 995, 1231
Mosses from an Old Manse, 469
Mosul, 57
Motifs, musical, 555
Motion, laws of, 1098–1101
Motivated behavior, 1295
Motley, William, 189
Motor response, 1293
Moulton, Forest Ray, 1074
Mount McKinley, 259
Mount Olympus, 13
Mount Vernon, 180, 182, 545
Mountains, 1060–1071
Mourir, conjugation of, 593
Moussorgsky, Modest, 508, 556
Mouth, 1241, 1274–1275
Movements, symphonic, 559
Mover, conjugation of, 650
Mozambique, 305
Mozart, Wolfgang Amadeus, 555, 557, 561
Mucous membrane, 1243
Mucus, 1243
Muhammad, 56
Mukden, 147
Multicellular organisms, 1198, 1201–1203
Multiplicand, 736
Multiplication, 736–738
    Algebra, 814–815, 829–840
    of Fractions, 751–755
    of Negative numbers, 814–815
    of Polynomials, 831–835
    of Positive numbers, 814–815
    Proving, 737
    Short-cuts, 738–740
Multiplier, 736
Mummers, 79
Mumps, 1274
Munich, 147
Munitions Assignment Board, 213
Murals
    Egyptian, 518
    Roman, 520–521
Murat, Joachim, 110
"Murders in the Rue Morgue, The," 469
Muriatic acid, 1159
Murillo, Bartolomé Esteban, 531
Muscles, 1203, 1249–1252
Muscovy, 74
Muses, 25
Museums of Constantinople, 56

Museums, Greek, 25
Music, 552–563
    Absolute, 560
    Ancient, 553
    Chamber, 559
    Church, 554
    Contemporary, 562–563
    Program, 560, 562
    Renaissance, 86
    Symphonic, 559–562
Musical scale, 1117–1118
Musical sounds, 1120–1121
Muslin, 57
Musset, Alfred de, 494
Mussolini, Benito, 123, 144, 147, 148, 149
Mycenæ, Lion Gateway at, 537
Myriapods, 1214
Myron, 547
Mystères de Paris, Les, 497
"Mysterious Stranger, The," 471

Nagasaki, 150, 154, 214
Nagy, Ferenc, 158
Nana, 497
Nantes, Edict of, 93, 100
Naples, 26, 110, 114, 284
Napoleon Bonaparte, 108–112, 114, 115, 121, 123, 182, 183
Napoleon, Louis, 121, 124
Napoleon II, 121
Napoleon III, 121, 124
Napoleonic Code, 109, 112
Nares, 1274
Narrative poetry, 430
Nasal sounds in French, 567–568
Nascent gas, 1170–1171
Nash, Ogden, 476
Nasser, Gamal Abdel, 162
Nathan the Wise, 501
National Assembly, 106, 107
    French, 125
    German, 123
National Convention, French, 107, 108
National Labor Relations Board, 209
National Peoples' Party, 146
National Recovery Administration, 209
Nationalism, 67, 161–164
Nationalists
    Chinese, 155, 158, 219, 297
    India, 135, 136
    Moslem, 136
Nations, Battle of, 111
Native Son, 477
NATO, 156, 218, 219, 222
Naturalization, 224, 227
Nature, fitness of, 1228–1232
Naumburg Cathedral, 550
Navarre, 71
Navarrete, Fernandez, 530
Nave, Canterbury, 543
Navigation Acts, 174, 175
Navigation, medieval, 83
Navy Department, 238
Nazis, 137, 146, 148, 149

Neanderthal Man, 1238
Nebraska, 203, 266
Nebuchadnezzar II, 5, 6, 8
Nebulae, 1000, 1030, 1031, 1033, 1035
Nebular Hypothesis, 1074
Necho II, 5
Nefud Desert, 291
Negative numbers, 808–809, 812–816
Negro
    Citizenship, 199
    in Legislatures, 201
    Protection of, 200, 221
    Slavery, 108, 119, 172, 185, 186, 189, 192–196, 199
Negroids, 1326
Nehru, Jawaharlal, 136, 137
Nelson, Lord, 109
Nemathelminthes, 1213
Nepal, 295
Neptune, 970, 1002–1003, 1004, 1024, 1025
Nero, 37, 553
Nerve
    Cells, 1218
    Optic, 1092
    Tissue, 1203
    Trunks, 1253
Nerves, 1252
    Cranial, 1253, 1254
    Olfactory, 1254
    Optic, 1254
    Spinal, 1253, 1254
Nervous fatigue, 1254
Nervous impulses, 1254
Nervous system, 1218, 1241, 1252–1257
    Autonomic, 1256–1257
    Central, 1241, 1252–1255
    Peripheral, 1253
Net loss, 764
Net proceeds, 769–770
Net profit, 764
Netherlands, 93, 94, 100, 112, 114, 130, 155, 156, 164, 275, 283
Netherlands Indies, Council of, 144
Neurons, types of, 1252
Neurosis, 1316
Neutrons, 986, 1166–1168
Nevada, 191, 262, 266
New Amsterdam, 170, 171
New Atlantis, The, 445
New Caledonia, 309
New Deal, 210, 216
New England, 170–172, 174, 175, 184, 194, 261, 262–263
    Confederation, 170
    Geography of, 262–263
    Hills, 261
New Frontier, 220, 221
New Guinea, 254, 270, 307
    Battle of, 214
New Hampshire, 170, 171, 213, 258
New Harmony, 189
New Haven, 170
New Hebrides, 270, 307
New Jersey, 171, 178, 263

New Mexico, 191, 193, 262, 266, 267
New Netherland, 170
New Netherlands, 98
New Orleans, 172, 196, 264
    Battle of, 185
New Testament, 479
New World, 72, 84, 100, 167, 168, 169, 170, 174, 178
New York, 98, 170, 171, 172, 178, 180, 181, 230, 258, 261, 263
New Zealand, 139, 269, 307
Newfoundland, 58, 100, 270
Newton, Sir Isaac, 446, 989, 1013
Newton's Laws of Motion, 1027, 1098-1101
Nexö, Martin Andersen, 506
Niagara Falls, 1044, 1051
Nibelungenlied, 78, 500
Nicaragua, 272-273
Nicholas I, 128
Nicholas II, 128, 143
Nicias, 21
Nickel, 1072, 1180, 1188
Nictitating membrane, 1232, 1233
Niels Klim's Underground Journey, 506
Niemen River, 73, 110
Nietzsche, Friedrich, 503
Niger, Republic of the, 163, 301
Nigeria, 163, 269, 303
Nihilists, 128
Nile River, 2, 3, 301
    Delta, 23, 1051
Nimitz, Admiral Chester, 149, 214
Nine Power Treaty, 146
Nineteenth Amendment, 139, 209, 246
Nineveh, 5, 6, 547
Ningpo, 132
Nitrates, 992-993, 1173-1174, 1179
Nitric acid, 1160, 1171
Nitrogen, 992, 1173-1175, 1179, 1180
Nixon, Richard M., 219, 220
Njalssaga, 505
NLRB, 209
No, Japanese, 479
Nobel, Alfred B., 139, 508
Nobel prizes, 139, 508
Nodes, plant, 905
Noises, 1302-1303
Nonconformists, 96
Non-fiction, 426, 428
Nonmetals, 1165, 1181
Nordics, 1326
Noric Alps, 286
Normandy, 59-60, 214
Normans, 53, 59-60, 67, 438, 439
Norris, Frank, 472
Norsemen, 58, 69
North Africa, 149, 150, 163, 211, 214
North America
    Animals of, 256-257

Countries of, 270-272
Map of, 271
Plants of, 257
North Atlantic Defense Pact, 156, 218, 221
North Atlantic Lowland, 261
North of Boston, 475
North Carolina, 180, 264
North Dakota, 203, 266
North, Lord, 176
North, Sir Thomas, 443
North star, 1012, 1032, 1036, 1037
Northmen, 51, 56, 58, 75, 84
Northumberland, Duke of, 92
Northumbria, monasteries of, 439
Northwest Ordinance, 181
Northwest Territory, 181
Norway, 52, 58, 77, 89, 114, 142, 148, 156, 287
Norwegian literature, 506-507
Note, promissory, 775
    Finding value of, 776-779
    Interest-bearing, 777-779
Notochord, 1214, 1235
Notre Dame Cathedral, 78, 542, 550
Notre-Dame de Paris, 494
Nouns, 348, 353, 354, 355-357
    Case of, 356-357
    Gender of, 355
    Latin, cases of, 677-678
    Number of, 355-356
    Person of, 356
    Problems of, 355-357
    Proper, 380-381
Nova Scotia, 58, 84, 100, 169, 270
Novae, 1033, 1038
"Novalis," 502
Novel, 427, 448
Novgorod, 74, 77
NRA, 209
Nuclear energy, 216, 985-987, 1102, 1145
Nuclear physics, 1088, 1145-1150
Nuclear reactors, 990
Nucleic acids, 1197-1198
Nucleus, atomic, 989, 1088
Nucleus, cell, 1196-1197
Nueces River, 190
Number
    of Nouns, 355-356
    of Pronouns, 357-359
Number System, Arabic, 729-730
Numbers
    French, cardinal, 600-601
    French, ordinal, 601
    Latin, 701-702
    Spanish, cardinal, 637
    Spanish, ordinal, 638
Numbers, mathematics
    Abstract, 738, 786
    Compound, 786
    Concrete, 738, 786
    Denominate, 786-792
    Natural, 804
    Negative, 808-809, 812-816
    Positive, 812-816

Reading, 729-730
    Square roots of, 964-966
    Writing, 729-731
Numerator, 744
Nuremberg, 77, 533
Nutcracker, 1092
Nyasaland, 305
Nylon, 1192

Oberlin College, 192
Oberon, 501
Oblique triangle, 961-962
Observation, 1290, 1305
Observatories, 1040-1041
Observatory, Lowell, 1025
O'Casey, Sean, 429, 463, 465
Occipital bone, 1246, 1253
Ocean
    Currents, 1063
    Testing depth of, 1118
    Tides, 1063
Oceans, 251
Octavius Caesar, 36
Ode, 429
Oder River, 73, 286
Odessa, 290
Odets, Clifford, 477
Odin, 58
Odoacer, 48
Odors, elementary, 1302
Odyssey, 12, 15, 430, 450, 479-481
Oedipus, 482
Oehlenschläger, Adam G., 506
Oesterreich, 53, 72
Office of Price Administration, 211, 326
Oglethorpe, James, 171
O'Hara, John, 477
Ohio River, 181, 259, 262, 264
Ohm's Law, 1133
Oil, 1072, 1073
    of vitriol, 1159
Oil scandals, 208
Oil wells, 162
Ofr, conjugation of, 653
Okinawa, 214
Oklahoma, 189, 264, 266
Olaf, King, 58
Old Hickory, 188
Old Ironsides, 184
"Old Ironsides," 469
Old Testament, 7-8, 479
Oler, conjugation of, 653
Olfactory nerves, 1254
Olympiads, 13
Olympic games, 13, 14
Omnibus Bill of 1850, 193
Omnivorous, 1216
One-celled organisms, 1198-1201
"One Hoss Shay," 469
O'Neill, Eugene, 429, 475
Onomatopoeia, 432, 433
Oozes, 1063
Open Door Policy, 146
Opera, 554-556
Operating expenses, 764
Optic nerves, 1125-1126
Optical illusions, 1311
Optics, 1088

Or San Michele, church of, 551
Oracles, 13, 14
Orange, Prince of, 94
Orangemen, 99
Oratorio, 556
Oratory, Athenian, 20, 22
Orbit, planetary, 1002
Orchestra, symphony, 560
Orders, fundamental, 172
Orders in Council, 110
Ordinance of Secession, 195
Ore, 1072
Oregon, 183, 194, 259
Organ, animal, 1203
Organ pipes, 1119
Organic chemistry, 1189–1193
Organic evolution, 1076, 1196
Organism, 1196
Organisms
  Many-celled, 1201–1203
  Multicellular, 1198, 1201–1203
  One-celled, 1198–1201
  Unicellular, 1198–1201
Organizations, religious, 1355–1356
Orient, 75, 79, 130–134
Oriental literature, 478–479
Orion, 1030, 1032, 1037, 1038
Orlando, 142
Orlando Furioso, 487
Orléanists, 124
Orléans, 70–71, 78, 121
Orthodox Church, Holy, 54
Os innominatum, 1248
Osaka, 298
Osmosis, 1208, 1217, 1222, 1245, 1266
Ossianic cycle, 463–464
Ostracism, 15
Ostrogoths, 48, 55
Othman, 75
Otis, James, 175
Ottava rima, 435
Otto, Nikolaus, 979
Otto I, 52
Otto the Great, 52, 53, 63, 72
Ottoman Turkish Empire, 86, 126
Ottoman Turks, 71, 73, 75, 83, 86
Outline of History, 461
Ova, 1220, 1282
Ovaries, 1220, 1282
Ovary, plant, 1212
Overture, 555
Ovid, 38, 485
Oviduct, 1222
Oviedo y Valdés, Gonzalo Fernández de, 510
Oviparous animals, 1222
Ovules, 1212
Ovum, 1284
Owen, Robert, 120
Oxford, 77
Oxford University, 78, 440
Oxidation, 969, 1154, 1156, 1169, 1218, 1271
Oxides, 1153–1154, 1179
Oxygen, 992, 1153–1154, 1155–1157, 1179, 1180, 1209

Nascent, 1170–1171
Preparing, 1155
Uses of, 1156
Oxyhydrogen blowpipe, 1156
Ozone, 1157

P.A.C., 212
Pacemaker, 1270
Padua, 78, 523
Paine, Thomas, 177, 466
Painting, 518–536
  American, 535–536
  British, 534–535
  Dutch, 532–533
  Egyptian, 518
  Flemish, 531–532
  French, 525–530
  German, 533–534
  Greek, 25, 519–520
  Italian, 86, 521–525
  Mesopotamian, 518
  Prehistoric, 518–519
  Roman, 520–521
  Spanish, 530–531
Pakistan, 135, 136, 161, 269, 295
Palace of Whitehall, 545
Palace, Pitti, 544
Palaces, Medici, 544
Palate, 1248
Palatine, 27
Palatine bones, 1248
Paleozoic Era, 1077, 1079–1081, 1236, 1237
Palestine, 4, 6, 8, 10, 23, 56, 137–138, 156, 162
Palestrina, 86, 554
Pali, 479
Pallas, 1021
Palmo, Ricardo, 510
Panama, 168, 205, 273
  Canal, 205, 250, 268, 273, 276
  Canal Zone, 205, 268, 273
Pancreas, 1217, 1242, 1259, 1276–1277
Pancreatic juice, 1217
Panic
  of 1837, 189
  of 1873, 201
Pankhurst, Emmeline, 139
Pantagruel, 492
Pantheon, 38, 539
Papal States, 114
Paper, 1192
  Early use of, 85
  Litmus, 1158
Paper, British White, 137
Papua, 307
Paradise Lost, 433, 447
Paraguay, 279
Parallel lines, 875–879
  Construction of, 879–882
Parallelepiped, 932
Parallelogram, 901
Parasites, 1201, 1230–1232
Parcel-post system, 232
Parenchyma, 1202
Parentheses, in algebra, 827–828
Pariahs, 1336–1337
Parietal bones, 1246

Paris, 69, 77, 105, 106, 107, 108, 111, 112, 124, 149, 179, 214, 282, 529
  Treaty of, 172
  Universities, 78
Parkman, Francis, 189
Parler, conjugation of, 585–588
Parliament, 69, 70, 85, 96, 98
  English, 70, 90, 96, 98, 99, 118, 127, 135, 171, 173, 176, 179, 269
  Long, 97
  Rump, 97
Parliamentary committee, 136
Parmenides, 16
Parnassians, 495
Parnell, Charles, 127
Parotitis, 1274
Parthenogenesis, 1221
Parthenon, 19, 20, 538, 547–548
Parthians, 24
Party caucuses, 233, 234
Party, National Peoples', 146
Pascal, Blaise, 493
Pascal's Law, 1103–1104
Pasiteles, 548
Passacaglia, 562
Passive voice, 369–370
  in Latin, 705–706
Past perfect tense, Latin, 688
Pasteur, Louis, 996
Pastoral symphony, 560, 561
Patella, 1248
Pater, Walter, 459, 485
Patriarchate, 1335
Patricians, 27–29
Patrick, St., 54
Patrilinear, 1335
Patrilocal, 1335
Patterns, psychological, 1302
"Paul, Jean," 501
Paul of Tarsus, 41
Payee, 780
Peace Corps, 221
Peale, Charles, 535
Pearl Harbor, 148, 150, 154, 155, 211, 268
Peat, 1055
Peel, Sir Robert, 119
Peer Gynt, 507
Peiping, 73, 133
Peking, 73, 133, 297
Peking Man, 1239
Pelléas and Mélisande, 500, 556
Pelle the Conqueror, 506
Peloponnesian League, 17, 18
Peloponnesian War, 20, 482
Peloponnesus, 10, 13
Pelvic girdle, 1248
Pendleton Act, 203
Pendulum, 1100–1101
Peneplane, 1052
Penguin Island, 498
Penicillin, 993–994
Peninsular War, 110
Penis, 1282
Penn, William, 171
Pennsylvania, 171, 186, 198, 258, 263, 331

INDEX

Pentagon, 849, 909
Pentameter, 432
"Penthali," 547
Penumbra, 1011
Pepin, Donation of, 50
Pepin the Short, 50
Pepita Jiminez, 490
Pepsin, 1217, 1277
Pepys, Samuel, 428, 448
Per cent, complement of, 767
Percentage, 754–761
  Problems, 756–761
  Reading, 755–756
Perception, 1309–1311
Perch of stone, 785, 800
Percussion instruments, 560
Pereda, José María de, 490
Perennials, 1205
Pergamum, 25
Pericardium, 1268
Pericles, 18–19, 21, 537
Perigee, 1014
Perimeters, 791–792
Period, 350, 382
Periodic law, 1165, 1177
Peristalsis, 1278
Peritoneum, 1242
Peritonitis, 1242
Peroxide, hydrogen, 1170
Perpendicular
  Angle, 859
  Dropping a, 856–857
  Lines, 859
Perrault, Claude, 545
Perry, Commodore Oliver
  Hazard, 134, 184
Persepolis, 23
Perseus, 551, 1038, 1039
Pershing, John J., 207
Persia (*See also* under
  "Iran"), 5, 6, 16, 17,
  42, 43, 57, 294
Persian Empire, 16
Persians, 6, 8, 16, 17, 55, 56
  War with, 16–18
Person
  of Nouns, 356
  of Pronouns, 357–359
Personality, 1315–1316
Perspiration, 1217, 1279
Persse, Augusta, 465
Peru, 276
Perugino, 523
Peter and the Wolf, 563
Peter Schlemihl, 503
Peter the Great, 101, 102, 128,
  508
Petition of Right, 97, 99
Petrarch, 85, 435, 487
Petrograd, 102
Petroleum, 264, 267, 270, 272,
  289, 1072, 1073, 1190
Phagocytes, 1267
Phalanges, 1248
Pharaoh Rameses II, 4
Pharaoh Thutmose III, 4
Pharos, 25
Pharsalus, battle of, 36
Pharynx, 1259, 1261, 1271, 1274
Phenolphthalein, 1158
Phidias, 19, 537, 547
Phidippides, 17

Philip Augustus, King, 64, 68
Philip of France, 66, 87
Philip II of Macedon, 22, 30,
  483
Philip II, 89, 92, 93, 94
Philip IV, 70, 87
Philippi, battle of, 36
Philippics, 22, 483
Philippine Commonwealth,
  144
Philippine Islands, 130, 131,
  132, 148, 149, 154, 155,
  160, 205, 211, 299
Philistines, 8, 10
Philosophy
  Athenian, 16, 20
  Dutch, 505
  German, 501, 503
  Greek, 25, 483
  Medieval, 79
Phobos, 1020
Phoenicians, 7, 8–9
Phonetic spelling
  French, 570–576
  Spanish, 621–623
Phonograph, 1119–1120
Phosphate, 264, 290
Phosphorus, 990, 1176–1177,
  1180
Photography, 1185–1186
Photosphere, 1007, 1008
Photosynthesis, 991–992, 1200,
  1206–1207, 1209, 1231
Phrase, prepositional, 355
Phrases, Latin, 717–720
Phratries, 1338
Physics, 1087–1151
Physiology, 1241–1287
Piano, grand, 1119
Pianoforte style, 556–558
Picasso, Pablo, 529
Pickwick Papers, 456
Picts, 48, 52
Picture of Dorian Gray, The,
  459
Piedmont Plateau, 261
Pierce, Franklin, 193, 195
"Pietà," 551
Pigments, 1127
Pilgrim Fathers, 96
Pilgrimages, 66
Pilgrims, 170, 172
Pilgrim's Progress, 448
Pillars of Society, 507
Pindar, 15, 481
Pinturicchio, 523
Pippin (Pepin) the Short, 50
Piraeus, 18
Pirandello, Luigi, 489
Pirates, 33, 182–183
Pisa, 77, 541
  Leaning Tower of, 541
Pisano, Andrea, 550
Pisano, Giovanni, 550
Pisano, Nicola, 550
Pisces, 1036, 1039
Pisistratus, 15
Pissarro, Camille, 527
Pistil, 1211–1212
Piston, 1109
Pitcairn Island, 270, 307

Pitch
  Musical, 1120, 1129
  of Voice, 1280
Pitt, William, 103, 118, 177
Pitti Palace, 544
Pituitary gland, 1257–1259
Pius VII, Pope, 109
Pizzicato, 554
Placenta, 1222, 1223
Plague
  Bubonic, 85
  Great, 448
  Roman, 38
Plain Tales from the Hills,
  459
Plane figures, 849–850
Plane geometry, 849–920
Plane, inclined, 1096–1097
Planetariums, 1040–1041
Planetesimal Hypothesis, 1074
Planetoids, 1005, 1021–1022
Planets, 1003–1006, 1018–1025
  Minor, 1005, 1021–1022
Planned economy, 343
Plant kingdom, 1203–1204
Plant lice, 1221, 1231–1232
Plant processes, 1207–1213
Plant reproduction, 1210–1213
Plant slips, 1211, 1227
Plantagenet, Royal House of,
  68
Plantation system, 186, 200
Plantations, 192
Plants, 991–992, 1203–1213
  Cork tissue of, 1202
  Epidermis of, 1202
  Growth of, 1207–1210
  Herbaceous, 1205
  Parts of, 1204–1207
  Seed-bearing, 1204
  Woody, 1205
Plassey, 135
Plaster of Paris, 1182
Plastics, 1191
Plataea, 18
Plateau, Piedmont, 261
Platelets, 1267
Platinum, 1180, 1187
Plato, 20, 25, 443, 483
Plattsburg, 184
Platyhelminthes, 1213
Platypus, 1222
Plautus, 38, 484
Plays (*See also* under
  "Drama"), 428–429
  Miracle, 79, 442
  Morality, 79, 442
Plebeians, 27–29, 34
Pleiades, 1038
Pleistocene Period, 1084–1085,
  1238
Pleura, 1242
Pleurisy, 1242
Plexus, 1254
Pliny the Elder, 40
Pliny the Younger, 38
Plow, iron, 115, 191
Plumule, 1212
Pluperfect tense, Latin, 688
Plutarch, 38, 428, 443, 483
Pluto, 1004, 1005, 1013, 1025
Plymouth, 96, 170

Pocket veto, 235
Poder, conjugation of, 654
Poe, Edgar Allan, 189, 427–428, 467, 469
Poetry, 426, 429–438
　　Elements of, 430–433
　　Gaucho, 510
　　Lyric, 429, 481
　　Narrative, 430
　　Roman, 484–485
Point Counter Point, 462
Poise, 401
Poitiers, 70
Poland, 52, 74, 102, 114, 128, 143, 147, 148, 152, 156, 157, 158, 159, 217, 289
Polar bear, 1229
Polaris, 1012, 1030, 1032, 1036, 1037
Poles, magnetic, 1129–1130
Poliomyelitis, 997
Polir, conjugation of, 588–589
Polish Corridor, 147
Polish Literature, 510
Political Action Committee, 212
Politics, 247
Polk, James K., 190, 193
Pollen, 1211
Pollination, 994, 1212
Pollock, Jackson, 536
Pollux, 1037
Polo, Marco, 73, 82
Polyandry, 1329
Polyclitus, 548
Polyeucte, 492
Polygamy, 1329
Polygnotus, 520
Polygons, 850, 909–913
Polygyny, 1329
Polyhedral angle, 922
Polyhedrons, 931–936
Polynesia, 309
Polynesians, 1326
Polynomials
　　Addition of, 817–818
　　Multiplication of, 831–835
Polyphonic choruses, 554
Pomerania, 73
Pompeii, 37, 520, 1068
Pompey, 34–36
Ponce de León, Juan, 168
Poner, conjugation of, 655
Poor Folk, 509
Poor Richard's Almanack, 180, 466
Pope, Alexander, 434, 449, 450
Popes, 62–64
Po River, 49, 284
Porifera, 1213, 1215
Pork barrel, 236
Porter, William Sidney, 472
Portugal, 71–72, 83, 91, 102, 114, 130, 155, 156, 285, 306
Portuguese Guinea, 302
Positive numbers, 812–816
Post Office Department, 232, 241
Post, Wiley, 209
Postal savings, 232
Posterior, 1241

Post-Impressionists, French, 528
Postulate, 859
Posture, 1251–1252
Potash, caustic, 1159
Potassium, 1171–1172, 1181
　　Chlorate, 1155–1156, 1177
　　Cyanide, 1184, 1185
　　Ferricyanide, 1184
　　Sulphate, 1173
Potato blight, 1231
Potential energy, 1101–1102
Potomac River, 180, 182, 198, 258, 261, 264
Potsdam Conference, 154, 159, 215
Poulenc, Francis, 563
Pound, Ezra, 474–475
Pound, foot, 1101
Poussin, Nicolas, 525
Pouvoir, conjugation of, 595
Po Valley, 254
Poverty, 1343–1344
Powder
　　Bleaching, 1182
　　Talcum, 1182
Power, in physics, 1101
Powers and roots, 809–810
Powers, Central, 141, 142, 144
Prague, University of, 88
Praxiteles, 20, 548
Prayer, The Book of Common, 90
Precipitation, 974, 975, 977, 1059, 1161
Prendre, conjugation of, 600
Preposition, 349
Prepositional phrase, 355
Prepuce, 1282
Presbyterian Church, 89
Presbyterians, 169
Prescott, William, 189
Present, historical, 369
President, U.S., 181, 226, 229, 230, 232, 233–235, 236–240, 243, 246
President's Cabinet, 240
Press, hydraulic, 1104
Pressure
　　Atmospheric, 977–978, 1058
　　Law of, 1106
　　Liquid, 1102–1104
Prévost, Abbé, 493
Price, 327–328
　　Finding list, 769–770
　　Normal, 328
　　Selling, 766, 767–770
Prices, inequitable, 328–330
Pride, Thomas, 97
Pride's Purge, 97
Primates, 1232, 1238
"Primavera," 523
Primitive peoples, 1323–1324, 1339–1340
Primitive work, 1339–1340
Prince, Black, 70
Prince, German Crown, 142
Prince of Orange, 94
Prince of Wales, 69
Prince of Wales Island, 267
Princeton, 174, 178

Principal, 771
Printing, invention of, 85
Prinz Friedrich von Homburg, 503
Prism, 931, 1126–1127
Privateers, 179
Prizes, Nobel, 139, 508
Problems
　　in Algebra, 826–828
　　in Bank Discount, 778–780
　　in Commission and Brokerage, 770
　　in Fractions, 752–754
　　in Interest, 772–774
　　in Measurement, 792, 796
　　in Percentage, 760–761
　　in Profit and Loss, 765–768
　　Tax, 781–783
Proceeds, net, 771–773
Procyon, 1032
Producer's credit, 322
Producers' goods, 311, 314
Product, in mathematics, 736, 835–838
Production, 338–341
Productivity, marginal, 328
Profit
　　Gross, 766–770
　　Net, 766
Profit and loss, 764–768
Program music, 560
Progressive party, 217
Prohibition Amendment, 209
Prokofiev, Sergei, 556, 563
Prometheus Bound, 481
Prometheus Unbound, 453
Prominences, solar, 1007, 1008, 1011
Promissory note, 775
Pronominal adjectives, Spanish, 635
Pronouns, 349, 353
　　Antecedents of, 358
　　Case of, 360–362
　　French, agreement of, 570
　　Gender of, 359
　　Latin, 721–726
　　　Interrogative, 693
　　Number of, 357–359
　　Person of, 357–359
　　Problems of, 357–362
　　Spanish, agreement of, 626
　　Spanish, demonstrative, 636–637
　　Spanish, possessive, 626
Pronunciation, 348, 350
　　French, 566–570
　　Key to, 388
　　Spanish, 620–622
Propeller, airplane, 983
Property, 312–313
　　Primitive, 1340–1341
Proportion in art, 514
Proportional, mean, 890
Proposition in geometry, 859
Prose, 426–429
Prostate gland, 1282

Proteins, 992, 1193, 1197-1198, 1209, 1273
Proterozoic Era, 1077, 1079, 1237
Protestantism, 89, 90, 91, 93, 95, 441, 442
Protestants, 88, 89 91, 92, 93, 94, 101, 118, 169, 170
Protons, 1166-1168
Protoplasm, 1196-1198, 1210, 1218 1244
Protozoa, 1200, 1213 1215, 1219, 1231
Proust, Marcel, 498
Provence, 71
Prud'hon, Pierre-Paul, 526
Prussia, 72-73, 101, 102, 103, 107, 109, 112, 114, 122, 123, 124, 125, 126, 172
Psammetichus, 5
Pseudopods, 1199
Psychoanalysis, 1318
Psychology, 1256 1288-1321
Psychosis, 1316
Psychosomatic, 1319
Psychozoic Era, 1077, 1084, 1236, 1237
Pteridophytes, 1204
Pterosaurs, 1236
Ptolemies, Greek, 5, 23
Ptolemy, 24
Ptyalin, 1217, 1277
Public Works Administration, 209
Puccini, Giacomo, 556
Puerto Rico, 205, 224, 243, 268
Pulaski, Casimir, 178
Pulley, 1095-1096
Pulmonary capillaries, 1271
Pulse, 1268
Pump, water, 1108-1109
Punctuation, 348, 382-385
Punic Wars, 29-33
Punishment, capital, 1348
Punjab, 23
Pupa, 1223
Pupil, eye, 1126, 1264
Pure Food and Drugs Act, 232, 997
Puritans, 96, 97, 98, 169-170, 443, 446, 448
Pushkin, Alexander, 508
PWA, 209
Pyeshkov, Alexei M., 509
Pygmies, 1326
Pylorus, 1275
Pym, John, 97
Pyramids, 3, 10, 536, 934-936
Pyrenees, 57, 71, 285
Pyrrhus, 26-27, 29
Pythagoras, 16
Pythagorean Theorem, 900

Qatar, 293
Quadrilaterals, 849, 901-909
Quakers, 169, 170, 172
Quality, sound, 1120
Quanta, 1209
Quantum theory, 968
Quartzite, 1049
Quatrains, 436

Quebec, 150, 172, 270
Battle of, 103
Queen Anne's War 100, 172
Quercia, Della, 551
Querer, conjugation of 656
Quicksilver, 1183
Quintus Fabius Maximus, 32
Quirinal, 27
Quo Vadis?, 511
Quotation marks, 384-385
Quotient, 742

Rabelais, François, 492
Race, human, divisions of, 1326
Races of mankind, 1238
Rachmaninoff, Sergei, 558
Racine, Jean, 492
Radar, 139, 1145
Radcliffe, Ann, 451
Radiation, 1114-1115 1138-1141
Radical, chemical, 1159
Radical, hydroxyl, 1160
Radio, 138, 139, 984-985, 1139-1140, 1142-1143
Radio telescope, 1040
Radioactive isotopes, 990-991
Radioactivity, 985, 1147-1148
Radiochemistry, 1193-1194
Radius, 791, 792, 937
Radius bone, 1248
Railroad
Baltimore & Ohio, 191
Berlin-Baghdad, 126
South Manchuria, 147
Underground, 192
Raleigh, Sir Walter, 169
Rameses II, Pharaoh, 4
Raphael, 524
Rate, interest, 771-772
Rate, tax, 783-786
Rationalization, 1313
Rationing, 211
Ravel, Maurice, 558, 559, 562
"Raven, The," 469
Ravenna, 42, 48, 50
Reactions, emotional, 1298-1300
Reade, Charles, 457
Realism, beginning of, 471-473
Realists, French, 496-497
Reaper, 117, 191, 467
Reasoning, 1312-1313
Rebuttal, 413
Recapitulation, musical, 558
Receiver
Radio, 1142-1143
Telephone, 1135, 1136
Television, 1143, 1144
Recessive characters, 1226
Recevoir, conjugation of, 595
Recitative, 554, 555
Reclamation Act, 266
Recognition, 1308
Reconstruction, 200-202, 246
Rectangle, 792-793, 901
Rectangular solid, 803
Rectum, 1276
Red Badge of Courage, The, 472

Red Cross, International, 139
Red Laugh, The, 509
Reducir, conjugation of 648-649
Reduction
Ascending, 787-789
Chemical, 1024
Descending, 787
of Denominate numbers, 786-790
of Fractions, 747
Reed instruments, 560
Reefs, 1062-1063
Reflection, diffused, 1121
Reflection, sound, 1118-1119
Reflex, 1254-1255 1291
Reform Bill of 1832, 118
Reform Bill of 1918, 139
Reform Bill of 1928, 139
Reformation, 82, 87-92, 441
Refraction of light, 1122-1124
Reichstag, 124
Reign of Terror, 107-108
Reims, 149, 214
Cathedral, 78, 543, 550
Reliefs, Chaldean, 547
Religion, 1327, 1354-1357
Greek, 13
Modern, 1356-1357
Primitive, 1354-1355
Roman, 28
Viking, 58
Religious organizations, 1355-1356
Remagen, 149
Rembrandt van Rijn, 532
Remembrance of Things Past, The, 498
Renaissance, 85-86, 103, 168, 441, 442, 443, 487-488
American, 467
Architecture, 543-545
Sculpture, 550-552
Rennin, 1217, 1277
Renoir, Pierre Auguste, 527
Repetition, rhythmic, 514, 515
Spaced, 1307
Representatives, House of, 186, 201, 209, 229-231, 233-235, 237, 239
Reproduction
Animal, 1219-1224
Cellular, 1199-1201
Plant, 1210-1213
Sexual, 1224
Vegetative, 1227
Reproduction of sound, 1119-1120
Reproductive system, 1281-1284
Female, 1282-1284
Male, 1281-1282
Reptiles, 1216
Age of, 1236
Mesozoic, 1081
Republic, 483
Republican party, 182, 188, 193, 201, 206, 209, 233
Republicans, 182, 185, 188 201, 202, 203, 216, 217,

Republicans (cont'd)
219, 220, 247
French, 125
Resistance, lever, 1090–1097
Resources, U.S., 261–268
Respiratory system, 1271–1272
Response, motor, 1293
Response, secondary, 1309
Responses to stimuli, 1291–1294
Restoration, 448
in England, 97–98
Resurrection, 509
Retina, 1125–1126, 1264
Returns, diminishing, 343–344
Returns, law of adequate, 328–330
Revere, Paul, 176
Revolution
Agricultural, 116–117
Algomian, 1079
Alpine-Cascadian, 1084
American, 105, 173, 175–179, 225, 450, 466
Appalachian - Hercynian, 1081
French, 103–108, 112, 114–115, 450
German, 121, 122, 123, 142
Industrial, 115–116, 131
Killarneyan, 1079
Laramide-Himalayan, 1082
Laurentian, 1079
Russian, 129
of 1688, 98–99
of 1848, 121, 123
Revolutionary War, 175–179, 181
Reymont, Wladyslaw Stanislaw, 510
Reynolds, Sir Joshua, 534
Rhine, 35, 49, 51, 52, 149, 214, 286, 1055
Rhineland, 146
Rhode Island, 170, 171, 172, 180, 230
Rhode Island College, 174
Rhodes, 25
Rhodesia, 163, 270, 305
Rhodesia, Northern, 305
Rhombus, 901
Rhone, 51, 1055
Rhyme, 430
Royal, 434–435
Rhyolite, 1047
Rhythm, poetic, 430
Rhythmic repetition, 514, 515
Rialto, 77
Ribs, 1248
Richard the Lion-Hearted, 66, 67, 68, 78
Richard I, 66, 67, 68
Richard II, 88, 444
Richardson, Samuel, 451
Richelieu, Cardinal, 93–94, 95, 99, 100
Richmond, 196, 198, 261
Richter, Jean Paul Friedrich, 501–502

Rigel, 1037
Rightist faction, Spanish, 146
Rights, Bill of, 99, 182, 245–246
Riley, James Whitcomb, 473
Rime of the Ancient Mariner, The, 452
Rio de Janeiro, 278, 279
Rio Grande, 190, 191, 258, 259, 266
Río de Oro, 301
Rio Muni, 304
Rire, conjugation of, 598
Rivers, in geology, 1050–1051
Robbia, Della, 551
Robin Hood, 78
Robespierre, Maximilien de, 107, 108
Robinson, Edwin Arlington, 474
Rochefoucauld, Duc de la, 493
Rockefeller Center, 546
Rocket bomb, 214
Rocket engine, 1114
Rocket ships, 989–990
Rocks
Archean, 1078–1079
Cenozoic, 1082–1084
Decomposition of, 1049
Disintegration of, 1049
Extrusive, 1047
Igneous, 1047, 1070
Intrusive, 1047
Mesozoic, 1082
Metamorphic, 1048–1049, 1070
Movements in, 1063–1064
Proterozoic, 1079
Sedimentary, 1047–1048, 1070, 1076
Weathering of, 1049
Rocky Mountains, 254, 258, 259, 261, 262, 265, 1044, 1055, 1070, 1082
Rococo period, 544
Rodin, Auguste, 552
Rodó, José Enrique, 510–511
Roland, 487–488, 491
Song of, 78, 488, 491
Rolland, Romain, 498
Rollo, 59
Romains, Jules, 498–499
Roman
Architecture, 38, 539
Forum, 717
Literature, 38, 40, 483–486
Religion, 28
Sculpture, 38, 548–549
Roman Catholic Church, 54, 62, 86, 89, 91, 93, 94, 96, 104, 109, 220
Roman Emperor, Holy, 52, 55, 63, 64, 72, 89, 90, 95
Roman Empire, 35–42, 46, 48, 50, 60, 73, 86, 94
Decline of, 40
Eastern, 50, 51, 54, 55, 60
Founding of, 35–37
Map of, 39
Western, 48, 51, 54, 55, 60

Roman Empire, Holy, 50, 53, 87, 88, 94, 101, 109, 112, 123
Map of, 65
Romance languages, 49, 484
Romance of Reynard, 491
Romanesque architecture, 78, 541–542
Romanoff, house of, 102
Romantic literature, English, 451–453
Romantic love, 1296
Romanticists, French, 494–496
Rome, 24, 25–42, 50, 55, 66, 79, 87, 109, 122, 123, 284
Map of, in 218 B.C., 31
Rome-Berlin-Tokyo Axis, 147
Romney, George, 534
Romulus Augustulus, 42, 46, 48
Rondeau finale, 559
Rondo form, symphonic, 559, 560
Roosevelt, Franklin D., 150, 151, 153, 209–211, 212, 213, 215, 237–238, 1349
Roosevelt, Theodore, 205, 206, 239
Root, square, 796–800, 964–966
Roots, plant, 1204–1205
Roses, War of, 71, 90
Rosetta stone, 3
Rossetti, Dante Gabriel, 457
Rostand, Edmond, 497–498
Rotten boroughs, 118
Rough Riders, 205
Round Table Conferences, London, 135–136
Roundheads, 97
Roundworms, 1213, 1215
Róusseau, Jean Jacques, 104, 178, 494
Rousseau, Théodore, 526
Royalists, 173
Rub El Khali Desert, 293
Rubáiyát of Omar Khayyám, 457, 478
Rubber, 1191
Rubens, Peter Paul, 532
Rubicon, 35
Rubinstein, Anton, 558
Rudolf of Hapsburg, 64, 72
Rumania, 75, 127, 148, 154, 156, 157, 217, 289
Rump Parliament, 97
Runeberg, Johan Ludvig, 507
Runoff, geologic, 1050
Rurik, 59
Ruskin, John, 311, 455–456
Russell, George William, 464
Russell, Lord John, 127
Russia, 56, 57, 59, 74, 77, 101, 102, 109, 110, 114, 124, 125, 126, 128–130, 132, 134, 137, 140, 142, 143, 148, 149, 150, 153, 154, 155, 156, 157, 158, 159, 164, 165, 213, 217, 221, 222, 289–290, 450
Russian Literature, 508–510

Russian Revolution, 129
Rwanda, 163, 304
Ryder, Albert, 535

Saar, the, 286
Saber, conjugation of, 656
Sacral bones, 1246
Sadowa, battle of, 124
Sage, René le, 493
Sagittarius, 1036
Saguntum, 30
Sahama, 279
St. Augustine, 53, 171, 439, 486
St. Bartholomew's Day, Massacre of, 93
St. Bayon altarpiece, 531
St. Bernard, 63
St. Dominic, 63
St. Francis, 550
St. Francis of Assisi, 63
St. Helena, 111, 269, 306
St. Ives, 76
St. Lawrence River, 168, 259
St. Mark's Cathedral, 77
St. Mark's Church, 540
St. Mihiel, 207
St. Patrick, 54
St. Paul's Cathedral, 543, 545
St. Peter's, 543, 544, 545
St. Petersburg, 102
Saint-Simon, 120
St. Sophia, Church of, 540
Sainte-Beuve, Charles Augustin, 497
Saipan, 214
Sakhalin, 134
Sakuntala, 479
Saladin, 66, 67
Salamanca, 78
Salamanders, 1216
Salamis, bay of, 18
Salammbô, 497
Salerno, 78
Salic Law, 49, 70
Salir, conjugation of, 653
Saliva, 1217, 1274, 1277
Salivary glands, 1274, 1277
Salome, 459
Salt
    Common, 251, 266, 1181
    Rock, 264
Salt lakes, 1054
Salts, 1073, 1158–1160
    Epsom, 1182
    Table of, 1178–1179
Salvador, 272
Salvation Army, 139
Samarkand, 73
Samnites, 29
Samoa, 307
    American, 268
San Francisco, 159, 213, 215, 266, 267
    Conference, 153, 213, 215
San Jacinto, battle of, 190
San José, 273
San Marino, 285
San Stefano, Treaty of, 126
Sand, George, 494, 495
Sandburg, Carl, 428, 437, 475
Sandstone, 1048

Sandworms, 1214
Sanskrit, 479
Santa Anna, 190
Santiago, 276
Santo Domingo, 273
Saorstat Eireann, 128
Sap, cell, 1197
Sapho, 497
Sappho, 15, 481
Saprophyte, 1200, 1230
Saracens, 56
Saratoga, 178
Sarawak, 296
Sardinia, 26, 30, 114, 122, 127, 284
Sardou, Victorien, 495
Sargent, John Singer, 535
Sargon I, 5
Sargon II, 5, 6, 10
Sarmiento, Domingo Faustino, 510
Sarto, Andrea del, 524, 525
Sartor Resartus, 455
Sartre, Jean Paul, 499
S'asseoir, conjugation of, 594
Satellites, artificial, 222, 988–991
Saturated solution, 1161
Saturn, 1004, 1005, 1006, 1022, 1023–1024, 1025, 1028
Saturnalia, 703
Saud, Ibn, 137
Saudi Arabia, 138, 162, 293
Saul, 8
Saving, 319–321
Savoir, conjugation of, 596
Saxons, 41, 48, 51, 52, 59, 438
Saxony, 52, 112, 114, 550
    West, 53
Scale, musical, 1117–1118
Scalene triangle, 861
Scandinavia, 52, 58, 89, 287
Scandinavian Literature, 505–508
Scapulas, 1248
Scarlatti, Domenico, 557, 558
Scarlet Letter, The, 469
Scheherazade, 478–479
Scherzo form, 560
Schiller, Friedrich von, 502, 561
Schism, Great, 87
Schist, 1049
Schlegel, August Wilhelm von, 501, 503
Schlegel, Friedrich von, 503
Schlüter, Andreas, 552
Schnitzler, Arthur, 504
Scholasticism, 78, 445
Schönberg, Arnold, 562
Schools, 1351
    Arabian, 57
Schopenhauer, Arthur, 503
Schubert, Franz, 553, 559, 561
Schumann, Robert, 553, 557, 559, 561
Schwyz, 72
Science
    Arabian, 57
    Greek, 25
    Modern, 138–140
Scientific method, 967–970

Scipio, 32
Scopas, 548
Scorpio, 1036
Scotland, 48, 54, 58, 69, 89, 95, 97, 269, 280, 438
Scots, 48, 69, 97
Scott, Dred, 193
Scott, Sir Walter, 431, 453
Scott, General Winfield, 190–191
Screw, 1096–1097
Scriabin, Alexander, 558
Scrotum, 1281
Sculpture, 546–552
    Assyrian, 547
    Athenian, 19–20
    Babylonian, 547
    Byzantine, 549
    Early Christian, 549
    Egyptian, 546
    Gothic, 549–550
    Greek, 25, 547–548
    Italian, 86
    Modern, 552
    Renaissance, 550–552
    Roman, 38, 548–549
    Romanesque, 549–550
Scythes, 191
Sea, 251, 1061–1063
Sea level, 250, 253
Seas, 251
Seasons, diagram of, 1012
Seaweed, 1178, 1203
Sebaceous glands, 1280
Secant, 913, 945
Secession, 194
Second International, 120
Secretariat, 153, 215
Secretary of Defense, 240
Secretary of State, 181, 239, 240–241
Secretary of the Treasury, 181, 240, 242
Security Council, 151, 153, 159, 215
Sedimentary rocks, 1047–1048, 1070, 1076
Sedimentation, 1063
Seed drill, 116
Seepage, 1053
Seine, 59
Seingault, Casanova de, 488
Seismographs, 1067, 1071–1072
Selassie, Emperor Haile, 144
Seleucus, 24, 42
Self-assertion, 1297
Self-consciousness, 400–401
Self-preservation, 1295, 1297, 1325, 1344
Seljuk Turks, 55, 66, 75
Selling price, 764–768
Semen, 1281, 1282
Semicircular canals, 1262
Semicolon, 384
Semilunar fold, 1232–1233
Seminal vesicle, 1282
Semitics, 25
Senate
    French, 125
    U.S., 186, 219, 221, 229–230, 231, 233–235, 237, 238, 239, 240, 244

Senatorial courtesy, 238
Seneca, 37, 38, 484, 485
Senegal, 163, 302
Sennacherib, 5, 6
Sensations, 1300–1303
Sense of balance, 1259, 1262
Sense spots, 1301
Senses, physiological, 1255, 1259–1260
Sentence, in Grammar, 350–353
  Kinds of, 351
  Parts of, 352–353
Sentir, conjugation of, 653
Separation Act, 112, 125
Separatists, 96
Sepoy Mutiny, 135
Serajevo, 140
Serbia, 75, 87, 127, 140, 143
Serf, 60
Serfdom, 85, 112
Serous membranes, 1242
Sertorius, 34
Servir, conjugation of, 651
Sestet, 436
Sets, mathematical, 803–805
Seven Weeks' War, 122, 124
Seven Years' War, 103, 135, 172
Seventeenth Amendment, 206, 246
Sevier, John, 183
Sexual reproduction, 1224
Seychelles, 269, 306
Seymour, Jane, 90
Shadows, sound, 1118
Shah Namah, 478
Shakespeare, William, 92, 96, 429, 432, 435, 436, 438, 441, 442, 443–444
Shale, 1048
Shall, use of, 377
Shang dynasty, 43
Shanghai, 132, 297
Shantung, 126
Shaw, George Bernard, 429, 460
Sheeler, Charles, 535
Sheep grazing, 202
Shelley, Mary Wollstonecraft, 453
Shelley, Percy Bysshe, 429, 437, 452–453
Shellfish, 1214
Shelves, continental, 1061
Sheridan, Richard Brinsley, 450, 464
Sherman Anti-Trust Law, 203
Sherman Silver Purchase Act, 203
Sherwood, Robert E., 477
Sherwood Forest, 78
Shi Hwang-ti, 43
Shiloh, battle of, 196
Shoguns, 134
Sholokhov, Mikhail, 510
Shore lines, 1061–1062
Short story, 427–428
Short-cuts in multiplication, 740–741
Shostakovitch, Dmitri, 563

Should, use of, 378
Shovel, 1093
Showers
  Leonid, 1029
  Meteoric, 1029
Siam, 130, 131, 132, 148, 149, 296
Sib, 1335
Sibelius, Jan, 508, 562
Siberia, 73, 128, 129, 298
Sicily, 16, 26, 27, 29, 30, 48, 55, 60, 86, 149, 150, 211, 284
Sicilies, Kingdom of Two, 60, 113, 114
Sidon, 8
Siegfried, epic of, 78
Siegfried Line, 149
Siena, 522
Sienese school, 522
Sienkiewicz, Henryk, 510
Sierra Leone, 163, 269, 302
Sieyès, Abbé, 106
Sighing, 1271
Sight, sense of, 1303
Signorelli, Luca, 523
Signs, of zodiac, 1036–1037
Sigurd, 505
Silas Marner, 456
Silent Don, The, 510
Silesia, 74
Silicon, 1072, 1180
Silk, 1192
Silver, 268, 1180, 1185–1186
  Coinage of, 203
  Mining of, 202
  Plating, 1185
  Sterling, 1185
Silver bromide, 1185–1186
Silver cyanide, 1185
Similidae, 1238
Simon Commission, 135
Simon, Lord, 135
Sinai peninsula, 8, 162
Sinclair, Upton, 474
Sine, 945, 962, 963
Singapore, 131, 269, 297
Sinn Feiners, 127
Sioux War of 1876, 202
Sirius, 1030, 1032
Sisley, Alfred, 527
Sixteenth Amendment, 206, 246
Sixty-day method, Interest by, 772–774
Skeleton, 1245–1249
  Appendicular, 1248
  Axial, 1246
Skin, 1279
  Sensations, 1301
Skull, 1243, 1246
Slate, 1049
Slavery, 119, 172, 173, 262, 467
  Negro, 108, 119, 172, 173, 185, 186, 189, 192–196, 199–200
  Roman, 34
Slavic tribes, 41, 52, 56
Slavs, 41, 52, 73, 128
Sleet, 975, 1059
Slide rule, 971
Slips, plant, 1211, 1227

Slot-machine scales, 1093
Smell, sense of, 1302
Smetana, Bedrich, 559
Smith, Adam, 104
Smith, Alfred E., 209
Smith, Captain John, 170
Smith Act of 1940, 220
Smollett, Tobias, 451
Sneezing, 1254, 1272
Snow, 974, 1059
Snow-Bound, 468
Snowfields, 1055, 1056
Snowline, 1055
Social associations, 1327, 1336–1339
Social change, 1357–1360
Social classes, 1327, 1336–1339
Social Contract, 104
Social evolution, 1357–1359
Social forces, 1357–1358
Social groups, 1357–1360
Social habits, 1358
Social institutions, 1326–1327
Social selection, 1358
Socialism, 117, 119–120, 335–337
Societies, secret, 1337–1338
Society
  Evolution of, 1324–1325
  Modern, 1359–1360
  Origin of, 1324–1325
Sociology, 1322–1361
Socotra, 293
Socrates, 20, 482, 483
Socratic dialogue, 20
Soda, caustic, 1159
Sodium, 1171–1172, 1181
  Carbonate, 1160
  Chloride, 251, 1158, 1159, 1177, 1181
  Hydroxide, 1158, 1159
  Hyposulphite, 1186
  Sulphate, 1173
Solar eclipse, 1009, 1010
Solar plexus, 1254
Solar prominences, 1007, 1008, 1011
Solar system, 1001–1029, 1033–1034
Solar year, 4
Solid geometry, 921–941
Solid, rectangular, 800
Solids, mechanics of, 1087, 1090–1098
Sologub, Feodor, 509
Solomon, 7, 8
Solomon Islands, 214
  British, 307
Solon, 15
Somalia, 163, 270, 301
Somatic cells, 1219
Somerset, Duke of, 90, 92
Somme offensive, 141, 142
Sonata, 558
  Form, 558, 559–560
Song, 553–554
Song of Roland, 78, 488, 491
Sonnet, 435–436
Sonnets from the Portuguese, 455
Sons of Liberty, 175
Sophocles, 20, 429, 481–482

Sororate, 1331
Sorrows of Werther, The, 503
Sortir, conjugation of, 599
Sound and the Fury, The, 477
Sound barrier, 987
Sound, in physics, 1116–1121, 1128, 1129
Sounds, 1294
South Africa, 163, 270, 306
South America, 222
  Animals of, 257
  Countries of, 275–280
  Literature of, 510–511
  Map of, 277
  Plants of, 257–258
South Arabia, Federation, 293
South Atlantic lowland, 261–262
South Carolina, 171, 174, 188, 194, 195, 199, 264
South Dakota, 203, 266
Southern States, 264
South-West Africa, 306
Sovereignty, popular, 193
Sovereignty, squatter, 193
Soviet Union (See Union of Soviet Socialist Republics; Russia)
"Sower, The," 526
Space travel, 987–991
Spain, 26, 30, 32, 33, 34, 35, 36, 38, 42, 48, 49, 50, 51, 55, 57, 71–72, 78, 83, 91, 92, 94, 102, 110, 114, 130, 142, 146, 155, 168, 169, 172, 179, 183, 184, 185, 204–205, 285
  Protestantism in, 93, 94
Spanish, 619–675
  Conjugations, 638–656
  Exercises translated, 657–661
  Phonetic spelling, 621–623
  Pronunciation, 620–622
  Topical, 657–661
  Vocabulary, 630–631, 634
Spanish-American War, 204–205
Spanish Armada, 93, 168, 169, 442
Spanish Guinea, 304
Spanish Inquisition, 91, 94
Spanish Literature, 489–491
Spanish Sahara, 301
Spanish Succession, War of, 100, 172
Sparta, 12, 13–16, 17, 18, 19, 20–22, 24, 480
Speaking, Effective, 399–425
Specific gravity, 25, 1105
  Table of, 1105
Spectator, The, 449
Spectroheliograph, 1008
Spectroscope, 1000, 1008, 1033, 1040, 1127–1128
Spectrum, 1040, 1126–1127, 1139
Speech
  Acquiring, 1292, 1294
  After-dinner, 414–415
  Beginning of, 402, 423–424

Body of, 402–403, 408
  Conclusion of, 403, 408
  Ending of, 403, 424
  Introduction of, 402, 408
  Material, 403–405
  Parts of, 348–350
  Preparing, 401–403
  Rehearsing, 415–416
  Subject Matter of, 405–406
Spelling, 348, 385–388
Spender, Stephen, 463
Spenser, Edmund, 435, 443
Spenserian stanza, 435
Spermatophytes, 1204, 1211
Spermatozoa, 1282, 1284
Sperm, 1219, 1220
Sphere, 937
Sphere, celestial, 1001
Sphincter, 1251, 1276
Sphinx, 3, 546
Spinal cord, 1214, 1241, 1243, 1250, 1253, 1255
Spinal nerves, 1243
Spinning jenny, 103
Spinoza, Baruch, 505
Spires, Diet of, 89
Spirillum, 1201
Spirit of Laws, The, 104
Spitteler, Carl, 505
Spleen, 1242
Spoils system, 188, 201
Sponges, 1213, 1217, 1222
Spoon River Anthology, 474
Sporangium, 1210
Spores, 1210
Spring, water, 1053
  Hot, 152, 1069
  Mineral, 1053
Square, 792–793, 901
Square measure, 784
Square root, 796–800
  Table of, 964–966
Squatter sovereignty, 193
Stabat Mater, 78
Stage fright, 399–401
Stalactites, 1054
Stalagmites, 1054
Stalin, Joseph, 129, 130, 143, 148, 150, 151, 154, 157, 164, 214, 215
Stamens, 1211
Stamp Act of 1765, 175, 176
Standard of living, 321
Stanton, Edwin M., 201
Stanza
  Ballad, 434
  Forms, 433–438
  Spenserian, 435
Stapes, 1256
Starfish, 1214, 1221
Stars, 999, 1001, 1002, 1003, 1012, 1028, 1029–1040
Star-Spangled Banner, 184
State, Department of, 240–241
State governments, 247
State, Secretary of, 181, 239, 240–241
State, the, 1327, 1344–1348
States, Southern, 264
States, War between, 192–200
States, Western, 265–267

Static electricity, 1130–1131
Steam engine, 103, 115, 978–979, 1115
Steamboat, 115, 191, 467
Steapsin, 1217
Steel, 116, 161, 1111, 1184
Steele, Richard, 428, 449
Steinbeck, John, 476
Stems, plant, 1205–1206
Stephen II, Pope, 50
Stephens, Alexander H., 195
Stephens, James, 465
Stephenson, George, 115
Sterling silver, 1185
Sterne, Laurence, 451
Sternum, 1246, 1248
Steuben, Baron von, 178
Stevenson, Adlai E., 219, 402
Stevenson, Robert Louis, 458
Stigma, flower, 1212
Stimuli, 1291–1294, 1301, 1305, 1307, 1310
  Responses to, 1291–1294
Stock market crash, 209
Stockton, Frank R., 472
Stoicism, 25
Stomach, 1217, 1241, 1242, 1273, 1275–1276
Stomata, 1207
Stone Age, 1–2
Stone, perch of, 787, 803
Stone work, measuring, 803
Stones, precious, 1073
Stops, full, 382
Storm and Stress period, the, 501
Story of Burnt Njal, 505
Story, short, 427–428
Stowe, Harriet Beecher, 194, 470
Strachey, Lytton, 462
Straight-edge, 852–853
Strange Interlude, 475
Strassburg, 77
Stratification, 1048
Stratosphere, 1045
Stratum, 1048, 1235
Strauss, Richard, 554, 556, 562
Stravinsky, Igor, 559, 562
Streams, 1050–1051
Streltsi, 101
Strikes, labor, 206, 210, 216, 1343
Strindberg, August, 507–508
String-choir instruments, 560
Strings, laws of vibrating, 1120–1121
Stuart, Gilbert, 535
Stuart, Henry, 93
Stuarts, 95, 96, 98, 170, 171, 448
Studs Lonigan, 477
Sturluson, Snorri, 505
Sturm und Drang, 501
Style, flower, 1212
Style in speaking, 408–410
Subject matter, speech, 405–406
Submarines, 982
Submergence, shore line of, 1062
Subordination in art, 514, 515

Subtraction, 734-737
  Algebraic, 819-820
  of Denominate numbers, 789-790
  of Fractions, 746
  of Negative numbers, 814
Subtrahend, 734
Sub-treasuries, 189
Succession, War of Austrian, 172
Succession, War of Spanish, 100, 172
Suckling, John, 446
Sudan, 270, 301
Sudermann, Hermann, 504
Sudeten areas, 147
Sue, Eugène, 497
Suez Canal, 4, 156, 162, 222, 250
Suffocation, 1271
Suffrage, women's, 139
Suivre, conjugation of, 599
Sulla, 34
Sulphates, 1160, 1173, 1179
Sulphides, 1173, 1179
Sulphites, 1173, 1179
Sulphur, 264, 274, 284, 295
  1172-1173, 1179
  Dioxide, 1172, 1173
  Trioxide, 1160, 1173
Sulphuric acid, 1132, 1160, 1171, 1173, 1187
Sulphurous acid, 1173
Sumatra, 254, 299, 1068
Sumer, 2, 5
Sumerian-Akkadian Empire, 5, 6
Sumerians, 5, 6
Summer 1914, 499
Sumner, William Graham, 1358
Sumter, Fort, 195
Sun, 986, 1001-1002, 1003, 1004, 1005, 1006-1011, 1016
  Eclipse of, 1009, 1010
  Spots, 1007-1008
  Temperature of, 1008
Sun Also Rises, The, 476
Sun Yat-sen, 133, 146-147
Sundial, 6
Superior maxilae, 1248
Superstitions, medieval, 79, 86
Supplementary angles, 858
Supremacy, Act of, 96
Supreme Court, U.S., 188, 193, 210, 220, 221, 226, 229, 238, 242-244, 245
Supply and demand, 327, 328, 329, 330
Surface, 849
Surface tension, 1105-1106
Surfaces, lateral, 795
Surrealistic painters, 529-530, 532
Sulphate of magnesia, 1182
Surinam, 278
Susa, 23, 547
Susquehanna River, 258
Svea, 507
Svevo, Italo, 488
Swamps, 1054-1055
Swaziland, 269, 306

Sweat glands, 1279
Sweden, 58, 89, 95, 101, 110, 114, 142, 287
Swedes (Northmen), 52, 59
Swedish invasion of Germany, 94-95
Swedish Literature, 507-508
Sweetbread, 1217
Swift, Jonathan, 449-450
Swinburne, Algernon Charles, 457-458
Swiss Guards, 107
Swiss Literature, 505
Switzerland, 51, 72, 89, 95, 114, 121, 141, 142, 181, 254, 284
Syagrius, 48
Symbiosis, 1230-1232
Symbolists, French, 496
Symbols, geometric, 860-861
Symmetry, 514
Symphonic music, 559-562
Symphony orchestra, 560
Syncline, 1064
Synge, John Millington, 459, 464
Synod of Whitby, 54
Syracuse, 12, 21, 25, 26, 32, 263
Syria, 2, 4, 5, 6, 7, 10, 16, 23, 24, 33, 42, 56, 57, 66, 74, 138, 143, 162, 291
Systole, 1270

Taboos, 86, 1335
Tacitus, 38, 485
Tadpoles, 1223
Taft, William Howard, 206
Taft-Hartley Labor Act, 216
Tagore, Rabindranath, 479
Tahiti, 309
Tail, vestigial, 1233
Taine, Hippolyte, 497
Taiwan, 158, 218, 297
Taj Mahal, 540
Talc, 1182
Talcum powder, 1182
Tale of Two Cities, 456
Tales of a Wayside Inn, 468
Talleyrand, 112
Talmud, 479
Talus, 1050
Tambora, 1068
Tamburlaine, 442, 443
Tamerlane, 74
Tangent, 913, 943, 945, 962-963
Tangent, angle, 943
Tangier, 299
Tanglewood Tales, 470
Tank, armored, 141
Tanzania, 163, 269, 305
Taoism, 43
Tapeworms, 1213, 1231
Taras Bulba, 509
Tarawa, 214
Tarentum, 26
Tariffs, 185, 192, 198, 209, 210
Tarik, 57
Tarim River, 44
Tarkington, Booth, 473
Tarpeia, 720-721
Tarquins, 26

Tarsals, 1248
Tartarin of Tarascon, 497
Tartuffe, 493
Tasmania, 306
Tasso, Torquato, 435, 488
Tastes, 1301-1302
Tatars, 41, 43, 74, 128, 290
Tatler, The, 449
Taurus, 1030, 1036, 1038
Tax rate, 783-786
Taxes, 780-783
  Direct, 780
  Excise, 231
  Farming, 34
  Indirect, 780
  Real-estate, 780
Taylor, Zachary, 190, 193
Tchaikovsky, Peter Ilyitch, 561, 562
Tecumseh, 184
Tegnér, Esaias, 507
Teheran Conference, 150, 152, 213
Telegraph, 139, 191, 984, 1133-1134
Telephone, 139, 984, 1135-1136
Telescope, 1000, 1040, 1125
Television, 138, 139, 985, 1143-1145
Temperature
  Atmospheric, 976, 1058
  Kindling, 1154
Tempi, symphonic, 559
Temples
  Egyptian, 536-537
  Greek, 537-539, 547
Temporal bones, 1246
Ten Thousand, retreat of, 21
Tender, legal, 318
Tendons, 1203, 1246
Tener, conjugation of, 655
Tenir, conjugation of, 594
Tennessee, 182, 195, 196, 198, 264
Tennessee River, 259
Tennyson, Alfred, 429, 432, 433, 434, 454
Tense
  Latin
    Future Indicative, 686-687
    Imperfect Indicative, 686-687
    Perfect, 688
  of Verbs, 367-370
Tension, surface, 1105-1106
Ter Borch, 532
Tercets, 437
Terence, 38, 484
Territorial growth of U.S., map of, 187
Territories, U.S., 268-269
Terza rima, 437
Test ban, 220
Testament, New, 479
Testament, Old, 7-8, 479
Testes, 1220, 1259, 1281
Testicles, 1281
Tetrameter, 432
Teutonic tribes, 73
Teutons, 41, 51

Texas, 190, 193, 195, 261, 264, 265, 266, 282
Textiles, 1191–1192
Thackeray, William Makepeace, 456
Thailand (See also Siam), 130, 131, 296
Thales of Miletus, 16
Thallophytes, 1203–1204
Than, comparisons with, 379–380
"Thanatopsis," 467
Thant, U, 153
Thapsus, 36
Thebes, 3, 4, 21, 22
Themes, musical, 559
Themistocles, 17, 18
Theodora, 55
Theodoric, 42, 48
Theodosius, 40, 41, 54, 55
Theorem in geometry, 859
Theotocópuli (El Greco), 530
Thermodynamics, 1087
Thermo-equilibrium, 1114
Thermometers, 1111–1112
Thermopylae, 17
Thespis, 481
Thessaly, 18, 22, 36, 87
Thibault, Jacques Anatole, 498
Thibaults, The, 499
Thiers, Louis, 124
Thinking, 1306
Third Coalition, 109
Third International, 120
Thirst, 1293, 1303
Thirteenth Amendment, 199
Thirty Tyrants, 21
Thirty Years' War, 94–95, 101, 501
Thirty-Nine Articles, 91
of Episcopal Church, 89
Thor, 58
Thoracic bones, 1246
Thoracic cavity, 1241
Thoreau, Henry David, 189, 428, 468
Thousand and One Nights, 57, 478
Three Musketeers, The, 495
Thucydides, 20, 482
Thumb, opposable, 1238
Thunder, 977, 1060
Thurber, James, 477
Thurmond, Strom, 217
Thus Spake Zarathustra, 503
Thutmose III, Pharaoh, 4
Thyroid gland, 1257, 1258
Tiberius, 37
Tibet, 297
Tibia, 1248
Ticonderoga, Fort, 177
Tidal marshes, 1062
Tides, 251, 1016–1017, 1063
Tiglath Pileser I, 96
Tiglath Pileser III, 5, 6, 8
Tigris River, 2, 5, 6, 16, 293
Tilden, Samuel J., 202
Till, glacial, 1057
Tilsit, Treaty of, 109
Timbre, 1120
Time, geologic, 1077–1085

Timur the Lame, 74
Tin, 296, 299, 1188
Tinfoil, 1188
Tintoretto, Jacopo, 524
Tinware, 1188
Tissue, 1203, 1243, 1249
Titian, 86, 524
Tito, Marshal, 151, 157, 159
Titus, 37–38
Toads, 1216
Toasts, after-dinner, 414–415
Tobago, 269, 274
Toga, Roman, 29
Togo Republic, 163, 303
Tokugawa family, 133
Tokyo, 155, 298
Toledo, 57
Tolima volcano, 275
Tolstoy, Leo, 509
Toulon revolt, 108
Tom Sawyer, 471
Tomb of the Medici, 551
Tombigbee River, 259
Ton, long, 789
Tone poem, 562
Tonga Islands, 270, 307
Tongue, 1274
Tonkin, 131, 160
Tonsils, 1274
Tories, 98, 176, 449, 466
Tornado, 976, 1059
Totemism, 1339
Toulouse-Lautrec, Henri de, 527
Tours, 50, 57, 71
Tower, Canterbury, 543
Tower, Leaning, of Pisa, 541
Tower of London, 68, 543
Town meetings, 172
Townshend Acts, 176
Townshend, Lord, 116
Tracer atoms, 1194
Trachea, 1218, 1271
Trade acceptance, 325
Trade discounts, 761–764
Trade routes, 75, 83–84
Trade unions, 76, 116, 117–118, 206
Trading centers, medieval, 84
Traer, conjugation of, 656
Trafalgar, battle of, 109
Tragedies, 429
Traits, acquired and native, 1294
Trajan, 38, 548
Trajan's column, 38
Transcendentalism, 467–468
Transistors, 1142
Trans-Jordan, 137, 138, 156, 162
Transmitter, telephone, 1135, 1136
Transylvania, 87
Trapezoid, 901
Treasure Island, 458
Treasury Department, 241
Treaty, Four Power, 146
Treaty, Nine Power, 146
Treaty of Frankfort, 125
Treaty of Guadalupe-Hidalgo, 191
Treaty of Mersen, 51

Treaty of Paris, 172
Treaty of Reconciliation, 159
Treaty of San Stefano, 126
Treaty of Tilsit, 109
Treaty of Utrecht, 100, 102
Treaty of Verdun, 51, 52
Treaty of Westphalia, 95
Tremolo, 554
Trenton, 178, 261
Triangle, 792, 793–794, 849, 861–864, 885–901, 909
Acute, 861
Altitude of, 857, 861
Equiangular, 862
Equilateral, 861, 869, 885
Isosceles, 861, 868, 869
Oblique, 961–962
Obtuse, 861
Right, 799, 861, 885–888
Scalene, 861
Triangles
Applying square root to, 798–800
Classification of, 861–864
Congruent, 862–863, 864
Equivalent, 862, 863
Measuring area of, 796–797
Similar, 862, 863, 889–901
Tribes, African, 1345
Tribunes, 28
Tributaries, 1051
Trichina, 1213
Trichina worm, 1231
Trieste, 284
Triglyphs, 538
Trigonometric functions, 952
Trigonometry, 942–966
Trihedral angle, 922
Trimeter, 432
Trinidad, 269, 274
Trinomial, 817, 831
Triple Alliance, 126, 140
Triple Entente, 140
Tripoli, war with, 182
Tristan da Cunha, 269
Tristram, 430
Tristram Shandy, 451
Triumvirate, second, 36
Trochaic foot, 431
Trojan War, 10, 12, 480
Trojans, 27
Trollope, Anthony, 457
Trombone, 1119
Tropic of Cancer, 252
Tropic of Capricorn, 252
Trotsky, Leon, 143
Troubadours, 78, 491
Troy, 10, 480
Troy weight, 786
Trucial Sheikdoms, 293
Truman, Harry S, 154, 156, 160, 212, 213, 215, 216, 217, 218, 219
Trust Territories, 268–269
Trusteeship Council, 215
Trypsin, 1217
Ts'in dynasty, 43
Tsunamis, 1067
Tuan, Prince, 133
Tube, Fallopian, 1222, 1283
Tube, pollen, 1212

Tuberculosis, 996
Tubes, Eustachian, 1261, 1274
Tudor, Henry, 90
Tudor, Mary, 92
Tudors, 90, 96, 543
Tuff, 1067
Tuileries, 106, 107
Tull, Jethro, 116
Tunis, 182, 299
Tunisia, 163, 299
Turbinate bones, inferior, 1248
Turbo-jet, 983, 1116
Turgenev, Ivan, 509
Turkey, 87, 89, 124, 126, 142, 143, 156, 157, 218, 291
Turkish Empire, Ottoman, 86, 126
Turks, Ottoman, 71, 73, 75, 83, 86
Turks, Seljuk, 55, 66, 75
Turn of the Screw, The, 472
Turner, Joseph William, 534
Turpentine, 264, 1170
Twain, Mark, 471
Twelfth Amendment, 246
Twelve Tables, 28
Twentieth Amendment, 209, 246
Twenty-first Amendment, 209, 246
Twenty-One Demands, 146
Twenty-second Amendment, 238, 246
Twenty-third Amendment, 246
Twice-Told Tales, 469
Two Sicilies, Kingdom of, 114
Tydings-McDuffie Acts, 144
Tyler, John, 190
Tympanum, 1260, 1261
Tyndale, William, 441
Typhoid, 995
Typhoons, 976, 1059
Tyrants, Thirty, 21
Tyre, 8, 23

Uganda, 163, 269, 304
Ukraine, 129, 290
"Ulalume," 469
Ulm, 77
Ulna, 1248
Ulster, 128
Ultraviolet, 1127, 1139, 1140
Ulysses, 462
Umbilical cord, 1222, 1223
Umbra, 1001
Uncle Tom's Cabin, 194, 470
Unconformity, geologic, 1066
Under Fire, 498
Underground railroad, 192
Underground water, 1052–1054
Undset, Sigrid, 507
Unemployment, 1343–1344
Unicellular organisms, 1198–1201
Union in 1861, Map of, 197
Union of Soviet Socialist Republics, 129, 143, 146, 150, 151, 152, 212, 213,

217, 218, 220, 221, 222, 289–290
(*See also* under Russia)
Unions, labor, 189, 1343
Unions, trade, 76, 116, 117–118, 206
United Arab Republic (*See* Egypt)
United Kingdom, 114, 118, 127, 128, 269–270, 280–282
United Nations, 138, 151, 152–153, 156, 159, 160, 162, 163, 164, 213, 218, 239, 269, 1346, 1349
Charter, 215
Conference, 153, 215
Organization, 153, 215
Relief and Rehabilitation Association, 152, 213
United States, 158–160, 162, 164, 165
Citizenship, 167, 224–225
Constitution, 99, 104, 180–181, 183, 225–229, 245–247
Education, 191–192, 261
Geography of, 258–268
Government, 224–248
Growth of, 185–192
History, 167–223
Literature, 189, 465–478
Map of, 187, 260, 1083
Physical features of, 258–259
Possessions, 268
Supreme Court, 188, 193, 210, 220, 226, 229, 238, 242–244, 245
Weather Bureau, 191
Universe, 1000–1001, 1034–1035
Universities, 25, 78, 174
University of France, 112
UNRRA, 152, 213
Unterwalden, 72
Untouchables, 136
Upper Volta, 163, 303
Ural Mountains, 290
Uranium, 266, 270, 282, 289, 298, 306, 985, 986, 1168
Uranus, 1004, 1005, 1006, 1024, 1025, 1028
Urban VI, Pope, 87
Urea, 1189
Ureters, 1279
Urethra, 1279, 1282, 1284
Urey, Harold, 986
Uri, 72
Urine, 1217, 1242, 1279
Ursa Major, 1030, 1032, 1036, 1037, 1039
Ursa Minor, 1036–1037, 1039
Uruguay, 510
Uruguay, 279
U S.A., 476
Usury, 77
Utah, 191, 193, 203, 262, 266
Uterus, 1222, 1283
Utility, marginal, 327, 328
Utopia, 441
Utopians, 120

Utrecht, Treaty of, 100, 102
Uvula, 1274

Vacuoles, 1197, 1198
Vacuum, 1107, 1113–1114
Vagina, 1283–1284
Valence, 1162–1165
Valera, Juan, 490
Valley Forge, 178
Valoir, conjugation of, 596
Valuation, assessed, 783–786
Value, maturity, 781–782
Valve, 1108–1109
Van Buren, Martin, 189, 190
Van Dyck, Anthony, 532, 534
Van Eyck, Hubert, 531
Van Eyck, Jan, 531
Van Gogh, Vincent, 527–528
Vandals, 41, 48, 55, 71
Vapor, water, 973, 1013, 1076, 1160
Variable stars, 1032–1033
Vas deferens, 1282
Vasari, Giorgio, 488
Vascular cylinder, 1204–1205
Vascular system, 1217–1218
Vases, Greek, 519
Vatican City, 123, 284–285
Vauban, 100
Veda, 479
Vega, Garcilaso de la, 510
Vega, Lope de, 490
Vegetative propagation, 1211
Vegetative reproduction, 1227
Veins, 1266
Velásquez, 530–531
Velocity of sound, 1118
Velocity of waves, 1128–1129
Vendre, conjugation of, 589
Venezuela, 278
Venice, 77, 86, 112, 122, 284
Venir, conjugation of, 655
Ventral cavity, 1241, 1242, 1243
Ventricle, 1268
Venus, 1002, 1004, 1005, 1011, 1019, 1021
Venus de Milo, 25
Ver, conjugation of, 656
Vera Cruz, 190–191
Verb, 349, 351–352, 353
and Subject, agreement, 365–367
Forms in Latin, 680–681
Verbs
Copulative, 363–364
Infinitive of, 364
Intransitive, 362–363
Irregular, 370–374
Moods of, 367–368
Participle of, 364–365
Principal Parts of Irregular, 371–374
Problems of, 362–370
Spanish, conjugations of, 638 656
Tenses of, 367 370
Transitive, 362–363
Verdi, Giuseppe 555 556
Verdun, 141
Treaty of, 52
Vergil, 484

Verhaeren, Emile, 500
Vermiform appendix, 1232, 1276
Vermont, 182, 210, 258
Verrocchio, Andrea del, 551
Versailles, 106, 142, 143, 207, 545
Treaty of, 143, 146, 207
Versunkene Glocke, Die, 504
Vertebrae, 1246, 1253
Vertebrata, 1235
Vertebrates, 1214, 1215, 1235
Vertical angles, 859, 865
Vespasian, 37
Vespucci, Amerigo, 168
Vesta, 1021
Vesuvius, Mount, 37, 520, 1068
Veto, 28, 235, 239
Vézelay, Church at, 541
Viaud, Louis Marie Julien, 497
Vibrating strings, laws of, 1120–1121
Vibration, 1116, 1117, 1118
Vicar of Wakefield, The, 450
Vice-president, U.S., 181, 230, 233, 236–238
Vicksburg, 196, 198
Victor Emmanuel II, 122
Victoria, Queen, 127, 128, 135, 454
Victorian Literature, English, 453–458
Vienna, 72, 87, 108, 111, 286
Congress of, 112–114
Vietnam, 160, 164, 296
Viking Age, 58
Vikings, 58–59
Villon, François, 492
Vinci, Leonardo da, 86
Virgil, 27, 38, 484, 485, 486–487
Virgin Islands, 268, 275
Virginia, 92, 171, 174, 175, 176, 180, 182, 194, 195, 196, 198, 199
Virginia Company, 171
Virus, 997
Viscera, 1249
Visigoths, 42, 48, 49, 55, 71
Vision of Piers Plowman, 440
Vision of Sir Launfal, The, 468
Vistula River, 73
Vitamin requirements, table of, 1272–1273
Vitamins, 1193, 1209, 1272
Vitreous humor, 1126, 1264
Vitriol, blue, 1185
Vitriol, oil of, 1159
Viviparous animals, 1222
V-J Day, 215
Vladimir, 59
Vocabulary, 408–410
English-Spanish, 665–669
French, 606–611
French, topical, 611–617
Spanish, business, 630–632
Spanish-English, 661–664
Spanish, topical, 669–673
Vocal cords, 1280

Vocative, Latin, 677, 678
Voice, human, 1280–1281
Voice, improvement of, 422–423
Voices of Freedom, 468
Voir, conjugation of, 596
Volcanoes, 1067–1069, 1071
Volksraad, 144
Volsunga Saga, 500, 505–506
Voltaic cell, 1132
Voltaire, 64, 104, 493
Volts, 1132
Volume, measuring, 800–803, 1089, 1090
Voluntary actions, 1316
Vomer, 1248
Vouloir, conjugation of, 596–597
Vowel sounds, 1280
French, 566–568
Vulva, 1284

Wagner, Richard, 555
Wagram, 110
Wake Island, 268
Walden, 468
Waldensians, 88
Waldo, Peter, 88
Wales, 53, 69, 269, 280, 438
Wales, Prince of, 69
Wall, Great, of China, 43, 73
Wallace, Henry A., 217
Wallace, Lew, 472
Wallace, William, 69
Wallenstein, 94
Walloons, 77
Walpole, Sir Robert, 103
War and Peace, 427, 509
War, Civil, 119, 185, 191, 192–200, 226, 246, 466
War, Cold, 129, 156–157
War, Crimean, 127
War, First World, 102, 120, 124, 131–132, 133, 135, 139, 140–143, 146, 147, 206–207
War, Franco-Prussian, 123, 124, 142
War, French and Indian, 103, 172
War, Hundred Years', 70
War, in Sociology, 1348–1350
War, King George's, 172
War, King William's, 100, 172
War, Korean, 160
War of 1812, 110, 118, 184–185
War of Austrian Succession, 172
War of Liberation, 111, 112
War of Spanish Succession, 100, 172
War of the Roses, 71, 90
War, Mexican, 190–191, 192
War, Peninsular, 110
War, Queen Anne's, 100, 172
War, Revolutionary, 175–179, 181
War, Second World, 120, 129, 131–132, 137, 147–155, 161, 210–215
War, Seven Weeks', 122, 124

War, Seven Years', 103, 135, 172
War, Sioux, of 1876, 202
War, Spanish-American, 204–205
War, Thirty Years', 94–95, 101, 501
War with Tripoli, 182
Warps, geologic, 1064–1065
Wars, Hussite, 88
Wars of the Succession, 24
Wars, Punic, 29–33
Warsaw, 110, 114, 152, 289
Washington, 203, 259, 266
Washington Conference, 146
Washington, D.C., 151, 153, 182, 189, 196, 198, 213, 226, 227, 246, 545
Washington, George, 106, 178, 179, 181, 182
Waste, 341–343
Waste Land, The, 475
Water, 1153, 1160–1161, 1244
Distillation of, 1160–1161
Electrolysis of, 1161
Expansion of, 1109
Formula of, 1162
Freezing, 1109
Pump, 1108–1109
Table, 1052–1053
Underground, 1052–1054
Vapor, 973, 1013, 1076, 1160
Waterloo, 111
Watt, 1101
Watt, James, 103, 115, 978
Watteau, Jean Antoine, 525
Wave motion, 1128–1129
Wealth, 311–313, 1339–1344
Weather, 972–978, 1058
Weather Bureau, U.S., 241
Weavers, The, 504
Weber, Carl Maria von, 555
Weber, Max, 536
Webster, Daniel, 470
Webster, Noah, 470
Wedge, 1097
Wehrmacht, 149
Weight, measures of, 786
Weight, units of, 1089
Weimar, 143
Welhaven, Sebastian C., 506
"Well-tempered Clavichord," 557
Wellesley, Sir Arthur, 110
Wellington, Duke of, 110, 111
Wells, artesian, 1053
Wells, H. G., 461
Welsh, 52, 53, 69
Welty, Eudora, 477
Wergeland, Henrik, 506
Wesleyan Female College, 192
Wessex, 53
West Germany, 156, 158, 164, 286
West Indies, 84, 168, 173, 273–275
West, Middle, 172, 202, 265
West, Nathanael, 477
West Virginia, 191, 194, 196, 198
Western Samoa, 307

Western States, 265-267
Westminster Abbey, 543
Westphalia, 110
  Peace of, 95
  Treaty of, 95
Weyden, van der, 531
Wharton, Edith, 473
Wheat, 202
Wheel, 1093-1095
Wheelbarrow, 1092
Whig party, 190, 194
Whigs, 98, 173, 176, 177, 188, 193, 194, 449
Whispering, 1281
Whistler, James, 535
Whitby, Synod of, 54
White Paper, British, 137
Whitehall, palace of, 545
Whitman, Walt, 429, 437, 438, 470
Whitney, Eli, 191
Whittier, John Greenleaf, 189, 468
Wieland, Christoph Martin, 501
Wigglesworth, Michael, 466
Wilde, Oscar, 430, 458-459, 464
Wilder, Thornton, 477
Wilhelm, Kaiser, 126, 142
Wilhelm Meister, 503
Wilhelm Tell, 502
Will, 1316-1317
Will, use of, 377
William and Mary, College of, 174
William I, 126
William II, 126
William III, 98, 99
William IV, 127
William the Conqueror, 60, 67-68
William, King of Prussia, 124
William of Normandy, Duke, 59-60
William of Orange, 98, 99, 100, 172
William the Silent, 94
Williams, Roger, 170, 172
Williams, Tennessee, 477
Willkie, Wendell L., 211
Wilson, Edmund, 428
Wilson, Woodrow, 142, 143, 206, 207, 1349
Winchester, 76
Windpipe, 1271, 1274
Winds, 973, 977, 1060-1061
Windsor, 170
Windstorms, 1058

Windward Islands, 269, 274, 275
Winter of Our Discontent, The, 476
Wisconsin, 193
Witchcraft, 79, 172
Wittenberg, 88
Woehler, Friedrich, 1189
Wohlgemuth, 533
Wolf, Hugo, 554
Wolfe, General James, 172
Wolfe, Thomas, 476
Wolsey, Cardinal, 90
Woman in White, 456
Womb, 1222, 1283
Wonder-Book, 470
Wood, cord of, 787, 803
Wood, Grant, 535
Wood, Leonard, 205
Wood-wind instruments, 560
Woody plants, 1205
Wool, 1192
Woolf, Virginia, 462
Woolworth Building, 545
Words frequently mispronounced, 388-394
Words frequently misspelled, 385-388
Words frequently misused, 394-396
Wordsworth, William, 429, 430, 435, 452
Work, 1101, 1327, 1339-1344
  Units of, 1101
World Court, 153
World War, First, 102, 120, 124, 131-132, 133, 135, 139, 140-143, 146, 147, 206-207, 221
World War, Second, 120, 129, 131-132, 137, 147-155, 161, 210-215
Worms, 64
Worms, Concordat of, 64
Worms, Diet of, 89
Would, use of, 378
Wren, Sir Christopher, 448, 545
Wright, Frances, 189
Wright, Frank Lloyd, 546
Wright, Richard, 477
Writs, court, 244
Wuthering Heights, 457
Wyant, Alexander, 535
Wycherly, William, 448
Wycliffe, John, 88, 440
Wyoming, 191, 203, 262, 266, 267

Xenophon, 21, 482
Xerxes, 17
X rays, 1140
Xylem, 1202, 1205

Yale, 174
Yalta Conference, 151, 152, 213, 215
Yangtze River, 42, 297
Yawning, 1271
Year, solar, 4
Yeast, 1200
Yeats, Jack Butler, 535
Yeats, William Butler, 429, 461, 464, 535
Yellow fever, 205, 994, 995
Yellow River, 297
Yemen, 162, 293
Yokohama, 298
Yolk, 1220
York, 77
York, Duke of, 98
York, house of, 90
Yorktown, 179
Ypres, 77
Ypres, battles of, 141
Young, Arthur, 117
Yugoslavia, 143, 148, 151, 156, 157, 159, 218, 288

Zadig, 493
Zama, battle of, 32
Zambia, 163, 269, 305
Zanzibar, 305, 306
Zend-Avesta, 478
Zenger, Peter, 172
Zeno, 25
Zeppelins, German, 141
Zeus, 13, 28, 480, 481, 548, 1036
Zeuxis of Ionia, 520
Zinc, 1110, 1132, 1180, 1182
  Chloride, 1158, 1171, 1182
  Nitrate, 1160
  Oxide, 1154, 1180, 1182
  Sulphate, 1160
  Sulphide, 1172
Zincite, 1182
Zionist, 137
Zodiac, 6, 1036-1040
Zodiacal light, 1031
Zola, Emile, 125, 497
Zollverein, 123
Zones, climate, 249, 252
Zoological classification, 1235
Zwingli, Ulrich, 89
Zygote, 1211, 1212, 1220, 1221, 1222, 1227, 1233